ADVANCED MICROPROCESSOR ARCHITECTURES

ELECTRONIC SYSTEMS ENGINEERING SERIES

Consulting Editor   **E L Dagless**
University of Bristol

OTHER TITLES IN THE SERIES

Modern Logic Design   *D Green*

Communications and Computer Networks   *F Halsall*

Microwave Components and Systems   *K F Sander*

ADVANCED MICROPROCESSOR ARCHITECTURES

Luigi Ciminiera
Adriano Valenzano
Politecnio di Torino, Italy

Addison-Wesley Publishing Company

Wokingham, England • Reading, Massachusetts • Menlo Park, California
New York • Don Mills, Ontario • Amsterdam • Bonn • Sydney
Singapore • Tokyo • Madrid • Bogota • Santiago • San Juan

The programs presented in this book have been included for their instructional value. They have been tested with care but are not guaranteed for any particular purpose. The publisher does not offer any warranties or representations, nor does it accept any liabilities with respect to the programs.

The Publishers have made every attempt to supply trademark information about company names and products mentioned in this book. Those listed are derived from various sources.

Cover design by Sampson/Tyrell Limited.
Illustrations by Chartwell Illustrators.
Typeset by Columns, Reading, Berks.
Printed in Great Britain by The Bath Press.

First printed 1987.

British Library Cataloguing in Publication Data
Ciminiera, Luigi
    Advanced microprocessor architectures.
    1. Microprocessors – Design and
    construction
    I. Title   II. Valenzano, Adriano
    621.392   TK7895.M5

    ISBN 0–201–14550–2

Library of Congress Cataloguing in Publication Data
Ciminiera, Luigi.
    Advanced microprocessor architectures.

    Includes bibliographies and index.
    1. Microprocessors.   2. Computer architecture.
    I. Valenzano, Adriano.   II. Title.
    QA76.5.C527   1987 ·   004.2′2   87–1081
    ISBN 0–201–14550–2

PREFACE

The advances achieved by microprocessors since their first appearance in the early 1970s are surprising, even in the rapidly evolving field of computers. The introduction of new features has caused technical innovations, in addition to changes in the technical background required to cope with them.

Early microprocessors were rather simple devices and the major problems encountered by users were concerned with developing programs in assembly language and interfacing to memory and I/O devices. In this framework, the typical microprocessor expert was usually an electronic engineer, with a hardware-oriented background, who was able to design rather small programs for modest application needs. From this point of view, the electronic engineer was regarded as a specialist in designing particular kinds of electronic circuits.

New 16- and 32-bit microprocessors include in their architectures features and supports that have been borrowed largely from mini-computer and mainframe technologies, and which rely heavily on the rapid progress achieved in the computer engineering and computer science fields. The main consequence of this is that microprocessor experts must now regard these devices as complex 'systems' rather than as special-purpose components. Hence, many of the basic concepts, such as those concerning operating systems, parallel processing and high-level language programming, must be included in the technical background of each modern microsystem designer.

Aims

The major goal of this book is to contribute to the technical knowledge needed by every modern microprocessor expert. It does this by addressing the main aspects underlying the design of modern micro-processor architectures. Since new commercial device families include sophisticated support for operating system implementation, memory management, high-level language programming, floating-point computations and so on, this book presents the main concepts on which these mechanisms are based, and discusses them in the light of their impact on modern microprocessor architectures. In addition, some important examples of commercial microprocessors are presented to illustrate how these basic principles are reflected in the 'real' world.

In other words, this book introduces advanced microprocessors from a point of view that does not merely use the conventional description of their hardware characteristics, but tries to offer a comprehensive picture of the philosophy that led to the design of modern architectures.

Intended Audience and Prerequisite Knowledge

This book is suited to undergraduate students in Electronic Engineering and Computer Engineering wishing to learn the fundamentals of advanced microprocessor architectures. At the same time, the book is also oriented to postgraduate students and engineers needing to be abreast of technical progress in modern device families.

Microprocessor-based system designers and computer engineering professionals will find in this book up-to-date material on the main features and characteristics of advanced microprocessors, together with the most important examples of commercial architectures.

The reader should be familiar with simple (8-bit) microprocessors, possibly by having attended a first-level course on microprocessor architectures. In particular, he or she is expected to have a knowledge of the basic organization of computers, and to have gained some experience in assembly and high-level language programming techniques.

The book is oriented to an advanced course on microprocessors. Since the early chapters present several fundamental concepts concerning operating systems and high-level languages, the reader can derive greater benefit from attending former or parallel courses on operating system principles and compiler construction. In this way, he or she will be able to understand, on the one hand, how operating system and compiler principles are implemented in practice, while, on the other hand, fundamental concepts will be mastered in detail.

Organization

The book is organized into two groups of chapters. Chapters 1 to 4 introduce the most important architectural characteristics of advanced microprocessors from a general point of view, without particular emphasis on any specific device. In contrast, Chapters 5 to 10 present the most popular and significant 'real' architectures, making use of the basic elements discussed in the early chapters.

- Chapter 1 summarizes the factors that led to modern design philosophy and deals with characteristics concerning data types, addressing modes and microprocessor instruction organization.

- Chapter 2 describes other important architectural features such as register organization, floating-point number representation and standardization, the role of the interrupt and trap mechanisms, and the function of some hardware and software debugging supports.

- Chapter 3 is devoted to multiprocessing and multitasking; thus, specific sections describe some basic concepts of operating systems such as process switching, mutual exclusion, process synchronization, process communication and process scheduling.

- Chapter 4 deals with memory management: memory hierarchy is discussed together with memory management mechanisms such as segmentation and paging. Further concepts, such as virtual memory and memory protection principles and supports, are also introduced.

- Chapters 5, 6, 7 and 8 present four popular 16- and 32-bit microprocessors: Zilog Z80000, Motorola MC68020, National Semiconductor NS32032 and Intel iAPX286.

- Chapter 9 describes the Intel iAPX432 system, perhaps the most important example of a 'capability-based' machine implemented on a few VLSI chips.

- The aim of the last chapter (Chapter 10) is to give the reader a taste of the emerging reduced instruction set (RISC) architecture approach, which has appeared in the last few years. For this purpose, some basic principles and examples concerning the RISC philosophy are presented.

Problems related to memory and I/O interfacing are not covered in this book, because advanced microprocessors do not show significant innovations in this field and, moreover, it is assumed that the reader has already been introduced to them by a previous course or by his or her own experience.

Each chapter is concluded by a set of questions and problems concerning the main topics introduced in the preceding sections. The main goal of these exercises is to supply the reader with an immediate and continuous means for checking his or her progress in understanding the concepts and principles presented throughout the book.

On the other hand, the set of problems presented in the appendix is oriented to typical aspects of modern microprocessor-based system design. The aim of these exercises is to lead the reader to a critical evaluation of the possible alternative solutions that can be adopted for 'real' problems. At the same time, some small design examples are proposed to spur the reader's fancy and creativity.

Luigi Ciminiera
Adriano Valenzano
July 1987

Acknowledgements

We are grateful to Professor Erik Dagless for his help and his many valuable comments and suggestions on early drafts of the book. We would also express our gratitude to Addison-Wesley for the cooperation and the comprehension shown by everyone during the preparation of the book. We would especially like to thank Simon Plumtree, Executive Editor, for his continuous encouragement and for solving several of the problems met in writing the manuscript. Finally, we would like to thank Zilog, Motorola, National Semiconductor, Intel and Inmos for supplying and providing permission to reproduce technical material that enhanced the accuracy of the book. The following material is adapted and reproduced courtesy of:

Zilog Corporation: *Z80000 CPU Preliminary Product Specifications* (1985) – Figures 4 (5.8), 5 (5.1), 7 and 8 (5.10), 10 (5.11) and Tables 2 (5.2), 5 (5.1).

Motorola Corporation: *MC68020 32 Bit Microprocessor User's Manual,* Prentice-Hall Inc. (1985) – Figures 1–1 (6.1), 1–2 (6.5), 1–3 (6.6), 4–1 (6.2), 8–4 (6.13), 8–8 (6.14), D–3 (6.11) and Tables 2–1 (6.8), 6–2 (6.2); Motorola Semiconductors: *MC68881 FPCP Technical Summary* (1985) – Figure 1(a) (6.21) and Tables 7 (6.4), 9 (6.5); Motorola Semiconductors: *MC68851 MMMU Pre-Specs* (1985) – Figure 9–3 (6.19).

National Semiconductor Corporation: *Series 320000 Databook* (1984) – Figures 1 (7.1), 2–6 (7.8), 2–8 (7.5), 3–2 (7.15), 3–5 (7.13), 3–10 (7.17), 3–22 (7.11), 3–23 (7.10).

Intel Corporation: *iAPX286 Hardware Reference Manual* (1983) – Figures 1 (8.19), 3–1 (8.1), 5 (8.21) and 6 and 9 (8.22), and Table 1 (8.1); *iAPX286 Programmer's Reference Manual* – 2–4 (8.2), 2–10 (8.5), 2–12 (8.3), 4–2a and 4–2b (8.6), 6–1 (8.7), 6–3 (8.9), 6–4 (8.11), 6–5 (8.12), 6–6 (8.8), 6–7 (8.10), 6–8 (8.13), 7.10 (8.14), 7–11 (8.15), 8–1 (8.17), 8–3 (8.16), 9–2 (8.18).

Inmos Limited: *Transputer Architecture* (1985) – (10.6); IMS T414 *Transputer Product Data* (1985) – (10.7).

IEEE: D. A. Patterson, C. H. Sequin, 'A VLSI RISC', *Computer,* September 1982, pp. 8–21 (©IEEE) – Figures 1 (10.2), 3 (10.1) and Table 4 (10.1); Whitby-Stevens, *Proc. 12th Ann. Symp. on Computer Architecture,* June 1985, pp. 292–300 (©IEEE) – Figures 1 (10.9), 2 (10.10).

Computer Science Press, Incorporated: S. A. Przybylski *et al.*, 'Organization and VLSI Implementation of MIPS', *J. VLSI and Computer*

Systems, **1** (2), pp. 170–208 – Figures 1 (10.5), 3 (10.3), 5 (10.4) and Tables 1 (10.2), 2 (10.3).

Trademarks

Z8000, Z80000, Z8070 and Zilog are trademarks of Zilog Corporation.

MC68000, MC68020, MC68851, MC68881, MC60008, MC68010 and Motorola are trademarks of Motorola Corporation.

NS32032, NS32202, NS32201, NS32081, NS32082 and National Semiconductor are trademarks of National Semiconductor Corporation.

8089, 80287, iAPX432, iAPX286, iAPX186/88, iAPX86/88 and Intel are trademarks of Intel Corporation.

Transputer, Occam, T414 and Inmos are trademarks of the Inmos Group of Companies.

VAX-11 is a trademark of Digital Equipment Corporation.

Am9511 is a trademark of Advanced Micro Devices Incorporated.

CONTENTS

Preface   v

**Chapter 1   Microprocessor Architecture: Data Types, Addressing Modes
and Instructions**   1

    1.1   The evolution of microcomputers: A brief history   2
    1.2   The semantic gap   4
    1.3   Architecture classification   5
    1.4   Memory allocation in high-level languages   8
    1.5   Data types   14
    1.6   Addressing modes   29
    1.7   Instructions   57
    1.8   Conclusion   65

Chapter 2   Other Architectural Features of Microprocessors   69

    2.1   Register organization   70
    2.2   Floating-point numbers   82
    2.3   Interrupts   88
    2.4   Traps   95
    2.5   Debugging supports   97
    2.6   Conclusion   100

Chapter 3   Multiprogramming and Multitasking   105

    3.1   Introduction   106
    3.2   Processes and processors   109
    3.3   Interleaved process execution   110
    3.4   Process switching   111
    3.5   Mutual exclusion   114
    3.6   Synchronization   121
    3.7   Process communication   126
    3.8   Processor scheduling   132
    3.9   Conclusion   139

xi

Chapter 4   Memory Management   143

    4.1   Introduction   144
    4.2   Program locality   145
    4.3   Virtual and physical addresses   146
    4.4   Memory hierarchy   146
    4.5   Simple management mechanisms   156
    4.6   Swapping   160
    4.7   Segmentation   161
    4.8   Paging   164
    4.9   Principles of memory protection   169
    4.10   Closed environments   170
    4.11   Multiple domains   172
    4.12   Privileged machine states   173
    4.13   Supports for capability checking   174
    4.14   Hardware memory protection   175
    4.15   Conclusion   181

Chapter 5   The Zilog Z80000 Family   187

    5.1   Introduction   188
    5.2   CPU architecture   188
    5.3   Cache memory   193
    5.4   Basic data types   195
    5.5   Registers   196
    5.6   Addressing modes   199
    5.7   Instruction set   202
    5.8   Exceptions   208
    5.9   Memory management   212
    5.10   Co-processors   217
    5.11   The Z8070 floating-point co-processor   218
    5.12   Conclusion   228

Chapter 6   The Motorola MC68020 Family   231

    6.1   Introduction   232
    6.2   CPU architecture   232
    6.3   Cache memory   236
    6.4   Basic data types   238
    6.5   Registers   240
    6.6   Addressing modes   244
    6.7   Instruction set   249
    6.8   Exceptions   259
    6.9   Co-processors   263
    6.10   Memory management   266
    6.11   The MC68881 floating-point co-processor   275
    6.12   Conclusion   279

Chapter 7 The National Semiconductor NS32032 Family   283

7.1	Introduction	284
7.2	CPU architecture	284
7.3	Basic data types	287
7.4	Registers	289
7.5	Addressing modes	292
7.6	Instruction set	298
7.7	Exceptions	305
7.8	Co-processors	312
7.9	Memory management	313
7.10	The NS32081 floating point co-processor	322
7.11	Custom co-processors	324
7.12	Conclusion	325

Chapter 8 The Intel iAPX286 System   329

8.1	Introduction	330
8.2	CPU architecture	331
8.3	Basic data types	336
8.4	Registers	337
8.5	Addressing modes	341
8.6	Instruction set	343
8.7	Memory management and protection	351
8.8	Privileged machine states	359
8.9	Task control information and switching	363
8.10	Interrupts and traps	368
8.11	The arithmetic co-processor	374
8.12	Conclusion	383

Chapter 9 The Intel iAPX432 System   387

9.1	Introduction	388
9.2	System architecture	389
9.3	Objects	391
9.4	Object addressing	392
9.5	Program organization	396
9.6	Objects for procedure execution	398
9.7	User-defined types	403
9.8	Multiprocessing support	407
9.9	Objects for memory management	416
9.10	The iAPX432 interconnect system	423
9.11	Fault handling in the iAPX432 system	430
9.12	Conclusion	437

Chapter 10 Reduced Architectures   441

10.1	Introduction	442
10.2	RISC approach	442

10.3   Berkeley RISC   443
10.4   MIPS   449
10.5   The Inmos Transputer   454
10.6   Conclusion   462

Appendix   Further Problems   465

Index   469

CHAPTER 1

MICROPROCESSOR ARCHITECTURE: DATA TYPES, ADDRESSING MODES AND INSTRUCTIONS

OBJECTIVES

The aims of this chapter are as follows:

- to look at the historical trends in the microprocessor evolution;
- to explain the typical memory allocation and operations required to run programs written in high-level languages;
- to explain how data types supported by advanced microprocessors can be used to implement data structures used in high-level languages;
- to show how the addressing modes of advanced microprocessors work, and how they can be used to access data in those memory organizations needed to implement programs written in high-level languages;
- to outline how some special instructions can be used to implement some typical operations required by high-level languages.

1.1 The evolution of micro-
    computers: A brief history
1.2 The semantic gap
1.3 Architecture classification
1.4 Memory allocation in high-
    level languages

1.5 Data types
1.6 Addressing modes
1.7 Instructions
1.8 Conclusion

1.1   The evolution of microcomputers: A brief history

In a book devoted to the most recent advances in microprocessor architecture, it is not possible to avoid a brief description of the short, but intense, history of microcomputers. In a field that is evolving so rapidly, the technological scenario is also changing continuously; thus, to understand the current state of the art it is necessary to know the trends of the microprocessor evolution and their bearing on future developments. The first section of this book is devoted to a brief description of the major events in the microprocessor evolution, therefore following microprocessors' original introduction to the market.

Although companies such as General Electric, RCA and Viatron contributed to microprocessor developments prior to 1971, the Intel 4004, introduced at the end of 1971, is generally acknowledged as the first microprocessor commercially available. Not long after, in 1972, other microprocessors were announced and introduced, such as the Rockwell International 4-bit PPS-4, the Intel 8-bit 8008 and the National Semiconductor 16-bit IMP-16.

The motivations leading to the first microprocessor implementations were dictated by the increased demand for large control circuits, which could not be effectively implemented with the dedicated chips then available. Thus, the microprocessor was originally seen as a programmable electronic device that could replace hard-wired circuits used in the implementation of small peripheral controllers, such as printers, intelligent terminals and pocket calculators. The field of application and the technology available dictated the technical characteristics of such a device; for example, the 8008 had an 8-bit data path, 14-bit address (16 Kbytes address space), an instruction set providing capabilities to perform simple arithmetic (addition, subtraction) and logical operations on 8-bit integers, and a stack implemented in hardware within the CPU, with a limited size, which prevented the execution of software with a complex structure.

With further developments in integration technology it became possible for an ever increasing number of transistors to be implemented on the same silicon area, so that the microprocessor designer was faced with the problem of using the area freed by the technological advances.

From 1973 to 1977, only a few years after their first appearance, microprocessors were characterized by an 8-bit data path and a 16-bit address (64 Kbytes addressing space); the instruction set was enlarged to include some 16-bit data manipulations, since this feature enabled address computations, and the stack was implemented in main memory, allowing subroutine nesting to a large degree. The typical applications for these microprocessors (often referred to as 8-bit) were still found in the field of real-time control, as well as in industrial applications. Software was almost always written in assembly language because the relatively low clock frequency (around 1 MHz) and the addressing space required compact and efficient coding; however, some high-level languages designed *ad hoc* were introduced. Another important feature of the new microcomputer systems was the introduction of special peripheral devices devoted to floating-point and extended integer arithmetic, which represented the first attempt to introduce complex computational capabilities in microprocessor-based systems. However, arithmetic slave processors were still relatively slow and the interfacing with CPU operations was so poor that a large fraction of the operation time was due to loading/storing data and programming the slave processor.

A true extension of data types to include floating-point numbers was achieved between the end of the 1970s and the beginning of the 1980s when a new class of microprocessors was introduced. Such microprocessors were provided with a floating-point unit, implemented in a separate chip, and represented a real extension of the CPU, as it was, in general, able to decode specific floating-point instructions, now included in the extended CPU instruction set. These new microprocessors also had a data path that was 16 bits wide and a memory address space increased to 16 Mbytes. Other enhancements included the extension of integer arithmetic to 32-bit data (useful for address manipulation), the introduction of instructions to manipulate variable-length strings of bytes and better support for the implementation of procedure call/return for high-level languages allowing recursive programming. A completely new feature was the introduction of specialized hardware intended to support some specific operating system tasks, such as memory management and protection.

All these new characteristics were reflected in new types of applications, such as personal computing, CAD/CAM workstations and even some time-sharing systems. With these new microprocessors having larger memories and improved speed, almost all the application programs were written using one of the high-level languages (such as FORTRAN, Pascal and C) already in use in larger computer systems, while assembly language was used only for writing routines closely tied to hardware details or software with special performance requirements.

The next step in the microprocessor evolution, resulting in the present state of the art, was the emergence of an architecture based on three major units: a central processing unit (CPU) devoted to the execution of general-purpose processing; a floating-point unit (FPU) capable of executing floating-point and extended precision arithmetic instructions; and a memory management unit (MMU) capable of implementing most of the basic functions required by virtual memory systems and providing hardware support for the protection of memory objects against misuse. These microprocessors have a data path of 32 bits and a virtual address space of up to 4 Gbytes.

This brief history shows that the new silicon area made available by the advances in integration technology has been used for two main purposes:

(1)   to provide support for the implementation of complex operating systems by introducing specialized hardware and special instructions;

(2)   to achieve more efficient execution of programs written in high-level languages by using more complex addressing modes and instructions.

Although these trends do not have any direct bearing on future microprocessor developments, they do highlight two points of interest as regards microprocessor architectures, given the even more extensive use of high–level languages and the introduction of microprocessors in application areas such as engineering workstations and powerful personal computers, both requiring complex operating systems. Therefore, this book will first illustrate the basic operations required by modern high-level languages and operating systems, pointing out the hardware mechanisms required for their implementations, and then describe real microprocessor systems available today, with particular emphasis on the description of the features devoted to operating systems and high-level language support.

1.2   The semantic gap

As a very large fraction of software for microcomputers is written using high-level languages, the key to improving the overall performance is therefore to improve the execution efficiency of such languages. The major problems to be overcome in achieving this goal are due to the so-called **semantic gap**; that is, the differences existing between the programmer's view of the high-level language and that of the actual target machine. Bridging this gap is the keypoint in determining, to a large degree, the overall execution efficiency and software reliability of the microprocessor.

Before discussing the different possible solutions to this problem, it is important to take a closer look at the semantic gap, in order to understand its true meaning. To do this, it is necessary first to describe and contrast the machine views of high-level and assembly language programmers. The most important differences are as follows:

(1)   In high-level languages the memory is seen as a set of named variables without any indication as to their proximity, while the

real machine has a memory organized as a linear array of equal-sized locations, each associated with an address.

(2) High-level languages use multidimensional data structures (arrays, for example), while the memory organization of a real machine can only handle unidimensional data structures.

(3) Structured programming in some high-level languages leads to an extensive use of procedure calls, which require parameter passing, dynamic storage allocation and updating of the variable scope, in addition to the jump-to-subroutine and return-from-subroutine instructions provided in any processor.

(4) High-level languages make a sharp distinction between data and code, while in the real machine's memory they are not distinct.

In addition to these differences, there are other machine features not present in high-level languages, such as the CPU registers and the binary arithmetic.

1.3 Architecture classification

The approach used to bridge the semantic gap between the programmer's view of the computing system and the elementary functions performed by the real machine can be used to classify different architectures. The difference between the classes lies in the amount of processing performed in the software and the hardware when executing a high-level language program. In a conventional computer, the source program must be processed by a compiler, translating the programmer's statements in more or less low-level instructions that can be then executed by the hardware; hence, both software and hardware processing are needed to execute a program. However, some machines require extensive translation, given the very low level of the instructions, and in such cases a large amount of processing is performed in the software. Furthermore, other computers, with high-level functions implemented in the hardware, require a simpler compilation process as the hardware is able to perform functions close to those used in the source language.

The classification of architectures adopted is shown in Figure 1.1 (see also References [1] and [2]). The two main classes are represented by **direct-** and **indirect-execution architectures**. The latter is in turn divided into **reduced** and **complex architecture**, with **language-directed** and **language-corresponding architecture** as subclasses of complex ones. Language-corresponding architectures are further divided into those requiring translation in the software and those employing hardware translation.

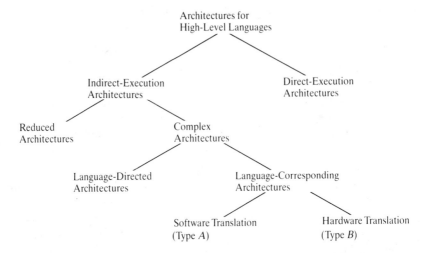

Figure 1.1 Architecture classification with respect to high-level language execution.

1.3.1   Direct-execution architectures

Computers in this class are able to execute the high-level language source directly, with no translation. The major advantages of such architectures are the high level of interactiveness, no compilation time and the representation of the program with a single file (source only, and no object or executable files). The disadvantages of this approach, on the other hand, are that only one or a few syntax errors are discovered for each execution, the syntax checking must always be performed even for correct programs, and the machine can only execute programs written in the programming language it is designed for.

As there is no example of a microprocessor in this category, it will not be discussed further in this book.

1.3.2   Reduced architectures

Computers with reduced architectures are oriented towards the enhancement of performance when executing high-level languages. To achieve this goal, only a few, simple instructions are implemented directly in the hardware, so that their execution can be optimized. Furthermore, the chip area saved by using a simple control unit may be employed to introduce architectural features leading to a faster program execution. In such an approach, the compiler has the burden of translating the source program into an executable code, using only low-level instructions.

This approach is relatively new and only a few commercial microprocessors are now available. Some examples of microprocessors belonging to this category will be discussed in Chapter 10, and references to other microprocessors not discussed in this book are given.

1.3.3 Language-directed architectures

The distinctive characteristic of computers falling in this class is that some machine code constructs directed towards a simplification of the compilation process, are introduced by implementing special addressing modes and instructions in the hardware to be used by the compiler to implement typical operations of high-level languages, such as access to complex data structures. The potential advantage of this approach lies in the possibility of implementing some typical high-level language functions in the hardware directly. On the other hand, the increased complexity of the machine may lead to a less optimized design, with a possible loss of speed for simple operations.

The bulk of today's most popular microprocessors can be classified in this category; the most relevant ones will be extensively treated in Chapters 5 to 9.

1.3.4 Language-corresponding architecture

The feature characterizing computers in this class is the one-to-one correspondence between the high-level language and the machine code. Consequently, for such machines, the compiler becomes quite similar to a mere assembler. The difference between the two types (A and B) is in the use of software translation in Type A machines instead of a hardware-implemented assembler, used in Type B architectures. Hence, they differ in their translation speed (higher for Type B) and hardware complexity (lower for Type A).

For both types, the potential advantages lie in the possibility of debugging a program in a high-level language directly, the performance improvements achievable by implementing complex functions in the hardware and better software reliability. Conversely, both types of language-corresponding architectures are strongly oriented towards the execution of programs written using the language the machine has been designed for.

Only a few examples exist of machines in this class, and no microprocessor falling in this category is available; hence, language-corresponding architectures will not be discussed further in this book.

1.3.5   Architectures and execution efficiency

The architectural characteristics having the most influence on the execution efficiency of programs written in high-level languages are as follows:

- data types, since the type of data efficiently manipulated by the target machine may be more or less identical to the type of variables in the high-level language;
- addressing modes, since they define the mechanism for accessing data in the real machine, and hence they may be used efficiently to map complex data structures on to a memory with a linear organization;
- instruction sets, since the hardware may provide instructions that implement the typical operations required in the program execution (as in language-directed architectures) or may provide a more optimized set in terms of execution time (as in reduced architectures).

All these aspects will be fully addressed in Sections 1.5 to 1.7.

The next section is devoted to a discussion of the memory allocation scheme used for the execution of a program in a high-level language. This discussion also outlines some typical operations required by this type of program, but which are usually hidden from the programmer by the compiler.

1.4   Memory allocation in high-level languages

Almost all the microprocessors available today bridge the semantic gap by using the compiler, or, to be more precise, the code generator that maps the high-level language statements and memory addressing on to the machine instruction and memory organization. The description that follows is applicable to block-structured languages allowing recursive programming, such as Pascal and C, which are the most popular ones in microprocessing.

The whole memory space occupied by a program may be divided into two main sections: a **read-only** section composed of code and constants, and a **read–write** section composed of all the declared and auxiliary variables used by the program. These two sections are generally allocated to two different memory areas (even though such areas may be contiguous). The data may in turn be divided into a **stack**, where all the declared variables are allocated, and a **heap**, which is used for dynamically created variables.

The following simple Pascal program illustrates how the memory is used by the compiler code generator:

```pascal
program mem (input, output);
   var i, j: integer;
         a: array [1..10] of real;
   procedure A (x: integer; y: real):
      var z, t: real;
      procedure B (m: boolean; y: real);
         var w: real;
         procedure C (var t: real);
            var z: real;
            begin {C}
            .
            .
            .
            end; {C}
         procedure D (var v: boolean);
            begin {D}
            .
            .
            .
            C(w);
            .
            .
            .
            end; {D}
         begin {B}
         .
         .
         .
         D(m);
         .
         .
         .
         end; {B}
   begin {A}
   .
   .
   .
   B(true, t);
   .
   .
   .
   end; {A}
```

begin *{main}*

.

.

.

A(i, a[j]);

.

.

.

end.

Figure 1.2(a) shows the memory section devoted to variable storage when the execution begins. The memory is represented by a linear array of memory locations; large boxes within this vector represent blocks of contiguous memory, while narrow boxes are used to indicate a single location (or a small set of locations to be regarded as a single variable). An arrow leaving a narrow box indicates that a pointer is stored in that memory location, while the pointed location is indicated by an arrowhead. (This representation will be used for all the memory diagrams in this chapter.)

In Figure 1.2, only the upper area is allocated to hold the variables *i*, *j* and *a*, defined in the main program. When the statement calling procedure *A* is executed, the memory allocation is modified according to Figure 1.2(b). Since Pascal allows recursive programming, each procedure activation must be provided with its own copy of the parameters and the variables defined within the procedure itself. Thus, the procedure

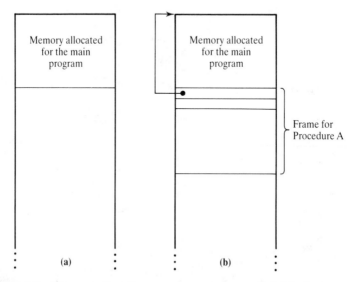

Figure 1.2 Memory allocation upon a procedure call: (a) before procedure *A* is called; (b) after procedure *A* has been called.

call causes the allocation of a new region of memory, referred to as a **frame**, to store the local variables of A, its parameters, the return address and any information needed to address variables defined outside of, but visible from, the procedure. In this case the other variables visible are only those defined in the main program.

A possible layout of a new frame allocated in memory upon a procedure call is shown in Figure 1.3. The display field is used to store the information required to access variables defined externally to the procedure itself; or, more precisely, the display field is a list of pointers to the frames of the last activation of each procedure encapsulating the procedure called. Thus, the display field of procedure A is composed only of the frame pointer of the global variables, because the declaration of procedure A is encapsulated only by the main program. The display field of procedure B is composed of the frame pointers of the main program and procedure A, since B is declared within A. Procedures C and D require a display field of three pointers to the frames of the main program, procedure A and procedure B. Note that the contents of the display field depend on the location of the procedure declaration, and not on the nesting of procedure activations.

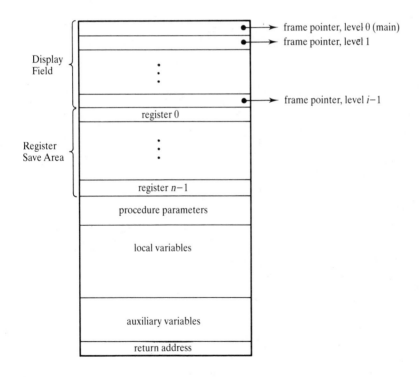

Figure 1.3 Format of the memory frame allocated for a procedure whose definition is placed at the $(i-1)$th level of nesting.

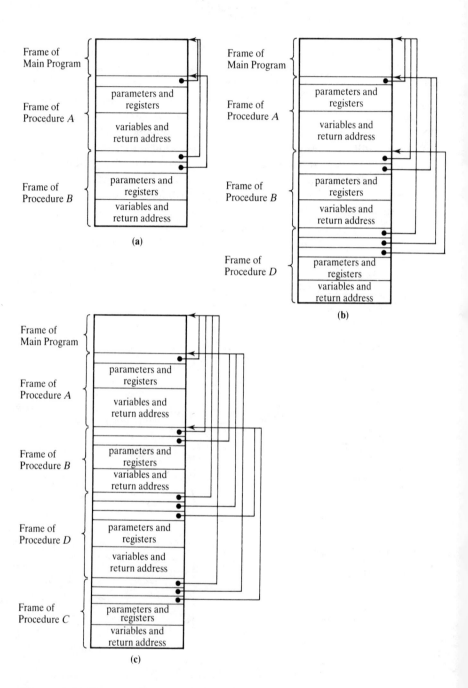

Figure 1.4 Memory allocation during the execution of a Pascal program: (a) after procedure *B* has been called; (b) after procedure *D* has been called; (c) after procedure *C* has been called.

Procedure *A* calls procedure *B*, causing the allocation of a new frame for *B*, as shown in Figure 1.4(a). Procedure *B* then calls *D* and the memory is as shown in Figure 1.4(b). Procedure *D* in turn calls *C*, causing a new frame allocation, and leads to the situation in Figure 1.4(c). It is interesting to note that the display field of *C* is the same as for *D*, since both procedures are declared at the same level of nesting, while they have different levels of activation nesting.

Once a procedure terminates, the corresponding frame is **de-allocated** (or freed); hence, the reverse operation required by procedure activation is performed. Note that to perform de-allocation it is necessary to hold the starting address of the caller's frame or the size of the current frame; the former, implementing a link for the frames, may also be added to the caller's display field, whenever the called procedure is defined at a nesting level higher than the calling one.

Given the memory organization just described, variable addressing is performed by using two types of information: the display level and the offset of the variable within the frame. For example, during the execution of procedure *C*, the variable *j* is accessed by adding the displacement within the frame of the main program to the first element of the display

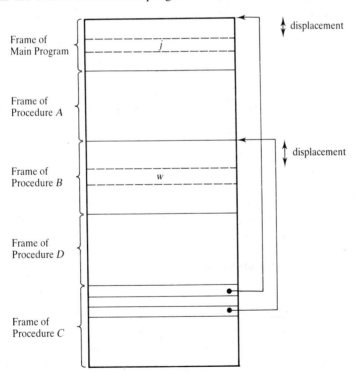

Figure 1.5 Addressing non-local variables through the frame pointers stored in the display.

field of the current frame; similar operations should be performed to address any other variable (local or not), as shown in Figure 1.5 for j and w.

The addressing modes most frequently used by a high-level language code generator are those that compute the operand address by adding something to a register, which has been previously loaded with one of the frame pointers stored in the display field. This may be easily verified since most of the compilers provide, in addition to the object code, an assembler source file with the code generated. On the other hand, some other addressing modes, such as those using the full address specified in the instruction itself, are not useful for generating code for high-level languages. Section 1.6 discusses the most common addressing modes found in modern microprocessors, in addition to explaining how they can be used to address memory according to the allocation scheme presented in this section.

1.5   Data types

Data play a very important role in a computer, since their manipulation is the basic goal of any program. A keypoint in data manipulation is the organization of the variables used by the program; therefore, all the most popular high-level languages provide flexible methods for defining the structure of complex data, since the language designers understood that, in most cases, the program is almost completely defined once the data structures to be manipulated have been designed.

In principle, all microprocessors are capable of manipulating any data structure defined in high-level language; however, given the semantic gap existing between the bare hardware and the programming language, the effort required to bridge the gap and the efficiency of the code obtained can vary greatly when different machines are considered.

A microprocessor is said to support a data type only if it is able to manipulate operands of that type with a reasonable efficiency. Two microprocessor characteristics are usually employed to support data types:

(1)   instructions performing operations on data represented according to the format of the type considered;

(2)   addressing modes allowing simple access to operands of the type considered.

Both of these factors will be considered in the following subsections to determine whether or not a microprocessor supports a specific data type.

1.5.1   Word length

One of the major factors affecting both the performance and the functionality of a microprocessor is the size of the **data word**. The importance of this parameter is shown by the fact that a typical classification is based on the word length; thus there are 8-bit, 16-bit and 32-bit microprocessors, where the three figures (8, 16, 32) refer to the size of the data word manipulated.

Although important, there is no unambiguous definition for the word length of a microprocessor. Consider the following two possible definitions:

(1)   the word length is given by the maximum number of bits that can be transferred between the CPU and the memory in a single cycle;

(2)   the word length is determined by the maximum size of an operand that can be handled by the arithmetic logic unit (ALU) in the CPU.

The first definition refers to the external data path of the microprocessor, while the second relates to the internal path. In most of the early microprocessors, the same result was obtained by applying both definitions, because the external data path matched the internal one.

With an increase in the size of the operand manipulated by the internal ALU, the microprocessor manufacturers released different versions of the same CPU with different external data bus sizes. This arose from the need to allow the insertion of the new CPUs in already existing microcomputer systems having memory and I/O subsystems designed for microprocessors with a narrower external data path. Consequently, the new microprocessors, with a reduced external data bus, could be used in conjunction with previously developed memory and I/O boards, preserving the investments required for implementing them.

It is important to note that all the different versions share the same instruction set, addressing modes, internal registers and ALU architecture, and interrupt/trap-handling mechanisms.

For example, in the National Semiconductor NS32000 microprocessor family (see also Chapter 7) the CPUs have three different external data path sizes: 8-bit (32008), 16-bit (32016) and 32-bit (32032). If the first definition of word length is used, then the three types of CPU would be classified as 8-bit, 16-bit and 32-bit microprocessors, respectively, although they all share the same internal architecture, and all the programs developed for one of them could be run without modifications on any other CPU in the family. However, the three versions of the NS32000 CPU are all considered 32-bit microprocessors if the second definition is applied, but significant performance differences arise from the different external bus sizes, leading to some confusion. Word length frequently implies a measure of performance; the larger the word size, the faster the microprocessor. In fact, a 32-bit microprocessor, with an 8-bit external data bus, might have a poorer performance than a 16-bit microprocessor with a 16-bit external data bus.

Thus, no adequate definition for the word length is available because the maximum data size supported by the internal hardware organization and that supported by the hardware mechanisms for external communications are different. Consequently, it is more appropriate to speak of two different word sizes: the internal and external ones. Internal word size is the major factor influencing the processing speed of the instruction operands, while the external size influences the overall memory access time to operands and instructions.

The increase of the operand size is not the only consequence of having a larger word size, since the possibility of efficiently manipulating larger sets of bits usually leads to the introduction of new data types. Microprocessors with a large word size are not only faster than those with a smaller word size, but they tend to have a richer set of data types supported by their instruction set and addressing modes. Hence, the influence of the word size is both quantitative and qualitative.

1.5.2 Memory organization

All microprocessors have a memory subsystem organized as a linear array of basic storage elements, each one associated with a specific address. The size of the basic storage element is selected by taking a compromise between two incompatible requirements:

(1)   to have a compact data representation;
(2)   to obtain efficient access to the data stored in memory.

A. BIT ADDRESSING

The need for compact data representation leads to the selection of small basic storage elements, because this implies that it is possible to tailor the memory space used to the size of the data format, wasting only a small amount of storage. The extreme case is a memory array with one bit as the smallest addressable unit. Here it is possible to store the different data types by assigning them to a string of contiguous bits, whose size is the one strictly needed by the data representation, and thereby achieve a full utilization of the memory space.

However, this memory organization incurs penalties in performance and cost. The main problem is that bit addressing requires that a memory bit should be capable of being transmitted from the memory to the CPU on different physical lines, since its position within the word

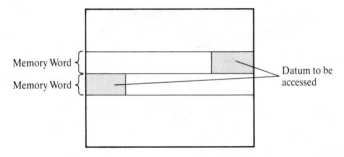

Figure 1.6 Datum placed across the word boundary in a bit-oriented memory organization.

read from memory depends on the difference between its own address and the bit address sent by the CPU. This implies that some multiplexing circuit should be implemented on the memory boards.

An alternative solution is to emulate bit addressing on a machine using larger basic storage blocks; in this case, the memory is addressed in larger blocks and the required bit field is extracted from the block by the CPU, using a suitable circuit (barrel-shifter) that is able to justify the addressed field in a single cycle. Performance penalties occur when the bit field, though smaller than the external word size, is placed across the border of two memory words as shown in Figure 1.6. (In this case, the memory word is the maximum block of data readable in a single cycle.) Accessing such a datum requires two memory cycles, because both words must be read to extract the whole operand.

The drawbacks of bit addressing were also the motivation for designing machines using larger elementary memory units. The increased efficiency of this type of addressing lies in the fact that it closely matches the physical memory-access operation. All the data and instructions are exchanged between the memory and the CPU over a limited set of physical connections, which constrains the number of bits exchanged in a single memory cycle. Hence, machines with fixed-size words are a natural consequence of the physical implementation of data transfers.

B. FIXED-WORD MACHINES

Since the external data path is composed, in the most recent microprocessors, of up to 32 bits, selecting a basic storage block equal to the external word size would lead to too much waste of memory, when data types requiring only a few bits (characters, for instance) are stored in memory. In general, therefore, the smallest addressable memory unit is an 8-bit byte, and all the addresses transmitted by the CPU are byte addresses. A datum larger than a single byte is then accessed by sending the address of its first byte together with the control signals indicating the size (up to the external word size) of the datum to be read. The possible sizes of the datum are also limited in number, to allow a simple implementation of the interfacing circuits, and they are, in general, an integral part of the whole word. The commonest data sizes, for 32-bit microprocessors, accessible in a single memory cycle are as follows:

- **longword**, corresponding to a 32-bit datum;
- **word**, corresponding to a 16-bit datum;
- **byte**, corresponding to an 8-bit datum.

The term **quadword** is often used to indicate a 64-bit datum; however, this type of data cannot be read in a single memory cycle. This classification of data sizes reflects a 16-bit microprocessor view, since the term 'word' is used for 16-bit data, while 32-bit data are long words. As this terminology is used by almost all the manufacturers, it will also be used in this book.

Byte addressing and fixed-word organization of memory do not solve the problem of accessing data placed across the word boundary; as Figure 1.7 shows, the same performance penalties arise in this case, as for bit addressing. Two solutions may be attempted:

(1)   avoid data allocation, as in Figure 1.7; or
(2)   handle such situations automatically.

In the first case, the starting address of the bytes holding a longword or a word is constrained to obey some specific rule. Longword

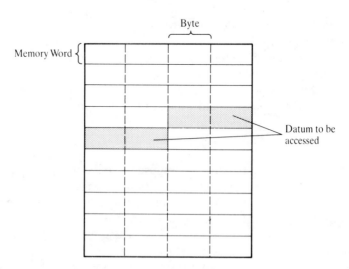

Figure 1.7   Datum placed across the word boundary in a byte-oriented memory organization.

addresses should be in general an integer multiple of four and word addresses should be even, so it is not usually possible to have a situation such as that in Figure 1.7. In the second case, however, no constraint is imposed on the addresses: when a situation such as Figure 1.7 is found, the microprocessor automatically performs all the memory cycles required to access the datum.,

1.5.3   Bit and bit fields

A single bit is the most natural internal representation for Boolean variables; however, due to the performance overhead caused by accessing a memory field smaller than a byte such variables are represented by a whole byte. Among the microprocessors considered in this book, only the NS32000 family provides some instruction for copying the content of one of the CPU flags into the least significant bit of a memory byte, word or longword. This type of operation is useful when it is necessary to assign the result of a comparison to a Boolean variable, and is normally indicated by the value of a flag.

A bit field is a set of contiguous bits in the memory, with no special interpretation associated with its content. Machines supporting this data type provide instructions for copying a bit field in a memory location, or in a register, justifying the result and performing, when required, sign extension. Such instructions and those performing the reverse operations are basically used to transform the bit-field value into the format of a different data type. For example, copying a bit field in a register, right justified and with sign extension, is equivalent to setting the register content to an integer value identical to the value stored in the bit field. In this way, it is possible to extract an integer from a bit field, perform some operation on it and store the result back in the bit field.

The advantage of using variable length bit fields is in the possibility of storing data in a very compact form. For example, consider the following Pascal definition of a record:

```
item = record
    switch    : boolean;
    workday  : (mon, tue, wed, thu, fri);
    count     : integer;
    code      : 0..1024
end;
```

If a vector of records of type *item* is to be stored in memory, then the memory allocation of a few records, when bit fields are not used, will be as shown in Figure 1.8(a), where the shaded areas indicate the amount of bits wasted in this representation. The use of bit fields allows the same data to be packed in to a smaller memory area, as shown in

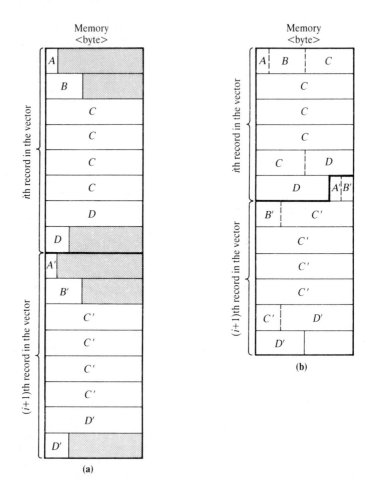

Figure 1.8 Memory allocation of an array of records: (a) normal; (b) using bit fields.

Figure 1.8(b), where solid vertical lines are used to indicate record boundaries and dashed lines represent field boundaries. Although the amount of memory saved with this new allocation is quite large, the benefit is offset by an increase in the time required to access the single record or record field, because the bit fields now span different memory words. They now require, typically, more memory cycles to be accessed. Bit fields are useful, though, to implement packed arrays and packed records.

Bit fields have the same advantages and disadvantages as bit addressing, since they can be used to emulate bit addressing on machines with fixed-word sizes and byte-structured memory.

Three pieces of information are needed to define a bit field:

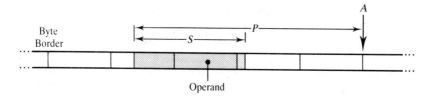

Figure 1.9 Example of access to a bit field, using the parameters A, P and S.

(1)   a **byte address**, A;

(2)   a **bit offset**, P;

(3)   a **field length**, S.

The first two parameters are used to locate the first bit in the field, as shown in Figure 1.9. In machines such as the VAX and MC68020, the offset is a signed number within the range ($-2^{(n-1)}$ to $2^{(n-1)} - 1$), which allows direct addressing of bit fields within large data structures. Other microprocessors, such as the NS32000, supporting bit fields, only allow three bits for this offset, and in these cases A is used as the address of the byte containing the first bit of the field, so that the three bits allowed for P can be used to indicate the position of the starting bit within the byte. In such schemes the benefit of having a separate base (A) and index (P) in a record is lost. The third parameter, S, indicates the length in bits of the addressed field, and the maximum field length is normally the same size as the internal data path.

1.5.4   Signed and unsigned integers

Two representations are generally used in microprocessors for storing integer values:

(1)   **two's complement notation**, where the value X stored in a string of n bits ($x_0, \ldots, x_{(n-1)}$) is given by:

$$X = (-x_0 + \sum_{i=1}^{n-1} x_i \, 2^{-i}) \, 2^{n-1} \qquad (1.1)$$

With this representation, the range of values allowed is $-2^{(n-1)}$ to $2^{(n-1)} - 1$;

(2)   **pure binary notation**, where the value X stored in a string of n bits ($x_0, \ldots, x_{n-1}$) is given by:

$$X = \sum_{i=0}^{n-1} x_{(n-1-i)} \, 2^i \qquad (1.2)$$

With this representation, the range of values allowed is 0 to $2^n - 1$.

It is important to note here that the two's complement notation allows the representation of negative numbers, while the pure binary notation does not. As integers are normally used for counting, as array subscripts and for representing memory addresses, the choice of representation should be made according to the use of the integer variable. For example, addresses should be represented in pure binary form, since only positive addresses are allowed.

Almost all microprocessors provide instructions that operate on both types of integers, and all the three main data sizes (byte, word and longword) are supported. In addition, several microprocessors are able to manipulate 64-bit integers. Longer formats for integers (up to 80 bits) can be handled when an arithmetic co-processor is available.

1.5.5   Characters

Textual information and numeric data are the most important types of data manipulated in a program, and therefore all microcomputers provide a method for the internal representation of characters. Normally, an unsigned integer (called a **character code**) is associated with each printable or control character, so that instructions for unsigned number comparison and manipulation can also be used for character comparison and manipulation. The commonest coding for character representation is the American Standard Code for Information Interchange (ASCII) code represented using a single byte.

An important structure based on characters is the **string**, which is equivalent to a vector of bytes. The length of a string can be fixed or variable, but when it is variable a special character must be used to indicate the end of the string. Often a maximum string length of 65 535 elements is imposed. Several microprocessors can also manipulate strings of words or longwords, in addition to character strings.

The most common operations on strings are comparisons and movement. Another operation involving strings is the use of a string for table lookup during the process of code translation. As the information needed to address a string is the address of the first or last string element and the string length, either the first or the last element should be indicated according to whether the instruction processes the string by scanning the different elements forwards or backwards.

Due to their size, strings cannot be held in the CPU registers, and so they are always manipulated in memory. However, in some microprocessors, the information for addressing a string must be stored in the registers because the instruction execution may require several accesses to this information – for example, for incrementing/decrementing the element pointer and counting down the number of elements processed.

1.5.6 Binary-coded decimal numbers

The binary representation of numbers is quite different from the decimal representation familiar to microprocessor users. As data are entered and output in decimal, a conversion between the two representations is necessary whenever data are prepared for output or for processing. Since binary arithmetic units are faster than decimal units, the conversion time required to translate the number between the two representations is more than compensated for by the processing time saved using binary arithmetic. In general, this is only valid when the amount of computation to be carried out is large. In those cases where only simple computations are required it is more convenient to represent the numbers in a form close to decimal, so that only simple conversions are required.

The **binary-coded decimal** (**BCD**) representation uses groups of four bits to represent the value of the individual decimal digits composing a number. The BCD representation of a number is therefore a string of BCD digits. Two methods are used to store the BCD digits in memory: **packed BCD** and **unpacked BCD**.

Packed BCD is a compact way of representing a BCD number: it packs two digits (each one represented by four bits) in a single byte, as shown in Figure 1.10(a). Unpacked BCD, in contrast, places each digit in a single byte, wasting the other four bits, as shown in Figure 1.10(b). The advantage of unpacked BCD is that it is closer to decimal representation and so only a simple operation is needed on each byte to yield the character string with the number to be printed.

Whole BCD numbers are not processed by CPU instructions as they usually only provide the basic arithmetic operations for one or a limited number of digits. A complete BCD operation can be implemented by using a suitable loop, processing the BCD digits in successive blocks. BCD operations on whole numbers are often provided in the arithmetic co-processor.

1.5.7 Arrays

This data type is not fully supported by microprocessors, since no instruction is provided that is specifically oriented to their manipulation, although some addressing modes and instructions permit easy access to single elements.

High-level languages allow the programmer to define arrays with several subscripts (up to a compiler-dependent number) and with elements of any standard or user-defined type. The compiler maps these multidimensional data structures on to the one-dimensional memory array of bytes. This mapping is performed by using n bytes per element, where the value of n is determined by the element type. The elements are

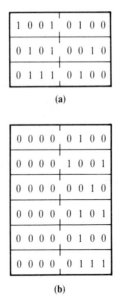

(a)

(b)

Figure 1.10 Representation of the number 745 294 using (a) packed BCD and (b) unpacked BCD.

then arranged in memory starting with the lowest subscript value and continuing with the other elements obtained by incrementing the subscript from the first to the last. Figure 1.11(a) shows an example of this allocation scheme for a 3 × 3 matrix of bytes (Figure 1.11(b)). Note that the first subscript values vary faster than the second subscript values.

Other types of allocation are possible if the subscripts are incremented in a different order, but they are all equivalent in terms of memory occupation and accessibility of single elements.

In some languages (Pascal, for example), the subscripts of an array can differ in type, though they should have a finite and discrete set of values so that the compiler can represent the subscript values internally with a set of integer numbers from 0 to $m - 1$, m being the number of possible values of the subscript considered. If the memory allocation described in Figure 1.11 is assumed, the address, a, of the array element defined by the subscripts $(d_o, ..., d_{n-1})$ is given by the following formula:

$$a = b + s \left(\sum_{i=0}^{n-2} d_i \prod_{x=i}^{n-2} m_{x+1} + d_{n-1} \right) \qquad (1.3)$$

where b is the starting address of the area reserved for the array; s is the size, in bytes, of a single array element; m_i is the number of possible values for the ith subscript; and n is the number of array subscripts.

The address computation of a single element is greatly simplified

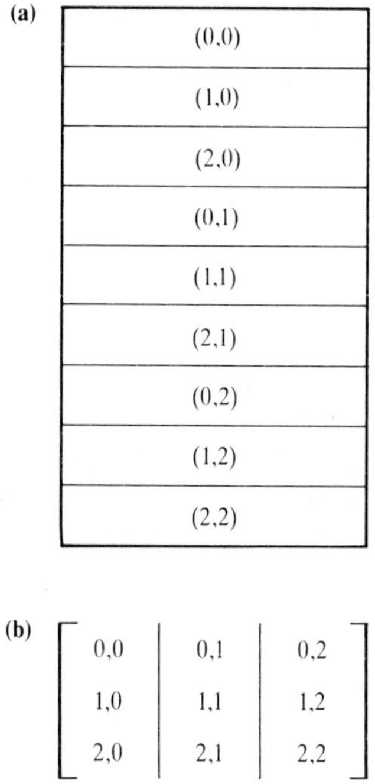

(a)

(0,0)
(1,0)
(2,0)
(0,1)
(1,1)
(2,1)
(0,2)
(1,2)
(2,2)

(b)

$$\begin{bmatrix} 0,0 & 0,1 & 0,2 \\ 1,0 & 1,1 & 1,2 \\ 2,0 & 2,1 & 2,2 \end{bmatrix}$$

Figure 1.11 (a) Location in memory of the nine components of a (b) 3×3 byte matrix where each element is identified by its subscripts.

when a one-dimensional array of standard type elements is considered because the number of multiplications reduces to one, and one of the factors, the element size, is a power of 2. This implies that an addition and a shift are the only operations required to access an element. Since these operations are simple, some microprocessors perform them in a special addressing mode.

When several subscripts are used, the value of the expression in parentheses, which gives the number of elements preceding the addressed one in the memory area reserved for the array, may be computed using the following recursive procedure:

$$k_0 = 0$$
$$k_i = k_{i-1} \, m_{i-1} + d_{i-1} \qquad i = 1, 2, \ldots, n$$

Note that $m_{i-1} - 1$ is also the maximum value allowed for d_{i-1} (the minimum being 0); hence, given k_{i-1}, m_{i-1} and d_{i-1}, it is possible to check whether the value of the subscript is in the correct range, and then perform one of the iteration steps required of the previous formula. This property allows some microprocessors to implement, in one instruction, a subscript range check and the computation of one iteration step. The iteration computes the number of array elements in the reserved memory area, which should be skipped in order to reach the addressed area. Once this number has been computed, the address is obtained by multiplying the number by the element size and adding the result to the starting address of the array.

1.5.8 Records

A data structure composed of heterogeneous smaller variables is called a **record**, whereas the single variables are called **fields**. A program may access either a whole record or single fields within the record. In the first case, it is convenient to consider a record as a string of bytes so that to record movement and comparisons can be performed by using string instructions. When a single field is addressed, however, the field address is computed by simply adding the record address and the field displacement within the record, as shown in Figure 1.12.

The support for record operations is supplied by string instructions for operation on whole records, and by addressing modes using base registers for accessing individual record fields.

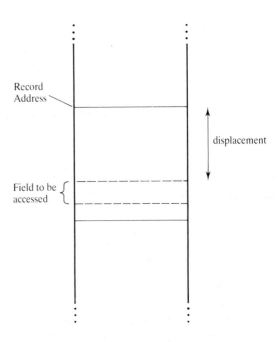

Figure 1.12 Access to a record field.

1.5.9   Discussion

Table 1.1 summarizes the main features of information storage in the memory for some popular microprocessors. All the microprocessors listed have a byte-oriented memory organization, and almost all also have an internal ALU capable of processing 32-bit operands (the exception being the iAPX286). Furthermore, all these microprocessors require that longwords and words are aligned to definite addresses, with the exception of the iAPX286, which allows words to be stored at any address.

Although the external data bus size is normally equal to the internal data path size, it can be seen from the table that this is not always the case. In fact, for some microprocessor families different versions of the CPU, with differing data bus sizes, can be obtained. An exception is the MC68020, which is able to emulate 8-, 16- and 32-bit data buses all in the same chip, by storing suitable values in an internal control register.

The data types supported by the same set of microprocessors are summarized in Table 1.2. Note that characters have been omitted because they are assigned to unsigned 8-bit integers. Where applicable, the entries in the table have been split into two parts to indicate the data types supported by the CPU and the FPU, respectively. An entry for floating-point numbers is also provided, but this topic will be covered in detail in Chapter 2.

There has been a remarkable increase in the repertoire of data types supported by the 8- and 16-bit microprocessors shown in the table. The early 8-bit microprocessors could only manipulate integers, BCD

Table 1.1   Characteristics of memory organization.

Characteristic	Microprocessor				
	NS32000	**Z80000**	**MC68020**	**iAPX286**	**VAX 11**
Minimum address unit	byte	byte	byte	byte	byte
External word size	32/16/8	32/16	32/16/8	16	32
Internal word size	32	32	32	16	32
Alignment of data longer than a byte	yes	yes	yes	no	yes
Bits of the virtual address	24	32/24/16	32	30	32

Note: The size of the virtual address may be selected in the Z80000 with two flags in the status word.

Table 1.2 Data types supported by common microprocessors.

Data Type	Microprocessor				
	VAX 11	iAPX286	Z80000	MC68020	NS32032
Bit			yes	yes	yes[1]
Bit field ⟨L⟩	⟨1⟩ to ⟨32⟩		⟨1⟩ to ⟨32⟩		⟨1⟩ to ⟨32⟩
Integer (signed) ⟨L⟩ two's complement	⟨8⟩, ⟨16⟩, ⟨32⟩ ⟨64⟩	⟨8⟩, ⟨16⟩ ⟨32⟩, ⟨64⟩ FPU	⟨8⟩, ⟨16⟩ ⟨32⟩, ⟨64⟩	⟨8⟩, ⟨16⟩ ⟨32⟩	⟨8⟩, ⟨16⟩, ⟨32⟩
Ordinal ⟨L⟩	⟨8⟩, ⟨16⟩, ⟨32⟩ ⟨64⟩	⟨8⟩, ⟨16⟩	⟨8⟩, ⟨16⟩ ⟨32⟩, ⟨64⟩	⟨16⟩, ⟨32⟩ ⟨8⟩	⟨8⟩, ⟨16⟩, ⟨32⟩
Address ⟨L⟩ [type][2]	⟨32⟩	⟨16⟩ [offset] ⟨16⟩ [selector]	⟨32⟩	⟨32⟩	⟨24⟩
String ⟨element length⟩ [string length bytes]	⟨8⟩ [1] to [64K]	⟨8⟩, ⟨16⟩ [1] to [64K]	⟨8, 16, 32⟩ [1] to [$2^{31} - 1$]	no	⟨8, 16, 32⟩ [1] to [$2^{24} - 1$]
Array structures	index 1, 2, 4, 8	no	no	index 1, 2, 4, 8	index *1, 2, 4, 8
Records	no	no	no	no	no
ASCII	no	yes	no	no	no
Unpacked BCD, 0–9/byte	string 1–31 digit	yes	no	yes	no
Packed BCD, 0–9/nibble		yes	yes	yes	yes
Floating point ⟨L⟩[3] [mantissa, exponent]	FP accelerator ⟨32⟩ [24, 8] ⟨64⟩ [56, 8]	FPU only ⟨32⟩ [24, 8] ⟨64⟩ [55, 11] ⟨80⟩ [65, 15]	FPU only ⟨32⟩ [24, 8] ⟨64⟩ [53, 11] ⟨80⟩ [65, 15]	FPU only ⟨32⟩ [24, 8] ⟨64⟩ [53, 11] ⟨80⟩ [65, 15]	FPU only ⟨32⟩ [24, 8] ⟨64⟩ [53, 11]

[1] Booleans represented by byte, word or doubleword.
[2] Address types are ordinal with no overflow.
[3] The sign bit is incorporated in the mantissa.

digits and, in some cases, bits, whereas the 16-bit microprocessors also contained string manipulation, and had floating-point and BCD numbers in the co-processor. The distinctive feature of advanced microprocessors is the introduction of bit-field instructions and addressing, in addition to an indexed addressing mode supporting access to array elements.

1.6   Addressing modes

Addressing modes are one of the main tools used to map the memory view of a programmer working in a high-level language into the machine view; in particular, they allow the programmer to build and use complex, multidimensional data structures, while the hardware can deal only with a linear array of fixed size elements. When an element in a fairly complex data structure is referenced it is necessary to compute the index or address in the memory vector corresponding to the first element of the referenced data structure. Such an operation is usually performed by using some combination of instructions with different addressing modes.

Of course, the more complex the computation performed by the addressing mode, the fewer the average number of instructions required to retrieve an element in a complex data structure. Furthermore, as complex addressing modes lengthen the instruction size, increase the execution time and complicate the control unit, they only provide a real benefit when used frequently.

1.6.1   Basic elements of addressing modes

Although a wide spectrum of addressing modes is used in different microprocessors, all the modes are obtained as a combination of a few basic **objects** and **functions**.

An object or function is considered fundamental if a machine without that object or function is not able to emulate any addressing mode. Thus, the fundamental objects are registers and displacements or offsets, stored in the instruction, while the fundamental functions are addition, shift and indirection. The shift operation is regarded as fundamental because the emulation of this function using addition/ subtraction would take so long that it would be of little practical value. Addition, in this case, is also meant to cover increment/decrement functions.

Since manufacturers often adopt different meanings for these terms, some standard definitions are given here as a guideline.

A.   REGISTERS

The registers in question are those of the CPU, FPU and MMU, irrespective of the specific unit they belong to. The main functions of registers in the addressing modes are as follows:

- **operand register**: the register contents are the operand referenced;
- **address register**: the register contents are the address of the referenced operand;
- **base register**: the register stores an address to be used in conjunction with the contents of another register or an instruction immediate field to obtain the full operand address.

B.   IMMEDIATE FIELD

The immediate field is a specific field, often optional, of the instruction devoted to holding some information to be used in retrieving the referenced operand. The most important uses of the immediate field are as follows:

- **immediate operand**:   the immediate field contents are the referenced operand;
- **immediate address**:   the immediate field contents are the memory address of the referenced operand;
- **offset/displacement**:   the immediate field holds an integer (signed, in general) value to be used in conjunction with register contents to produce the final address of the referenced operand.

C.   ADDITION

The role of addition in the addressing modes has been recognized to be as important as in data manipulation, since all but the simplest addressing modes involve the addition of two or more components. A special case is the increment/decrement operation, used in the autoincrement/decrement modes.

D.   INDIRECTION

This function takes the result of previous computations (possibly performed by the same addressing mode in previous steps) and uses it to address the memory to find the final operand. This operation is the most widely used in addressing modes because it is needed by all of them, except those directly using the registers as operands. In complex addressing modes this function may be applied more than once to obtain the referenced operand.

E. SHIFT (LEFT)

The shift function is used to perform the indexing operation. In this case, indexing is the operation that produces the offset of an element of a linear array, starting from the element subscript. If i is the subscript (or index) of the referenced element, and assuming that subscripts start with 0, then the offset of the ith element within the vector is given by $i * w$, where w is the length of a single array element. In general, indexing requires one multiplication. However, for vectors of variables of scalar data types, the values for w are 1, 2 or 4 bytes; hence, in these cases the multiplication $i * w$ becomes a left shift of i by a number of bits equal to $\log_2 w$. The use of the shift function shortens the time of the x indexing operation and it does make sense to include it in addressing modes.

F. DISCUSSION

There is a correspondence between the basic functions and objects manipulated by an addressing mode, and the memory and ALU cycles required to address the operand expressed by that addressing mode. In fact, each application of the indirect function produces one additional memory cycle, since the result of the previous computation has to be used as the address in a memory reference. The same effect also occurs with the use of an immediate field because it is a part of the instruction that should be read from memory. However, since these literals are often shorter than the microprocessor data path, they can be read together with the opcode or another instruction component, and no extra memory cycles are needed. In general, addition and shift require one ALU cycle each, unless some barrel-shifter circuit is implemented allowing shift and addition to be performed in one cycle.

It is also possible to describe the addressing modes in algebraic notation, by using the basic functions and objects introduced. Table 1.3 shows the notation adopted here to define the operations required by the addressing modes. The registers are given different symbols to take account of the possible different organizations. Addition is not included in the table since the standard arithmetic symbol is used.

Using this algebraic notation, it is possible to describe any addressing mode by an addressing expression, which returns the value of the referenced operand.

The addressing modes found in some of the most widely used microcomputers are reviewed in the following sections, where particular

Table 1.3 Notation for describing addressing modes.

Symbol	Meaning
g	Number or name of a register accessible to the programmer in assembly language
PC	Contents of the program counter
$M[x]$	Indirect function applied to the value x; it gives the value stored in main memory at address x
$G[g]$	Value stored in the register g
$a.sht.b$	The value of a is shifted b positions left
d	Value of a displacement, stored in an instruction field

emphasis is placed on the possibility of using them to address data structure elements, as used in high-level languages. For this purpose, many references will be made to the memory allocation scheme illustrated in Section 1.4.

1.6.2   Register operand addressing

The simplest addressing mode is one not requiring the application of any of the basic functions to obtain the operand value. The only mode in this class is the register operand.

In this case, the operand is stored in a register, so no memory or ALU cycle is needed to extract its value, and the operand value is given by $G[g]$. This is the fastest and most compact addressing mode, and is used to manipulate operands frequently used in the current program portion. These operands are usually loaded into registers for fast access.

1.6.3   Register indirect addressing

This addressing mode requires that a register, g, is specified in an instruction, whose content is used as the address of the operand, as shown in Figure 1.13. In this case, the operand's value is given by $M[G[g]]$. Since an indirect operation is used, the addressing mode requires an additional memory cycle to extract the operand.

Register indirect addressing is useful to access elements of complex data structures not directly accessible with a single addressing mode allowed by the machine. This address computation requires a sequence of instructions to calculate the result in a register, and the indirect register mode is used to access the operand.

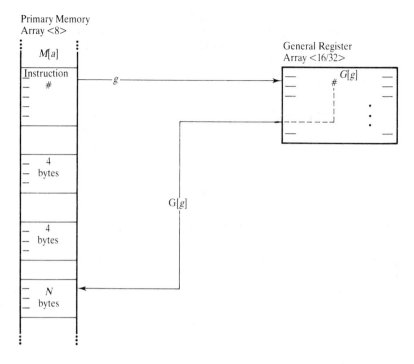

Primary Memory
Array <8>

$M[a]$

Instruction
#

4
bytes

4
bytes

N
bytes

General Register
Array <16/32>

$G[g]$
#

g

$G[g]$

Figure 1.13 Addressing mechanism for register indirect mode.

1.6.4 Autoincrement/decrement addressing

This is a very important addressing mode as it is the basis of addressing modes implemented in all computers. However, it is not normally recognized as existing in a given machine because its use is limited to special registers, such as the program counter or the stack pointer.

The autoincrement/decrement addressing mode functions in a manner similar to the register indirect mode, since the register g, specified (explicitly or implicitly) in the instruction, holds the address of the operand. In addition, the contents of the register are incremented/decremented by the length of the referenced operand. Since this addressing mode refers to operands that are scalar data types, the value of the increment is, in general, 1, 2, 4 or 8.

The problem of deciding whether the increment/decrement should precede or follow the application of the indirection function to the register contents is normally solved by implementing the increment after and the decrement before the indirection, leading to postincrement and predecrement addressing modes. The reasons for this are as follows. First, the postincrement mode is the one used to fetch the code from memory, when the register g is the program counter; and second, it is important that decrement and increment are not performed both before or both after the indirection, to implement the push and pop operation on a LIFO stack, by using the stack pointer as the register involved.

The following example illustrates this point. Assume that the contents of the stack pointer are SP. If predecrement/increment modes are used, then SP is the address of the top of stack. When an operand four bytes long is pushed, then the stack pointer is incremented to SP + 4 and the operand is then stored at the address SP + 4. When a pop of the same operand is executed, then the predecrement mode leads to a decrement of the stack pointer to SP and an operand fetch from that location, which holds the second rather than the topmost element of the stack.

A similar situation arises if postincrement/decrement is used. In this case, a pop following a push leads to an operand fetch of the first empty location above the top of stack. If the increment and decrement operations are not performed both before or both after the indirection, correct stack operations can still be implemented, but in this situation there is no difference between using autoincrement for push and autodecrement for pop operations, or vice versa.

Figure 1.14 illustrates how the predecrement and postincrement modes work. The autoincrement/decrement modes are the only ones having side effects because, in addition to operand addressing, they lead to the alteration of the contents of the register involved. Hence, while the operand of a postincrement mode may be expressed as $M[G[g]]$, as in register indirect mode, in this case it is necessary to add an assignment operation, $G[g] := G[g] + N$, to take account of the increment performed. The operand of the predecrement mode is given by $M[G[g] - N]$, and the side effect is expressed as $G[g] := G[g] - N$.

The autoincrement/decrement modes are useful as they make possible the implementation of stack operations. In addition, if these modes are allowed on registers other than the program counter and stack pointer, they provide a straightforward mechanism for implementing memory buffer scanning, since it is possible, in one cycle, to reference an operand and prepare the address for the next one. This is the reason why these modes are used implicitly or explicitly in string instructions, where they may be applied to specialized or general-purpose registers.

As a byproduct of the postincrement mode, it is possible to obtain the immediate operand addressing mode, which is used in all computers to introduce constants into the instruction stream. The immediate operand mode is obtained by using the standard postincrement mode and specifying the program counter as the register to be used. Since the program counter points to the word after the first one composing the instruction, the next instruction field is read and the program counter is incremented to point to the following word. In this way, instructions composed of more than one word can be processed.

Frequently, immediate operands have different lengths: a statistical

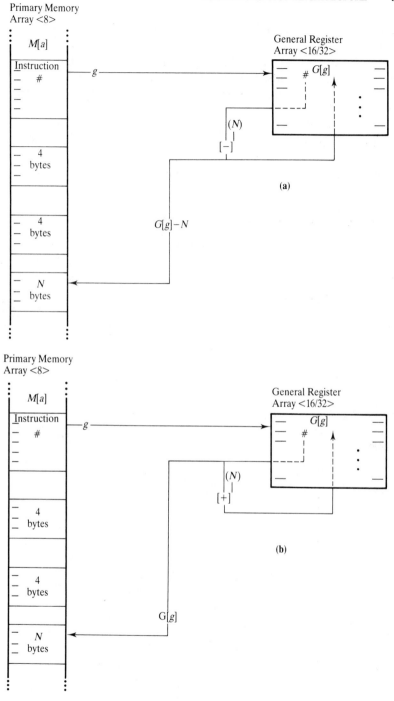

Figure 1.14 Operations involved in (a) the predecrement indirect mode and (b) the postincrement indirect mode.

study on the use of constants in high-level languages [3] has shown that the frequency of occurrence of small constants is higher than that of large ones. Thus, to achieve a shorter average instruction length, different immediate formats are allowed. In some cases, the Z80000 and MC68000 microprocessors for example, it is possible to store small constants in the same word as the opcode and addressing mode specification. Consequently, no extra memory cycle is required to fetch the immediate operand. It is obvious that the immediate operand mode is meaningful only for read operations, since it does not make sense to store computation results in an instruction field.

1.6.5   Autoincrement/decrement indirect addressing

This addressing mode may be obtained from the normal autoincrement/decrement modes by applying a further indirection, so that the final effect is as represented in Figure 1.15, for postincrement and predecrement addressing modes.

The contents of the specified register are used as in the normal autoincrement/decrement modes; however, the result obtained by such a

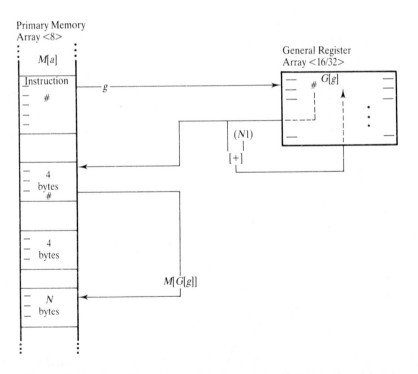

Figure 1.15   Operations involved in the postincrement indirect mode.

manipulation is used to address a memory location holding the address of the operand, rather than the operand itself.

For the postincrement mode, the operand may be expressed by $M[M[G[g]]]$. Once again, a side effect occurs and this is expressed as $G[g] := G[g] + N$, where N is the length of the pointer. The operand specified using the predecrement mode is given by $M[M[G[g] - N]]$, and the side effect is expressed as $G[g] := G[g] - N$.

When applied to the program counter, postincrement indirect mode gives rise to one of the commonest addressing modes found in all the microprocessors: **direct addressing**. This mode uses the operand address stored as a field of the instruction. Since the instructions are fetched using postincrement mode on the program counter, the latter always points to the word following the last one read. If postincrement indirect mode is applied to the program counter, the next instruction word is read; then the program counter is incremented and the word read is used to address the memory to access the operand. Some 8- and 16-bit microprocessors have an address size larger than the word size, and so they need more than a single memory cycle to get the whole address stored in the instruction.

As direct addressing specifies an operand address as part of the instruction, it is set at compile time and cannot be changed during program execution. As explained in Section 1.4, memory usage by a program written in a high-level language that allows recursive programming cannot make much use of direct addressing results for addressing variables. This is because most of them, excluding global variables, have a memory address assigned at run time. This implies that the addresses of local variables must be computed and so cannot be inserted into the instruction.

Although not often used for referencing variables, addresses stored in the instruction may still be employed in the code segment to specify the target label of instructions, such as conditional/unconditional jump and jump-to-subroutine.

1.6.6   Base displacement indirect addressing

It has already been pointed out, in Section 1.6.1, that a register is considered a base register if its contents, added to some other object manipulated by the addressing mode, can be used to determine the operand address. Base plus displacement mode computes the operand address by summing the contents of the specified base register and the value of an instruction field, called **displacement**.

Figure 1.16 illustrates the operations involved in the base plus displacement addressing mode. The addressing expression associated with this mode is $M[G[g] + d]$. Note that the displacement fetch requires a memory cycle and an increment of the program counter; hence, the total number of memory cycles needed to address the operand is two. The operations performed are an addition and an increment of the program counter. Like immediate operands, displacements may have different lengths, which may shorten the average instruction length. In the case of short displacements, it is possible to store a field in the same word as the opcode or the addressing mode indication, avoiding the need for extra memory cycles. Long displacements, however, may be larger than the word size, leading to more than one extra memory cycle to get the whole displacement.

Base plus displacement addressing is very useful in the execution of programs written in high-level languages as it represents the most natural way of addressing scalar variables. To understand this, consider the memory allocation for the Pascal program in Figure 1.4(c). This shows the memory allocation during the execution of the procedure *C*. The local variable *z* is stored within the frame allocated to *C*. Since the absolute frame addresses are determined by the sequence of procedure activations, they change at each activation of procedure *C*. When the compiler translates *C*, it can generate the displacements of all the fields and local variables stored in the procedure frame, but not their absolute addresses nor even the total displacement within the data segment.

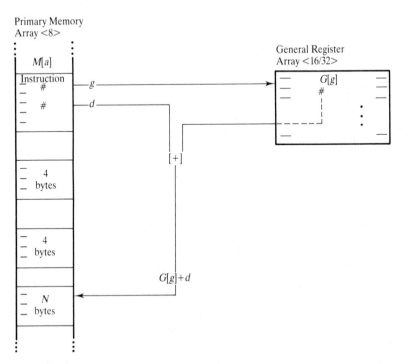

Figure 1.16 Operations involved in the base plus displacement mode.

The base addressing mode solves the problem of addressing local variables and control information in the following way. The piece of assembler code implementing the procedure call also sets a specific register, general purpose or specialized, to point at the beginning of the new frame – this register is referred to as the **local frame pointer**. The compiler can then generate instructions calling local variables by using the local frame pointer as a base register, and the sum of the lengths of the fields and variables preceding the referenced variable as a displacement. This type of addressing is illustrated in Figure 1.17, which parallels the situation in Figure 1.4(c), but with the addition of base registers.

Figure 1.17 also shows how non-local variables can be addressed by a mechanism similar to that of local variable addressing. However, in this case, the frame pointer of the procedure where the referenced variable is defined is retrieved from the display field. Display information may be seen as normal, local variables, hence the desired variable is copied into a

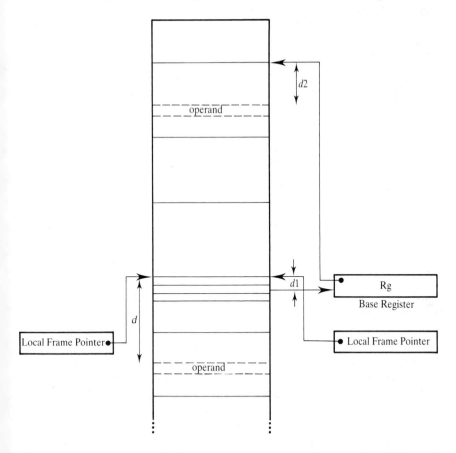

Figure 1.17 Using base displacement indirect mode to access local (left-hand side) and non-local (right-hand side) variables.

register by computing its displacement within the current frame and using base plus displacement addressing with the local frame pointer (LFP) as base register. The information in the register, Rg, is the pointer to the frame where the non-local variable is stored, and it is now simple to address the variable, by using Rg as base register and the proper displacement within the new procedure frame, as shown in Figure 1.17.

The local frame pointer is nearly always held in a register since it represents the key information needed to reach all the local variables, and since the probability of calling them within the procedure where they are defined is high. Another frame pointer, often held in a register, is that pointing to the global variables, which are referenced everywhere. A third register may be reserved, when required, for storing the pointer to the frame of a procedure that may be defined at any level between the local procedure and the main program.

Base displacement indirect addressing mode is frequently used to access both local and non-local variables, provided that they are scalar. In complex data structures this addressing mode only provides the starting address of the memory area allocated for the whole structure, and further calculation is required to locate the single element.

When the program counter is used as the base register, the resulting addressing mode is often referred to as relative, since the field in the instruction only indicates the relative position of the operand with respect to the value of the program counter or the instruction address. This addressing mode requires that a signed integer is used as displacement, while operand addressing modes normally require only positive displacements. The need for signed displacements is stronger if jump instructions are considered, because both forward (positive displacement) and backward (negative displacement) jumps can co-exist in the same program.

1.6.7   Base displacement indirect indirect addressing

This addressing mode is obtained by applying a further indirection to a base displacement indirect mode. In other words, the contents of the base register, specified in the instruction, are added to a displacement stored as a field of the instruction itself, and the result is used as the address of a memory location, whose contents indicate the operand address.

The whole addressing process is shown in Figure 1.18. The addressing expression associated with this mode is $M[M[G[g] + d]]$. The number of memory cycles required to extract the operand is one more than for a simple base displacement indirect mode, while the operation performed is exactly the same, since only one more indirection is used.

The base displacement indirect indirect mode may be used to access variables referenced through a pointer. As the base register is

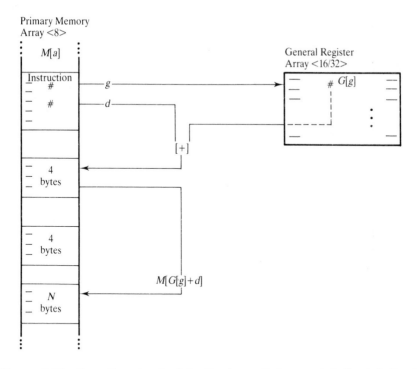

Figure 1.18 Operations involved in the base displacement indirect indirect mode.

always used to point to the frame starting address, the displacement corresponds to the pointer variable position within the procedure frame, and the double indirection is used to get first the pointer value and then the actual operand. Figure 1.19 shows how this mode is used to address a variable stored in the heap and referenced through a pointer variable, P.

Another typical application of the base displacement indirect indirect mode is to access procedure parameters passed by reference. In such applications, only the address of the parameter variable is stored, for the parameters within the procedure frame. Hence a simple base displacement indirect mode is only able to access the pointer to the parameter, whereas a further indirection extracts the operand value.

1.6.8 Base indexed indirect addressing

Linear arrays of scalars are the simplest data structure allowed in high-level languages. Scalars are, in general, represented by 8-, 16- or 32-bit memory fields and the computation of the displacement within the linear array of an element is obtained by shifting the number representing the array index of the element 0, 1 or 2 positions respectively, assuming that

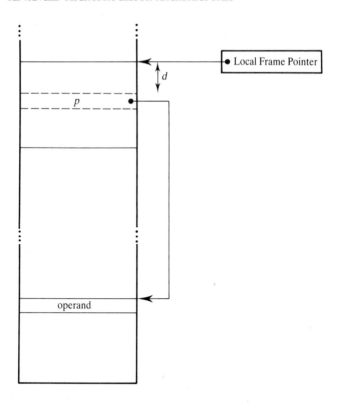

Figure 1.19 Using base displacement indirect indirect mode to access a variable through a pointer *P*.

the indices start with 0. It is also worth noting here that compilers of languages such as Pascal, which allow the programmer to use non-integer indices, internally translate the index value into an integer. The same operation is performed when the index is an integer, but its lowest value is not 0. Thus, a simple constant addition, performed at compile time, is sufficient to adjust the index.

The base indexed indirect mode is immediately able to perform the computation required by such an indexing operation, plus the addition of the displacement to the base address of the data structure. Two registers are required for this addressing mode: $g1$ and $g2$. As the contents of $g2$ are interpreted as the index in the array, they are shifted left by 0, 1 or 2 positions according to the type of operand manipulated by the instruction. After this shift operation, the result is added to the contents of $g1$, which should hold the starting address of the array. The whole computation process is shown in Figure 1.20. The addressing expression associated with the base indexed indirect mode is $M[G[g1]$

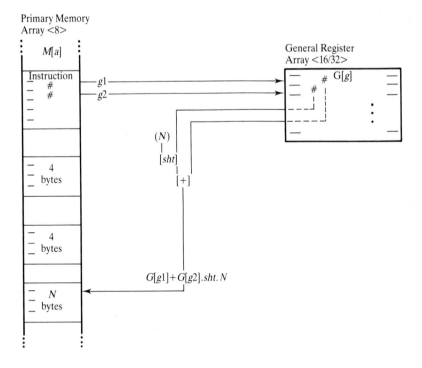

Figure 1.20 Operations involved in the base indexed indirect mode.

+ $G[g2].sht.N]$. This addressing mode needs only one memory cycle, plus one addition and one shift operation.

The base indexed indirect mode may be used to access an element in a vector of scalars whose starting address is stored in the base register.

1.6.9 Postincrement indexed indirect addressing

This addressing mode is derived from the base indexed indirect mode by adding an increment operation on one of the two registers used after the operand fetch. Thus, the contents of the register $g2$ are shifted by 0, 1, 2 or 3 positions; the result is added to the contents of the register $g1$; the result of the addition is used as the address of the operand; and the register $g1$ is incremented by the value of $N1 = 1, 2$ or 4.

Figure 1.21 shows the whole address computation process. The expression giving the operand value is the same as for base indexed indirect addressing, $M[G[g1] + G[g2].sht.N]$. The full description of the addressing mode operation requires the assignment $G[g1] := G[g1] + N1$, as for all the autoincrement/decrement modes, to express the side effect on the register contents.

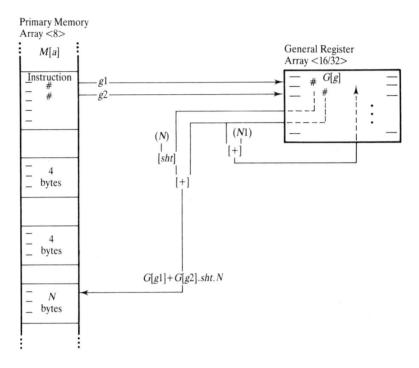

Figure 1.21   Operations involved in the postincrement indexed indirect mode.

1.6.10   Predecrement indexed indirect addressing

The postincrement indexed indirect mode is similar to the predecrement indexed mode in that the two registers $g1$ and $g2$ are also used in this mode. The contents of the register $g1$ are decremented by $N1 = 1$, 2 or 4, while register $g2$ is shifted by N positions ($N = 0$, 1 or 2). The new value of $g1$ is added to the result of the shift of $g2$ to give the operand address.

Figure 1.22 describes the whole addressing operation. The expression giving the operand value is still the same as for base indexed indirect addressing, $M[G[g1] + G[g2].sht.N]$, but it is necessary to insert the assignment $G[g1] := G[g1] - N1$ before this expression to account for the side effect on the register contents due to the initial decrement of the register $g1$.

1.6.11   Base displacement indexed indirect addressing

Three objects are involved in this addressing mode: a base register, $g1$, a displacement d stored in an instruction field, and a second register $g2$. The contents of the register $g2$ are shifted by N (where $N = 0$, 1 or 2) in accordance with the type of operand manipulated by the instruction. The

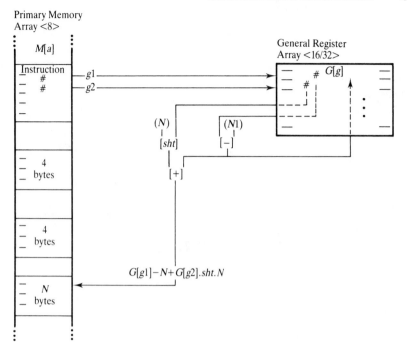

Figure 1.22   Operations involved in the predecrement indexed indirect mode.

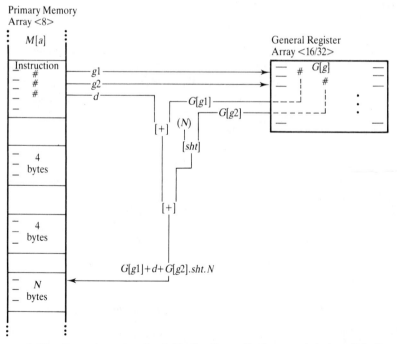

Figure 1.23   Operations involved in the base displacement indexed indirect mode.

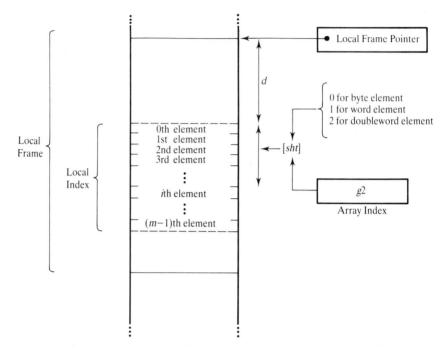

Figure 1.24 Access to an element of a local vector using the base displacement index indirect mode.

result is then added to both the displacement and the base register contents to obtain the address of the operand.

This address computation process is depicted in Figure 1.23. The expression giving the operand value is $M[G[g1] + d + G[g2].sht.N]$. The access to the operand only requires one memory cycle, plus one shift and two additions.

When access to elements of a linear array of scalars is considered, the base displacement indexed indirect mode represents an enhancement of both base displacement indirect and base indexed indirect. In fact, if the local frame pointer is used for $g1$, the array index is stored in $g2$ and the displacement indicates the starting address, within the frame, of the memory area reserved for the array, then this addressing mode provides the means for addressing any element of a local array of scalars in a single instruction. This is shown in Figure 1.24.

1.6.12   Postincrement indirect indexed indirect addressing

Two registers are used in this addressing mode, $g1$ and $g2$. The contents of $g1$ are used as an address to fetch the contents of a memory location, which is then added to the value of $g2$ and shifted by $N1$ positions

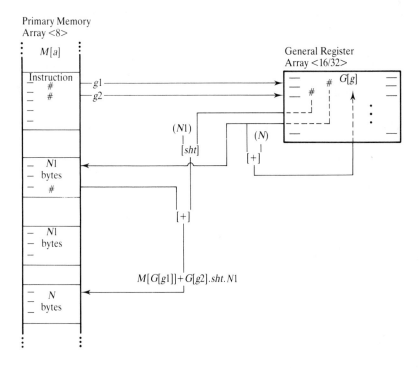

Figure 1.25 Operations involved in the postincrement indirect indexed indirect mode.

($N1 = 0$, 1 or 2) to obtain the operand address, and finally the contents of $g1$ are incremented by a constant, N, which depends on the address size. The constant $N1$ depends on the size of the operand manipulated by the instruction, and is not related to N.

Figure 1.25 explains the computations involved in this addressing mode. The expression giving the operand value is $M[M[G[g1]] + G[g2].sht.N1]$. As in the other postincrement-based modes, there is a side effect on the contents of $g1$, which is accounted for by the assignment $G[g1] := G[g1] + N$. Two memory cycles, one addition and one shift are required to find the operand value in this addressing mode.

1.6.13 Base displacement indirect indexed indirect addressing

The objects involved in this mode are two registers, $g1$ and $g2$, and a displacement stored in an instruction field. The contents of the register $g1$ are added to the displacement and the subsequent result used as an

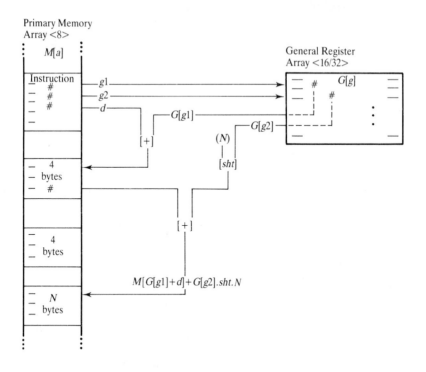

Figure 1.26 Operations involved in the base displacement indirect indexed indirect mode.

address to extract the value of the corresponding memory location. This value is then added to the contents of register $g2$ and shifted by N positions (where $N = 0$, 1 or 2) to obtain the operand address.

The computation is shown in Figure 1.26. The expression giving the operand value is $M[M[G[g1] + d] + G[g2].sht.N]$. From this expression it can be derived that two additions, one shift and two memory cycles are needed to access the operand.

A possible use of this addressing mode is for accessing single elements of an array of scalars pointed to by a variable. Arrays passed as procedure parameters have their starting addresses stored in the parameter field of the current procedure frame, and a single element can therefore be reached by using the local frame pointer as register $g1$, a proper displacement value indicating the position of the array address within the current frame, together with the element index in the register $g2$. Figure 1.27 shows this addressing mechanism for an array passed as a parameter and defined in the main program.

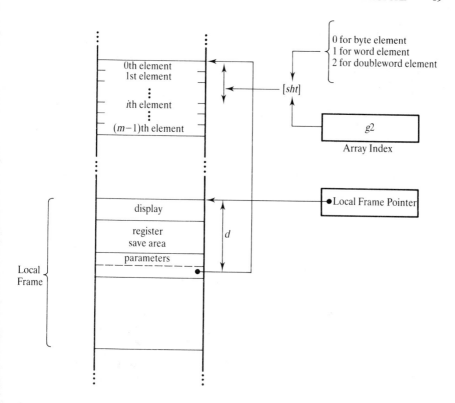

Figure 1.27 Accessing elements of a vector passed as a parameter by using the base displacement indirect indexed indirect mode.

1.6.14 Base displacement indirect displacement indirect addressing

This addressing mode uses two displacements stored in two instruction fields and one base register. The contents of the register g and the displacement $d1$ are added and the result is used as the address to find the value of the corresponding memory location. This value is then added to the second displacement, $d2$, to obtain the operand address.

Figure 1.28 shows how this addressing mode works. The expression giving the operand value is $M[M[G[g] + d1] + d2]$. Two memory cycles and two additions are required to access the operand.

This addressing mode can be used to access non-local scalar variables in a single instruction by using the local frame pointer as g, the displacement of the display item pointing to the frame where the variable is stored as $d1$, and the variable displacement within its frame as $d2$. This addressing mechanism is shown on the left-hand side of Figure 1.29. The right-hand side of Figure 1.29 shows another possible use of this mode;

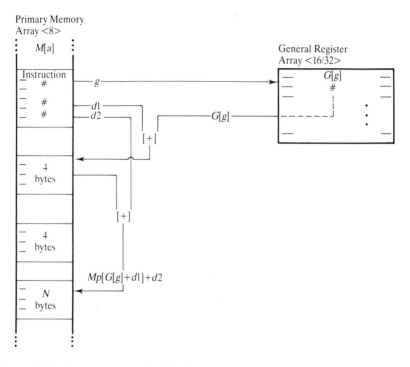

Figure 1.28 Operations involved in the base displacement indirect displacement indirect mode.

that is, to address a field of a record referenced through a local pointer variable. In this case, g is always the local frame pointer, $d1$ is the displacement of the local pointer variable within the frame, and $d2$ is the displacement of the referenced field within the record.

1.6.15   Base displacement indirect displacement indexed indirect addressing

Two registers, $g1$ and $g2$, and two displacements, $d1$ and $d2$, stored in two instruction fields, are the objects manipulated by this addressing mode. The contents of $g1$ and $d1$ are added and the result is used as an address to find the value in the corresponding memory location. To find the operand address, the value stored in $g2$ is first shifted by N positions (where $N = 0$, 1 or 2) and then added, respectively, to $d2$ and to the value previously fetched from memory.

The operations involved in this rather complicated mode are shown

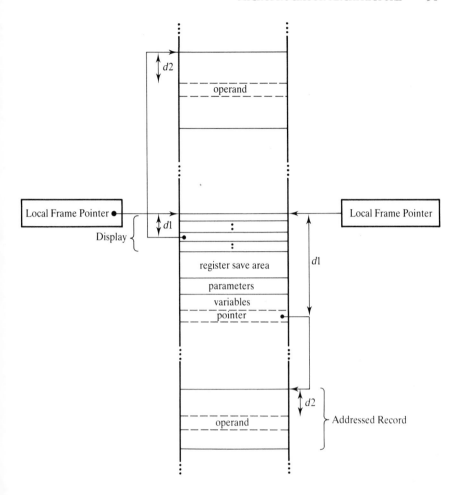

Figure 1.29 Using the base displacement indirect displacement indirect mode to access a non-local operand (left-hand side) or a field in a record reached through a pointer (right-hand side).

in Figure 1.30. The expression giving the operand value is $M[M[G[g1] + d1] + d2 + G[g2].sht.N]$, which represents three additions, one shift and two memory cycles.

Since the base displacement indirect displacement mode may be used to access non-local scalar variables, this addressing mode is able to support references to individual elements of non-local vectors of scalars, as a result of the indexing function. The reference can be made using the local frame pointer as $g1$, the displacement of the display item pointing to the frame where the vector is stored as $d1$, the displacement of the vector

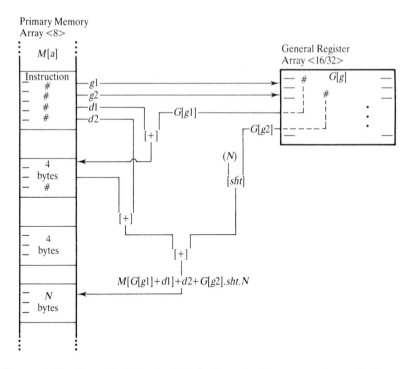

Figure 1.30 Operations involved in the base displacement indirect displacement indexed indirect mode.

memory area within the frame as *d2*, and the array index stored in *g2*. Figure 1.31 shows how this is performed.

1.6.16 Base displacement indexed indirect displacement indirect addressing

As in the previous mode, two registers, *g1* and *g2*, and two displacements, *d1* and *d2*, are used. *g2* is shifted left by *N* positions (where $N = 0$, 1 or 2), according to the operand size, and then it is added to *d1* and *g1*, the result being used to access a memory cell whose contents are added to *d2* to obtain the operand address. Figure 1.32 shows the whole address computation process. The addressing expression here is $M[[G[g1] + d1 + G[g2].sht.N] + d2]$, and although it requires the same computations as the previous mode, the order they may be performed in differs.

This addressing mode is not very useful for basic operations; hence, it may be used only in particular situations or in conjunction with microprocessor specific data structures.

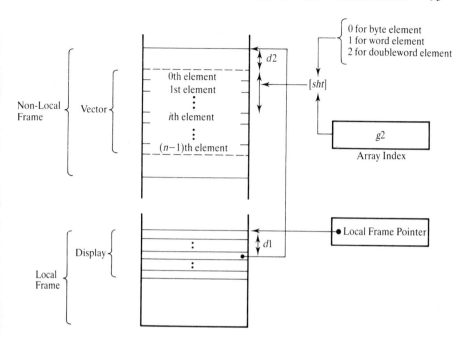

Figure 1.31 Accessing an element of a non-local vector by using the base displacement indirect displacement indexed indirect mode.

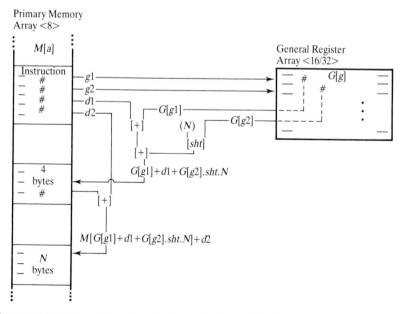

Figure 1.32 Operations involved in the base displacement indexed indirect displacement indirect mode.

1.6.17   Base indirect displacement indirect displacement indirect addressing

The objects used in this addressing mode are two displacements, $d1$ and $d2$, stored in two instruction fields, and a base register, g. The contents of g are used to address the memory. The value obtained is then added to $d1$ and the result used as the address for the value of the corresponding memory location. This value is then added to $d2$ and the result used, once again, as an address to access that location's value, which is used as the operand address.

Figure 1.33 illustrates this mechanism of accessing the operand. The expression giving the operand value is $M[M[M[G[g]] + d1] + d2]]$, which means that three memory cycles and two additions are required for this addressing mode.

This addressing mode is used in the NS32000 microprocessor to access operands through particular control structures (see Chapter 7), but is otherwise fairly limited.

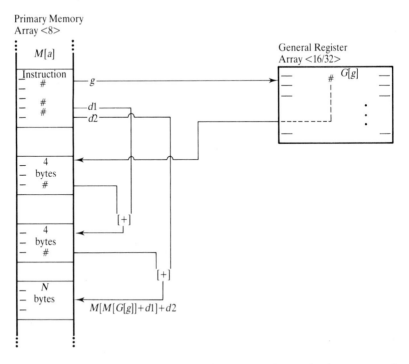

Figure 1.33 Operations involved in the base indirect displacement indirect displacement indirect mode.

1.6.18   Base indirect displacement indirect displacement indexed indirect addressing

Basically, this addressing mode is obtained from the previous one by the introduction of an indexing function before the last indirection. The memory location pointed to by the contents of register $g1$ is read and its value added to $d1$; the result is then added, respectively, to $d2$ and to the value stored in register $g2$, which is shifted by N positions (where $N = 0$, 1 or 2), to obtain the operand address.

The process is defined in Figure 1.34. The expression giving the operand value is $M[M[M[G[g1]] + d1] + d2 + G[g2].sht.N]$, which represents three memory cycles, three additions and one shift. This is in addition to possible extra memory cycles and program counter increments required to read the two displacements.

Once again, this addressing mode is typical of the NS32000 microprocessor and may be used with certain control structures to access data in different program modules.

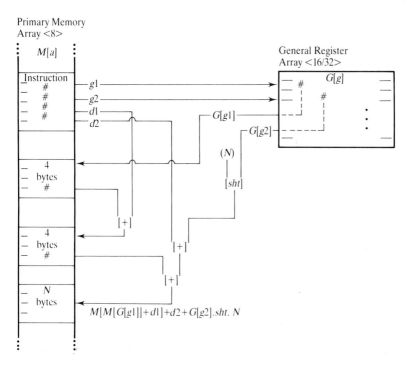

Figure 1.34 Operations involved in the base indirect displacement indirect displacement indexed indirect mode.

1.6.19   Discussion

The addressing modes may be grouped into three main categories:

(1)   simple modes, such as register operand, register indirect, immediate and direct addressing;

(2)   modes basing their address computation process on the addition of
register contents to one or more displacements, read from the
instruction, with the possible use of an additional indexing
function;

(3)   modes based on the addition of one or more register contents, plus
a possible use of an indexing function, followed by an increment,
or preceded by a decrement, of one of the registers involved.

In general, all computers use the simple modes, which represent
the basic operand addressing modes, and all of these are useful for
executing programs written in high-level languages. The exception here is
the direct addressing mode, which is only useful for the code segment.

The addressing modes using base registers and displacements are
also used for operand addressing because, as shown in Section 1.4,
recursive programming leads to the dynamic allocation of variables
defined inside the procedures or functions. This dynamic allocation makes
it impossible for the compiler and the linker/loader to put the addresses
of the manipulated variables into the code. At compile time, the only
information available about the location of variables is the displacement
of those variables within the memory area reserved for the procedures or
frames where they are defined. Hence, the use of a base register holding
the starting address of the frames, and the addressing modes, using such
registers and displacements inserted into the code by the compiler prove
very useful.

The modes based on autoincrement/decrement procedures perform
almost the same address computations as several modes using base
registers. The difference is that register increment/decrement is used
instead of or in addition to displacement addition. All computers allow
simple postincrement mode on the program counter to fetch instructions
as well as immediate and direct addressing modes. Autoincrement/
decrement modes are also used by the stack pointer to obtain pop and
push operations. The application of autoincrement/decrement modes for
general-purpose registers is not, however, allowed in all microcomputers.

The simple autoincrement/decrement modes are not only useful for
stack operations and fetching operands, but also for implementing
operations on strings, which require the automatic increment of the
pointer to the string element. Complex modes based on register
autoincrement are used only in a limited number of cases; for example,

when manipulating a block of operands whose addresses are stored in a string of contiguous locations.

The same relationship between complexity and usefulness of an addressing mode also applies to modes using base registers; in particular, the last two modes discussed in the previous subsection are only used in special cases.

Although more useful, the addressing modes using base registers are slowed down by the need for extra memory cycles to fetch the displacement value. Hence, almost all computers allow different sizes for the displacement, so that the average instruction execution time and length are both decreased by using the shortest possible displacement format.

A classification of the addressing modes of the most popular microprocessors is presented in Table 1.4. The terminology and notation described earlier in this chapter has also been adopted in this table, since different manufacturers give equivalent addressing modes different names.

1.7　Instructions

1.7.1　Instruction encoding

All executable programs are made up of a sequence of machine instructions. Each machine instruction contains two types of information: the operation to be performed, and where the input operands and the results should be located in memory or internal registers. As these two types of information are normally encoded in different instruction fields, the usual number of instruction fields is three, since the information used to locate the operands and the result are composed of an addressing mode specifier and the data to be used in the address computation, when the addressing mode specified requires them. Therefore, a typical instruction format is composed of the following three parts:

(1)　an opcode specifying the operation;
(2)　an addressing mode specification for each of the input operand and for the result;
(3)　data to be used in the address computation by the addressing modes specified (for example, immediate and direct addressing both require the immediate value or the address in the instruction).

Obviously, the machine instructions will have different lengths, depending on the number of operands and addressing modes used. The number of operands to be specified should be kept as small as possible, to

Table 1.4 Addressing modes supported by common microprocessors.

Addressing Modes ⟨instruction content⟩[1]	Operand Fetch	Microprocessor				
		VAX 11	iAPX286[3]	Z80000	MC68020	NS32032
Register direct ⟨g⟩	G[g]	⟨R0:R15⟩	⟨AX/CX/DX/BX SP/BP/SI/DI⟩	⟨16⟩[8]	⟨D0:D7⟩ (data) ⟨A0:A7⟩ (addr.)	⟨R0:R7⟩
Register indirect ⟨g⟩	M[G[g]]	⟨R0:R14⟩[6]	⟨BX/BI/SI/DI⟩	⟨RR2:RR30⟩	⟨A0:A7⟩	
Register indexed indirect ⟨g1, g2⟩	M[G[g1] + G[g2].sht.N]	⟨R0:R15, R0:R15⟩[6]	⟨BX/BI,SI/DI⟩ N = 0[7]			⟨SP0:SP1⟩
Autoincrement indirect ⟨g⟩	M[G[g]]; G[g] := G[g] + N	⟨R0:R14⟩ (R14 = SP)	SP only		⟨A0:A7⟩	
Immediate[2] (g = PC) ⟨length operand⟩	M[[PC]]; PC := PC + N	PC = R15 ⟨6, n/m/l⟩	⟨n/m⟩	⟨n/m/l⟩	⟨n/m/l⟩	⟨4/n/m/l⟩
Autoincrement indexed indirect ⟨g1, g2⟩	M[G[g1] + G[g2].sht.N]; G[g1] := G[g1] + N	⟨R0:R15, R0:R15⟩				⟨SP0/SP1, R0:R7⟩
Autodecrement indirect ⟨g⟩	G[g] := G[g] − N; M[G[g]]	⟨R0:R14⟩ (R14 = SP)	SP only		⟨A0:A7⟩ ⟨n/m/l⟩	⟨SP0/SP1⟩
Autodecrement indexed indirect ⟨g1, g2⟩	G[g1] := G[g1] − N; M[G[g1] + G[g2].sht.N]	⟨R0:R14, R0:R14⟩				⟨SP0/SP1, R0:R7⟩
Autoincrement indirect indirect ⟨g⟩	M[M[G[g]]]; G[g] := G[g] + N1	⟨R0:R14⟩[6]				
Memory direct g = PC, ⟨length⟩	M[M[⟨PC⟩]]; PC := [PC] + N 1	g = R15 = PC ⟨l⟩	⟨0:n/m⟩	⟨m/l⟩	⟨m/l⟩	⟨l⟩
Autoincrement indirect indexed indirect ⟨g1, g2⟩	M[M[G[g1] + G[g2].sht.N]; G[g1] := G[g1] + N1	⟨R0:R15⟩[6]		⟨PC, R15⟩, N = 1[9]		⟨PC, R0:R7⟩
Base displacement indirect (g, d) (A)	M[G[g] + d]	⟨R0:R14, n/m/l⟩	⟨BX/BP, n/m⟩[4] ⟨SI/DI, n/m⟩[5]	⟨R15, n/m/l⟩	⟨A0:A7, m⟩	⟨R0:R7, (E)⟩ ⟨SP/SB/FP, (E)⟩

Table 1.4 (cont.)

		⟨R15, n/m/l⟩	⟨BX/BI, n/m, SI/DI⟩ N = 0	⟨PC, n/m/l⟩	⟨PC, m⟩	⟨PC, (E)⟩
(Relative (g = PC))	M[[PC] + d]	⟨R0:R15, n/m/l, R0:R15⟩		⟨R15/PC, n/m/l, 15⟩ N = 1 (C)	⟨A0:A7/PC, n/m/l, D0:D7/A0:A7⟩ N = 0, 1, 2, 3	⟨R0:R7/SP/ SB/FP/PC, (E), R0:R7⟩
Base displacement indexed indirect ⟨g1, d, g2⟩	M[G[g1] + d + G[g2].sht.N]					⟨SB/FP/SP, (E), (E)⟩
Base displacement indirect indexed ⟨g, d⟩	M[M[G[g] + d]]	⟨R0:R14, n/m/l⟩[6]				
(Relative indirect)	M[M[[PC] + d]]	⟨R15, n/m/l⟩				
Base displacement indirect indexed indirect ⟨g1, d, g2⟩	M[M[G[g1] + d] + G[g2].sht.N]	⟨R0:R15, n/m/l, R0:R15⟩[6]				
Base displacement indirect displacement indirect ⟨g1, d1, d2⟩	M[M[G[g1] + d1] + d2]					
Base displacement indirect displacement index indirect ⟨g1, g2, d2⟩	M[M[G[g1] + d1] + d2 + G[g2].sht.N]				⟨A0:A7/PC, m/l, A0:A7/ D0:D7⟩ N = 0, 1, 2, 3	⟨SB/FP/SP, (E), (E), R0:R7]
Base indirect displacement indirect displacement indirect ⟨g1, d1, d2⟩	M[M[M[G[g1]] + d1] + d2]					⟨MOD, (E), (E)⟩ (F)
Base indirect displacement indirect displacement indexed indirect ⟨g1, d1, d2, g2⟩	M[M[M[G[g1]] + d1] + d2 + G[g2].sht.N]					⟨MOD, (E), (E), R0:R7⟩ (F)

Table 1.4   (cont.)

Addressing Modes ⟨instruction content⟩[1]	Operand Fetch	Microprocessor				
		VAX 11	iAPX286[3]	Z80000	MC68020	NS32032
Base displacement indexed indirect displacement indirect ⟨g1, d1, d2, g2⟩	$M[M[G[g1] + d1 + G[g2].sht.N] + d2]$				⟨A0:A7/PC, m/l, m/l, A0:A7/ D0:D7⟩ $N = 0, 1, 2, 3$	

1   ⟨n, g⟩: n and g present; ⟨n/m⟩: n or m present.
2   When performed at the beginning of an instruction, the operation is the instruction fetch access.
3   All references inside the segment.
4   Called based mode by Intel.
5   Called indexed mode by Intel.
6   Indirect is called deferred by DEC.
7   Called based indexed mode by Intel.
8   Names depend on size: RL, RH(0–15)–8 bits; R(0–15)–16 bits; RR(0–15)–32 bits; RQ(0–7)–64 bits.
9   Called index mode by Zilog.

(A)   Base refers to an unsigned address used as a base.
(B)   Index refers to signed value that is scaled to suit the data type used. Most other types of index are really base address mode.
(C)   The PC mode is called relative indexed by Zilog.
(D)   Called top of stack mode.
(E)   Literals are 7/14/30 bits long.
(F)   Called external mode.

N   Length of operand in bytes, or position shifted.
N1   Length of memory address.
n   Eight-bit value (byte).
m   Sixteen-bit value (word).
l   Thirty-two bit value (longword).
d   Displacement values n, m or l.

keep the average instruction length small. If the operation performed by an instruction needs *n* input operands to produce a result, *n* + 1 addressing modes should be specified, and up to *n* + 1 data fields required for address computation should be included in the instruction.

A common method of shortening the average instruction length involves using one of the input operands as the destination of the result. However, this solution limits the addressing capabilities, since it forces the result to be stored in a predefined input operand. Nevertheless, it does lead to substantial memory savings, as both the addressing mode and, possibly, the data field are specified for *n* operands rather than for *n* + 1. Furthermore, a study performed on a set of FORTRAN programs [4] has shown that most of the assignment statements are of the form $A := A \circ B$, where $\circ$ indicates any operation on two operands

For these reasons, almost all processors use one of the input operands to store the result of the operation, though there are exceptions, such as the VAX 11, which adopts three operand instructions for operations on two input values.

1.7.2 Orthogonality

The addressing modes and the instruction set are said to be **orthogonal** when the processor allows any possible combination of addressing modes and opcodes, except for those that are meaningless. Orthogonality is a desirable feature for instructions as it simplifies the activity of the compiler code generator by avoiding any artificial constraint on the use of addressing modes with different opcodes. However, orthogonality also leads to a moderate increase in the average instruction length. One reason for the increased average instruction length is the need to reserve the same number of bits to specify the addressing mode of each operand specified in the instruction. There is also a possibility of having more than a single immediate operand, address or displacement in the instruction, which will lengthen the instruction.

A solution often adopted in microprocessors with short memory words, of 8 or 16 bits, is to only address one operand at most in any of the eligible modes, while the others must be in a CPU register. In this way, the addressing mode for the operands in the register can be specified by just giving their register number. Furthermore, it is no longer possible to have more than one immediate operand, address or displacement in an instruction.

Other solutions are also possible: a limited subset of instructions – often those used for data movement – are allowed to use any possible combination of addressing modes for their operands, while all other instructions are only allowed to use specific combinations of the addressing modes.

Although orthogonality is a desirable feature, the instruction set of several microprocessors is not fully orthogonal and in some is not orthogonal at all. The search for more compact code is the main reason for violating the orthogonality principle, which often complicates the optimization of the code generated by a compiler.

1.7.3 Special operations

This subsection discusses those instructions that support the efficient implementation of operations typical of programs written in high-level languages. Although these instructions are not the only parameters that support efficient execution, they do represent a set of operations peculiar to programs written in high-level languages, and which are not found in other types of programs.

A. PROCEDURE CALLS

The whole mechanism of procedure calling, in a language allowing recursive programming, has already been shown in Section 1.4. It is possible to distinguish different phases in these operations:

- allocation of the memory for the new frame;
- preparation of the new display fields, by copying the corresponding values from the caller's frame and adding a new frame pointer, if the called procedure is defined within the calling one;
- jump to the subroutine;
- saving the registers (if any) used by the procedure in the reserved area.

Among the listed operations, only the jump-to-subroutine instruction is found in all microprocessors, including the early ones. New types of instructions have been added in more recent microprocessors to directly support procedure calls in all phases.

Table 1.5 summarizes the supports for procedure calls provided in each instruction set for all the microprocessors considered in this book. An X has been placed at the cross-point of each phase (row) supported by an instruction (column). Note that all the microprocessors shown in the table have more than just a jump-to-subroutine instruction, since they all also support other phases of a procedure call operation. Most of them do not have a single instruction to perform the complete procedure call, so it is possible to implement (for example, in an assembly language program) a simple jump-to-subroutine, thereby avoiding the overhead due to the whole procedure call process.

Table 1.5 Supports for procedure calls in common microprocessors.

Operation	NS32000		Z80000		MC68020		iAPX286		VAX 11
	JSR	ENTER	CALL	ENTER	JSR	LINK	JSR	ENTER	CALLS
Frame allocation		X		X		X		X	
Jump-to-subroutine	X		X		X		X		X
Display or link set		X		X		X		X	X
Register saving		X		X					

B.   ARRAY ELEMENT REFERENCING

The allocation and accessing methods for the elements of a multidimensional array have been presented in Section 1.5.7. In particular, this section outlined iterative algorithm that may be used to compute, in several steps, the address of an array element, given the set of associated subscript values.

Another important operation associated with the access of an array element is to check that each subscript value is within the range specified by the array declaration. The possibility of implementing such checks efficiently and with a small increase in the size of the program encourages the programmer to keep these controls active, even when the program has been debugged. In this way, the reliability of the software is enhanced, because any errors leading to the access of non-existent array elements are detected, and latent errors in the program can also be found.

It has already been pointed out that the compiler can map any possible set of subscript values on to the set of integer values from 0 to $m - 1$, where m is the cardinality of the original set of values. Hence, a bound-check operation would require only the subscript value and the maximum value allowed, the minimum being 0. However, some microprocessors implement bound-check instructions with both end values as parameters, and this simplifies the compiler's task, since it avoids mapping the original set of subscript values on to the interval 0 to $m - 1$.

The instructions provided by several microprocessors for accessing elements of multidimensional arrays are shown in Table 1.6. All the microprocessors considered have a bound-check instruction, and, in the Z80000 microprocessor, this check is integrated with the computation of a

Table 1.6 Supports for array element access in common microprocessors.

Operation	NS32000	Z80000		MC68020	iAPX286	VAX 11
	INDEX	CHECK	INDEX	CHK2	CHK	INDEX
Bound check	X	X		X	X	X
Single step of offset computation	X		X			X

Note: The CHECK instruction in the NS32000 compares an index against an upper and a lower bound, and gives the corresponding index value in the range 0 to $m - 1$, m being the number of possible values for the index.

step of the iterative procedure used to compute the element address. The microprocessors, with the exception of the iAPX286, have a different instruction for this operation.

1.8 Conclusion

The high computational speed reached by microprocessors and the decreasing costs of memory has encouraged the use of high-level languages for writing software for microprocessors, so that nowadays only routines for hardware-related operations are encoded in assembly language.

This chapter has analyzed the three main features used to map the programmer's view of the computer on to the real microprocessor: data types, addressing modes and special instructions.

Following a description of the typical memory use in a program written in Pascal, this chapter has shown the possible use of data types, addressing modes and special instructions available in most advanced microprocessors.

EXERCISES

1.1 Given the following Pascal program:

```
program Greek (input, output);
type rec = record
            key  : char;
            code : integer
        end;
        string=array [1..10] of char;
var i,j: integer
    a: string;
    r: rec;
procedure alfa (x: integer);
  var  c: char;
       k: integer;
  procedure beta (ch : char; var cod : integer);
  begin
    if ch in ['A'..'Z','0'..'9','a'..'z']
       then cod := ord(ch)
       else cod := 0
  end; {beta}
```

```
       begin {alfa}
       c := a[x];
       beta(c,k);
       if k>r.code then begin r.code := k;r.key := c end
       end; {alfa}
   begin {main}
   i := 1;
   while (i <= 10) and not eoln do
      begin
      read(a[i]);
      i := i + 1
      end;
   readln; for j := i to 10 do a[j] := ' ';
   r.key := ' ';
   r.code := 0;
   for i := 1 to 10 do alfa(i)
   end.
```

show the memory allocation at the following point in the execution:

(a)   when the main program is executed;

(b)   when procedure *alfa* is executed;

(c)   when procedure *beta* is executed.

1.2 Compute the size of the memory occupied in the three parts of Exercise 1.1, assuming that integers and addresses (pointers) are one doubleword (32 bits), a character is represented using a byte, and the machine has a byte-oriented memory without imposing alignment of data.

1.3 Assume the following definition:

```
   rec = record
            key   : [0..511];
            count : integer;
            ch    : char;
            flag  : boolean;
         end;
```

Compute how many bits are necessary to store a vector of five records of the type defined in a machine having a memory with the following parameters:

(a)   bit addressing and an external word of 32 bits;

(b)   byte addressing, an external word of 32 bits and no constraint on the allocation of data;

(c)   byte addressing, an external word of 32 bits and data aligned with the word or doubleword boundary.

How many bits are wasted in each of these cases?

1.4 For the three cases in Exercise 1.3, compute the average number (among the five records in the vector) of memory access required to read the count field of a record.

1.5 Write the BCD representation for the number 32 569 for both packed and unpacked formats. How many bytes are used in each case? What kind of operations are required to transform each BCD format into a string of ASCII characters?

1.6 Show the memory allocation for a matrix A defined as follows:

$$A : \textbf{array } [1..4, \text{`e'}..\text{`m'}, -4..4, \ 10..18] \textbf{ of } integer$$

How many multiplications are required to compute the offset of an element within the memory area reserved for the matrix?

1.7 Which of the addressing modes in Section 1.6 is most suitable to perform the following operations required by the program in Exercise 1.1:

(a)   access to the variable $a[x]$ within the procedure *alfa*, assuming that the value of x is stored in a register;

(b)   access to the variable *r.count* within the procedure *alfa*;

(c)   access to the variable *ch* within the procedure *beta*;

(d)   access to the variable *cod* within the procedure *beta*;

(e)   access to the variable *c* within the procedure *alfa*.

1.8 How many memory references and additions are required to read an operand addressed using the base displacement indirect displacement indirect mode? Discuss the advantages and disadvantages of using 8-, 16- and 32-bit displacements in a machine with a 32-bit external word.

1.9 Discuss the opportunity of using only positive displacements. What type of addressing must allow positive as well as negative displacements?

1.10 Assume that a microprocessor has the instruction INDEX A,B,C, performing the operation $C := A * B + C$, plus the check that the value of A is not negative and less than B. Write a small program to compute the offset of an element in a matrix with five subscripts:

the subscripts are stored at the locations $A1...A5$, while their bounds are stored in the locations $B1...B5$. (*Note*: Also use the instruction **DJNZ reg, label**, which decrements **reg** and jumps to **label** if not zero.)

References

[1]   G. J. Myers, *Advances in Computer Architecture*, John Wiley & Sons Inc., New York, 1982.

[2]   A. Silbey, V. Milutinovic and V. Mendoza-Grado, 'A Survey of Advanced Microprocessor and HLL Computer Architectures', *Computer* **19**(8), August 1986.

[3]   W. G. Alexander and D. B. Wortman, 'Static and Dynamic Characteristics of XPL Programs', *Computer* **8**(11), August 1975, pp. 41–46.

[4]   D. E. Knuth, 'An Empirical Study of FORTRAN Programs', *Software Practice and Experience* **1**(2), pp. 105–133.

Further reading

Special Issue on High-Level Language Computer Architecture, *Computer* **14**(7), July 1981. (All the papers are worth reading.)

H. El-Alabi and D. P. Agrawal, 'Some Remarks on Direct Execution Computers', *Computer Architecture News* **10**(1), pp. 23–27, March 1982.

K. Itano, 'Pasdec: A Pascal Interactive Direct Execution Computer', *Proceedings of an International Workshop on High-Level Language Computer Architecture*, pp. 161–169, 1980.

P. Bose and E. S. Davidson, 'Design of Instruction Set Architectures for Support of High-Level Languages', *Proceedings of the 11th Annual Symposium on Computer Architecture*, pp. 198–207, June 1984.

Additional references on reduced architectures may be found at the end of Chapter 10.

CHAPTER 2

OTHER ARCHITECTURAL FEATURES OF MICROPROCESSORS

OBJECTIVES

The aims of this chapter are as follows:

- to examine different register organizations of microprocessors;
- to illustrate the main features of the IEEE 754 Floating-Point Standard;
- to outline the trap and interrupt mechanisms in advanced microprocessors;
- to examine some microprocessor features intended to support debugging operations.

2.1   Register organization
2.2   Floating-point numbers
2.3   Interrupts

2.4   Traps
2.5   Debugging supports
2.6   Conclusion

2.1   Register organization

Although registers are regarded as an essential feature of computer architecture, several researchers have argued that registers should be eliminated. However, studies on machines lacking registers have shown that a substantial performance improvement is achieved by the introduction of registers.

The beneficial effect of using registers is mainly due to the following two reasons:

(1)   Operations on register contents are faster than on operands stored in memory, since the former have direct access to the ALU. Thus, it is possible to use the registers to speed up the program by keeping the most frequently used data in the registers.

(2)   The average program length is decreased because the instructions calling operands in registers do not need an address, only a small bit field with the register number.

On the other hand, register contents constitute a state of the computation that must be saved when an interrupt or trap occurs, or it is necessary to switch the program executed in multiprogrammed systems (see also Chapter 3). Therefore, a large register set leads, in general, to a longer time for performing program switching or interrupt/trap handling.

The rest of this section is devoted to examining some of the most important register organizations. However, before doing so, it is worth examining the commonest operations performed by a computer during program execution, since some of the register organizations have been designed bearing in mind what a computer has to do for most of the execution time.

2.1.1   Basic CPU operations

The two commonest activities performed during the execution of a program are data movement and the evaluation of expressions. This observation is supported by the fact that in almost all the algorithmic languages, such as C, Pascal and FORTRAN, all the executable statements fall either in the assignment class or in the flow-control class (**if, while, for** statements). In general, assignment statements require the evaluation of an expression and the assignment of the result to some variable, whereas program flow-control statements require the evaluation of a predicate (that is, a logical expression) and a branch on the value of the predicate to different blocks of instructions.

The use of parentheses and operators with different priorities leads to a general form of an expression that is not suitable for direct evaluation. For example, consider the following arithmetic expression:

$$(A + B) * ((C + D)/(E - F))$$

The order in which these different operations are performed is quite different from the order of their occurrence in the string; thus, the compiler re-orders the expression so that it is more suitable for code generation. The form usually adopted is the reverse polish notation, where each operator indicated is applied to the operands immediately to its left in the expression – note that one or more operands may be the result of subexpressions previously evaluated. Using this notation, the expression assumes the following form, where the parentheses are used only to indicate the order of the operations:

$$((A\ B\ +)((C\ D\ +)(E\ F\ -)/)*)$$

A stack is a data structure highly suited to storing the operands of an expression during its evaluation, and Figure 2.1 shows a sequence of steps leading to the correct evaluation of this arithmetic expression. All the arithmetic operations required are performed only on operands stored in the n topmost locations of the stack, for an n operand instruction. This approach to evaluating expressions has led to various proposals for register organization that closely support such stack operations.

2.1.2   Stack machines

The organization of the registers to store and automatically manage the topmost part of an evaluation stack is the basic idea behind the **stack machine**. The instructions of a pure stack machine only operate on the set of registers storing the contents of the topmost stack locations, with the exception of data movement instructions that are used to load/store the top of stack register from/to memory. Since the stack can grow beyond the limited storage capabilities offered by the register set, the bottom part of the stack is held in memory. For this reason, automatic mechanisms must be provided to handle certain situations, such as loading an operand on top of the stack when all the registers are busy (**register overflow**), or executing an instruction with a number of operands greater than the stack items currently stored in the registers (**register underflow**). Register overflow implies that part of the register's contents – that holding the stack items farthest from top – is copied to memory to free the register; register underflow, on the other hand, implies that the portion of stack just below the elements currently in the register is loaded from memory to the part of the register file not currently used to provide enough operands for the instruction execution.

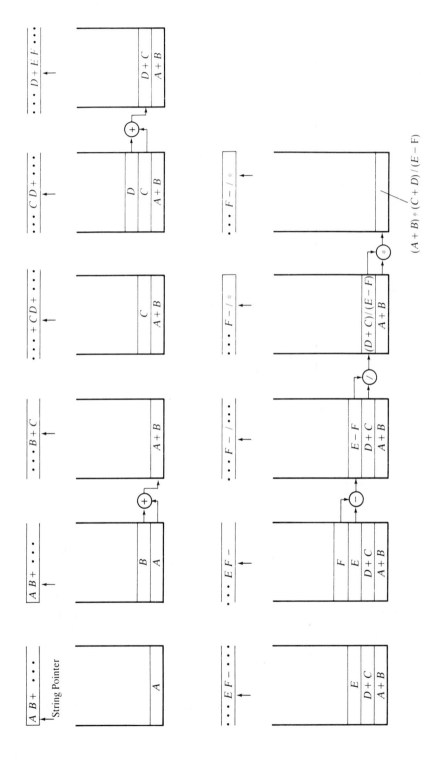

Figure 2.1 Evaluation of an arithmetic expression written in reverse polish notation using a stack.

Only a few stack machines have actually been built, and some of them have been designed for arithmetic processors, rather than general-purpose ones, since stacks are highly suited for the evaluation of expressions. Particular mention should be made here of the Am2911, a peripheral device used as a slave floating-point processor for extended integer arithmetic. This device has internal registers organized as a small stack. The arithmetic co-processor of the iAPX286 family (the 80287, see Chapter 8) also manages its internal data registers as a small stack, but it also allows instructions to operate between the top of a stack and another register.

In the class of processors used for general-purpose computations, the most relevant of the recently developed microprocessors is the Inmos Transputer (see also Chapter 10), which implements 4 Kbytes of memory on the same chip and has three registers dedicated to storing the topmost part of a stack.

Although seldom used in real systems, the stack machine concept has been widely used in designing abstract machines as intermediate target machines for code generation. The intermediate target is used to implement compilers having a sharp separation between the language-dependent (front end) and the real target machine-dependent (back end) parts. Such compilers have a front end that performs lessical, syntactical analysis and code generation for the intermediate target machine, while the back end performs the actual code generation task by deriving the code for the real target machine from that generated for the intermediate machine. This approach allows users to re-target the compiler for a new machine by rewriting the back end only. Furthermore, a compiler for an old machine and a new language can be implemented by rewriting the front end only and generating a code for the same abstract intermediate machine.

2.1.3 Accumulator-based machines

Almost all early computers had only one or a few registers for data manipulation, and these were called **accumulators**. An accumulator register was often an implicit operand for all the instructions of such machines, which resulted in an address in the instruction that specified the second operand (unless, of course, the instructions operated on two accumulators). The addressing modes available were instruction address-ing and indirect addressing, which represents a poor set of modes for modern high-level languages, where the actual location of some variables is determined at run time and cannot be 'hard wired' in the code at compile time. The basic function of the accumulator was to act as the top of the evaluation stack, since it was an operand for all the instructions.

2.1.4   Machines with index registers

A major departure from the early accumulator-based organization was the introduction of the **index register**, which allows easy address computation at run time. The index register provides a number which is added to an address stored in the instruction itself to yield the full operand address. Another class of registers with a similar function is **base registers**.

Sometimes, both types of register are found in the same machine. The distinguishing feature of such machines is only due to the fact that the full address of the operand can be obtained from the addition of the contents of one index register, one base register and, possibly, an offset stored in the instruction. A typical example of this type of microprocessor is the iAPX286 (see Chapter 8), which provides index, base and segment registers for use in address computation.

The introduction of index registers usually shortens the instruction length, since it is possible to specify only a short offset in the instruction rather than a full-sized address, even though this effect is partially compensated for by the number of extra bits required to specify the index register to be used, if more than one exists.

2.1.5   General-purpose register organization

This type of machine provides a set of internal registers that can be used for all possible functions, since all the instructions are applied to registers, irrespective of the registers' names used (with a few exceptions for processor control registers). Such machines are said to have an orthogonal instruction set and register file. Each register may assume a variety of functions:

- **accumulator**:   since it may be used in evaluating expressions;
- **index/base**:   since each register may be specified as an index or base register for operand address computation; hence, it is possible to use any register for storing information, such as a stack frame pointer or an item in the display field;
- **variable pointer**:   in this case, the register is used to store the address of a variable, or it is used to scan a long data type, such as a character string;
- **stack pointer**:   this allows the development of user stacks;
- **control register**:   processor control information is stored in a register, such as a general-purpose register acting as program counter.

Orthogonality between the register file and the instruction set has to be regarded as a support for efficient high-level language execution, because it simplifies the optimization of register use made by the compiler during the code-generation phase. In fact, it has been pointed out [1] that code optimization becomes easier when there are either a few alternatives or the set of alternatives is uniform. Of course, orthogonality represents a contribution to uniformity, and it allows users to partition the register set dynamically among the different functions – accumulators, index/base registers and scanning registers, for example – to match the particular needs of each program. For these reasons, general-purpose register organization is the commonest organization in microprocessors now appearing on the market, though some exceptions do exist.

The average instruction length of this type of register organization is short. This is because several operations can be performed on register operands, hence eliminating the need for an instruction address, which is replaced with a shorter bit field indicating the registers to be used. The same principle applies to index and/or base registers when they are used to specify a memory operand. Note that addressing modes using register contents for address computations represent a large proportion of the addressing modes used by high-level languages to address the variables. This is because, as shown in Section 1.4, the actual variable address is known only at run time.

A minor departure from the pure general-purpose register organization is represented by those machines, such as the Motorola MC68XXX family, where some distinction is made between data and address registers; the former can be used in any arithmetic, logic and movement instructions as source or destination, while the latter can only be used to store partial or full addresses of the operands. However, this distinction is not very sharp, since address registers can also be used in some arithmetic instructions as operands. Furthermore, if the two subsets are large enough, the distinction between data and address registers does not impose hard constraints on the register allocation.

So far, only the registers of the CPU have been implicitly considered, but the advent of arithmetic co-processors (FPUs) also raises the problem of register organization. Several FPUs, such as the NS32081 (see Chapter 7) and MC68881 (see Chapter 6), show the same general-purpose organization of the main CPU; moreover, they are logically part of the same register file as the CPU registers and share the same instruction set, except for extended arithmetic operations reserved for operands in the FPU registers and for addressing modes that cannot use FPU registers to compute operand addresses. In this way, a real, almost uniform, register set is seen by the assembler programmer and compiler code generator.

2.1.6 Machines without registers

Although registers lead to enhanced performance and compact code, they are not without disadvantages; for example, they can result in internal CPU state-to-be-saved when the execution should, in fact, be switched to another program. A more subtle problem can arise in a multiprocessor system where data shared among programs running on different CPUs is copied into and then modified by the registers of one CPU. Since the registers are not accessible from the external devices, these modifications are hidden from the other CPUs.

These problems are solved in register-based computers by means of either special instructions, used to manipulate critical shared data, or special language features, which indicate to the compiler which variables cannot be copied or manipulated in the registers. However, some proposals and implementations of microcomputers without registers exist. The main advantages sought by their designers are to have fast context switching (see Chapter 3) and to eliminate any problem connected with the manipulation of shared variables. It is not surprising therefore that the most relevant example of this type of internal organization is represented by the iAPX432 (see Chapter 9), which is a machine expressly conceived for multiprocessor configurations.

Of course, such CPUs also have drawbacks: their average instruction length is increased by the need to specify all the addresses of the operands and the results (if different) within the instruction; and the average execution time of an instruction is longer, because both the operand fetch and the result store require access to the memory, which is slower than register access.

2.1.7 Registers and code compactness

Register organization has an important influence on the average instruction length. Since almost all the operations in a program involve an operand in a register, the number of bits therefore used to specify such an operand can lengthen the instruction.

The two extremes of this situation are represented by machines without registers, which need to specify all the operands by using their full addresses, and by stack machines, where memory addresses are used only in load/store instructions. Intermediate situations are found in accumulator-based machines, requiring an address for the second operand (not in the accumulator), and in general-purpose register machines, requiring one or more instruction fields to specify registers and/or addresses for the operands.

The average instruction length is not the only parameter for evaluating the compactness of code achieved. It is also necessary to take account of the number of instructions needed to implement specific

Table 2.1 Comparison of stack, register and accumulator machines.

Stack Machine

Instruction coding

| op | addr. (a) |

Instruction: S1 of 12 bits

| op (f) |

Instruction: S2 of 6 bits

Operations (f)

$M[a] := s$
$s := M[a]$

$s := s.f.s$

Program	Instruction	Type	Stack contents
push a	$s := M[a]$	S1	a
push b	$s := M[b]$	S1	a, b
subtract	$s := s - s$	S2	$a - b$
push c	$s := M[c]$	S1	$a - b, c$
push d	$s := M[d]$	S1	$a - b, c, d$
push e	$s := M[e]$	S1	$a - b, c, d, e$
multiply	$s := s*s$	S2	$a - b, c, d*e$
subtract	$s := s - s$	S2	$a - b, c - d*e$
divide	$s := s/s$	S2	$a - b/c - d*e$
pop f	$M[f] := s$	S1	empty

Program size: $(6*S1) + (4*S2) = 96$ bits
Memory references = 6
Real m/c B5000: 144 bits

General Register Machine

Instruction coding

| op (f) | g | addr. (a) |

Instruction: R1 of 20 bits

| op (f) | g1 | g2 |

Instruction: R2 of 14 bits

Operations (f)

$G[g] := G[g].f.M[a]$
$G[g] := M[a]$
$M[a] := G[g]$

$G[g1] := G[g1].f.G[g2]$

Program	Instruction	Type
load g1, a	$G[g1] := M[a]$	R1
subtract g1, b	$G[g1] := G[g1] - M[b]$	R1
load g2, d	$G[g2] := M[d]$	R1
multiply g2, e	$G[g2] := G[g2] * M[e]$	R1
inv subtract g2, c	$G[g2] := M[c] - G[g2]$	R1
divide g1, g2	$G[g1] := G[g1]/ G[g2]$	R2
store g1, f	$M[f] := G[g1]$	R1

Program size: $(6*R1) + (1*R2) = 134$ bits
Memory references = 6
Real m/c IBM360: 224 bits (208)

Accumulator Machine

Instruction coding

| op (f) | addr. (a) |

Instruction: O1 of 16 bits

Operations (f)

	Type
$AC := AC.f.M.[a]$	O1
$AC := M[a]$	O1
$M[a] := AC$	O1

Program	Instruction	Type
load d	$AC := M[d]$	O1
multiply e	$AC := AC*M[e]$	O1
inv subtract c	$AC := M[c] - AC$	O1
store temp	$M[temp] := AC$	O1
load a	$AC := M[a]$	O1
subtract b	$AC := AC - M[b]$	O1
divide temp	$AC := AC/M[temp]$	O1
store f	$M[f] := AC$	O1

Program size: $(8*O1) = 128$ bits
Memory references = 8
Real m/c PDP-8: 180 bits (96)

Note: Computation of the function $r := (a - b)/(c - d * e)$. Variable addresses referred to by variable name. The lower bit count given in parentheses assumes that inverse subtract is available. Higher bit count is true value.

operations. To highlight the advantages and disadvantages of the different register organizations, Table 2.1 shows the translation of a simple program for stack, general-purpose and accumulator machines. Two parameters are taken into account: the memory space required by the program and the number of instructions executed.

The programming example in Table 2.1 illustrates the typical drawback of accumulator machines; that is, they require a larger number of load/store operations due to the small register set. Stack and general-purpose register machines execute the same number of instructions in this example, but the program for the stack machine is more compact. However, a machine with a general-purpose register set can emulate a stack machine with the same number of internal registers by means of a suitable register allocation policy. The former can never execute more instructions than the latter to run the same operations, while the latter can. Exercise 2.1 at the end of this chapter describes a typical situation where the stack machine requires more instructions.

2.1.8 Discussion

The number, size and function of the registers used are the key factors for evaluating the internal organization of a processor, including its extensions such as an FPU.

The size of the registers depends on both the external data path and the size of the address given by the CPU, since the addresses are a special type of operand manipulated in registers. In 8-bit and 16-bit microprocessors, where the data path is smaller than the address size, special instructions and register storage mechanisms are provided to allow simple operations on addresses. The 32-bit microprocessors no longer have this problem because their data path is equal to or larger than their addresses. They do not therefore require any special operation or register storage allocation.

When the data types being manipulated are shorter than the register length, different schemes are used to place them into the registers. To illustrate the three main schemes, consider a register file composed of sixteen 32-bit registers. Figure 2.2 shows how byte and 16-bit data can be stored in the registers. In Figure 2.2(a), each 32-bit register can only store one datum, no matter what the operand length. Therefore, a byte operand requires a full 32-bit register as a 32-bit operand. The scheme in Figure 2.2(b) shows that the 16 registers may also be seen as 32 registers each of 16 bits, or 64 registers each one byte long. Since the word, half-word and byte registers all share the same

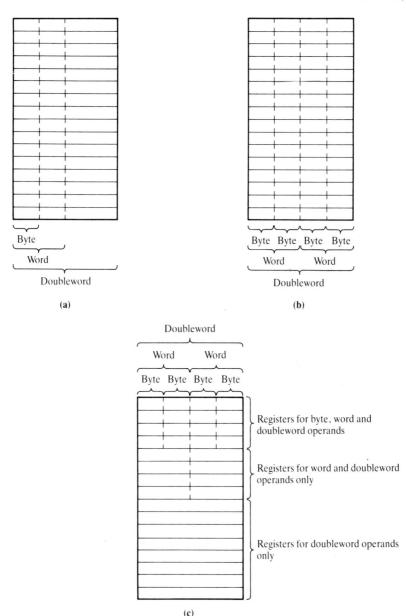

Figure 2.2 Different allocation schemes allowed for operands of different sizes in registers.

physical locations, then it is possible to have any combination of active registers of all the types at a given instant, provided they do not overlap. Finally, the third scheme, in Figure 2.2(c), is a derivation of the second, where the number of registers is always the same (16), regardless of the type considered. Thus, some 32-bit registers can never be used to store short operands.

It is obvious that the first scheme is the simplest because use of the register is independent of the operand length, although in the case of operands with different lengths, the amount of data that can be held in the registers is less than in the other cases. The second scheme preserves orthogonality, to some extent, and introduces more flexibility in the use of registers. However, it also introduces some complications in their optimization, since the amount of data that can be held in the registers depends on the arrangement of the operands in the registers. The third scheme is the one with the least orthogonality, since it constrains the use of registers. This is because some registers cannot be used in instructions manipulating short operands.

In addition to registers used to store data or addresses of different types (for example, pointers, stack pointers and procedure frame pointers), there is a class of registers devoted to special functions. This class includes flag registers, program counters and segment/page registers. Although these registers are all dedicated to their function, they are, in some cases, duplicated so that one copy is available for the user mode and a separate one for the supervisor mode.

The register organization of several important machines is reported in Table 2.2. Note that the VAX 11, MC68020 and NS32000 use the register organization of Figure 2.2(a), whereas the iAPX286 and Z80000 use the register organization of Figure 2.2(c). The iAPX286 and the MC68020 have general-purpose registers distinguished from those used for addresses. The VAX 11, NS32032 and Z80000, in contrast, do not have such a distinction. They normally use some of the general-purpose registers to store address information, such as stack pointers, program counters and frame pointers, and therefore a number of such registers are listed in separate lines – for example, the address registers for the iAPX286 and Z80000.

The address registers shown in the second line of Table 2.2 are the same as the general-purpose registers for the VAX 11, NS32032 and Z80000 (except R0 for the latter), since these processors make no distinction between general and address registers. The MC68020 and the iAPX286 have distinct address registers, which can also be used as operands in some instructions. The NS32000, in addition to the general registers, also has three base registers in the set of special registers.

In the third line of Table 2.2, only the registers normally used as stack pointers have been indicated; however, all the machines with autoincrement/decrement modes can use any address register as a stack pointer. All the other registers in the table are dedicated ones and their function depends on the specific processor considered.

Table 2.2 Comparison of register organizations.

Register	Microprocessor				
	VAX 11/780	iAPX286	Z80000	MC68020	NS32032
General registers (Accumulators) 64	6		8	4	4
32	12		16	8	8
16	12	2	16	8	8
8	12	8	16	8	8
Memory address registers ⟨L⟩[3] [type]	12[4] ⟨32⟩ [indirect, base, index][2]	2[4] ⟨16⟩ [base], 2[4] ⟨16⟩ [index]	15[5] ⟨32⟩ [indirect, base, index]	7[4] ⟨32⟩ [indirect, base, index], 1 ⟨32⟩ [interrupt]	8[4] ⟨32⟩ [indirect, index, base]
Stack pointer(s) ⟨L⟩[3] [type]	5 ⟨32⟩ [stack]	1 ⟨16⟩ [stack]	1 ⟨32⟩ [stack]	1 ⟨32⟩ [stack], 1 ⟨32⟩ [supervisor]	1 ⟨24⟩ [user], 1 ⟨24⟩ [interrupt]
Segment/page registers ⟨L⟩[3] [type]	6	1 ⟨16⟩ [code], 1 ⟨16⟩ [data], 1 ⟨16⟩ [stack], 1 ⟨16⟩ [extra]	2 ⟨32⟩ [data], 2 ⟨32⟩ [code]	2 ⟨32⟩	
Special registers ⟨L⟩[3] [type]	1 ⟨32⟩ [frame pointer], 1 ⟨32⟩ [argument pointer], 2 ⟨32⟩ [process descriptor]	1[4] ⟨16⟩ [loop/shift/repeat count]	1 ⟨32⟩ [overflow SP], 1 ⟨32⟩ [H/W interface]	2 ⟨32⟩ [cache], 1 ⟨32⟩ [vector]	1 ⟨16⟩ [modules descr.], 1 ⟨24⟩ [frame pointer], 1 ⟨24⟩ [integer base], 1 ⟨24⟩ [static base]
Processor state ⟨L⟩[3] [type]	1 ⟨32⟩ [status word]	1 ⟨16⟩ [flags], 1 ⟨16⟩ [m/c status]	1 ⟨16⟩ [flag, control], 1 ⟨8⟩ [system config.]	1 ⟨16⟩ [status]	1 ⟨16⟩ [(8) user], [(8) supervisor]
Program counter ⟨L⟩[3]	1 ⟨32⟩	1 ⟨16⟩	1 ⟨32⟩	1 ⟨32⟩	1 ⟨24⟩

[1] The VAX uses opcodes to distinguish operand size.
[2] Two of these are frame and argument pointers.
[3] Register size in bits.
[4] These registers can also be used as general registers in some instructions.
[5] These registers are a subset of the general registers.

2.2   Floating-point numbers

2.2.1   Representation of real numbers

Real numbers are a very important data type, especially for scientific and engineering applications of microcomputers. Unfortunately the set of real numbers is convex; that is, an infinite number of real values are included in any interval, regardless of the interval size. However, only a discrete set of values can be represented precisely in a computer, as each datum must be represented with a finite number of bits, and this leads to only a finite number of possible values, or bit patterns. Any representation of real numbers on a digital computer is therefore only an approximation of the actual values.

Another important characteristic of real data is that in many cases the data assume values drawn from a large range. However, in almost all cases, it is important to represent such values with a given relative precision, no matter what the absolute value. For example, it is necessary to represent a value so that the five most significant decimal digits are exact.

One method for separating the range and the precision is to represent the numbers in the following form:

$$x = (-1)^s \ (j.m) \ K^e$$

where s is the sign bit; $(j.m)$ is the significand, composed of an integer part j (no longer than one digit) and a mantissa m $(0 < m < 1)$; K is the radix of the representation, and is normally an integer; and e is the exponent. Sometimes, the integer part of the significand is not represented in calculating the maximum number of the bits reserved for the significand.

The value of K is a parameter of the specific representation, and is implicit for the representation chosen. The value can be indicated by specifying only four elements:

(1)   the sign of the significand;
(2)   the integer part of the significand;
(3)   the value of the mantissa; and
(4)   the value of the exponent.

If n bits are reserved for real-number representation, then the general format for a floating-point number is that shown in Figure 2.3.

It is interesting to note that there is a relationship between the representation of the significand and the value of K: floating-point numbers may be more efficiently used if K is a power of the base selected for the significand representation. Therefore, if decimal representation is

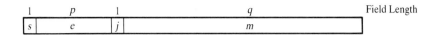

Figure 2.3   Generic floating-point format.

used, it is more convenient to use a power of 10 for K, so that the actual position of the decimal point is determined by counting digit positions in the significand. However, if binary representation is used, as in computers, a power of two is the most convenient choice for K.

The value of K, together with the number of bits used for the significand and exponent, defines the range and precision characteristics of a floating-point representation. The range is given by the minimum (except 0) and maximum absolute values allowed by the representation. Such values are:

$$K^{-(q+2^{(p-1)}-1)} \qquad \text{for the minimum}$$
$$K^{(2^{(p-1)}-1)} \qquad \text{for the maximum}$$

where it is assumed that the exponent values range from $-2^{(p-1)}$ to $2^{(p-1)} - 1$, and the mantissa is represented in binary.

The relative precision is given by the maximum value of the ratio $(x_{i+1} - x_i)/x_i$, where x_i and x_{i+1} are two values such that no intermediate value is allowed by the representation. Such a ratio is maximum when the value of the mantissa is minimum. Hence, the relative precision is given by $2^{(q-1)}$, whereas the absolute precision is given by $2^{(q-1)} K^{2^{(p-1)}-1}$.

These formulae show that the range and precision requirements are not compatible, since high values for K and p improve the former and worsen the latter, while high values for q and small values for K improve the latter and worsen the former.

Many floating-point formats use a normalized representation for the mantissa to increase the precision of the computations. The mantissa is represented in normalized form when it is no longer possible to obtain another valid representation of the same number by multiplying the significand and decrementing the exponent. In other words, the normalized representation of a floating-point number is the one where the significand has been shifted as far left as possible.

Normalized numbers increase the precision of the computations because the arithmetic unit sometimes generates the mantissa of the result with a number of bits greater than that allowed in the format used. Thus, if the result is normalized before being truncated or rounded to fit the data format, then a larger number of significant digits is kept after the operation. It should be noted, however, that using only normalized numbers can lead to problems, such as the impossibility (in principle) of representing a 0 value or an increase in the lowest absolute value allowed.

This problem arises due to the fact that the lower limit refers to a non-normalized representation.

Overflow and underflow are also distinctive features of a floating-point representation, because some of them include special bit patterns to indicate absolute values greater than maximum or less than the minimum allowed.

Another feature of this representation is the method used to round up the result of an operation.

2.2.2   IEEE 754 Floating-Point Standard

Section 2.2.1 highlighted the fact that several degrees of freedom are offered to the designer of a floating-point representation. However, this freedom has led, in the past, to a proliferation of different standards, since different manufacturers used their own personally designed floating-point system. This in turn has also given rise to problems in porting the same program on to different machines.

More recently, the IEEE 754 Floating-Point Standard [2 – 5] has been widely accepted by the computer manufacturers, and this has resulted in a unification of the different representations used. At present, all floating-point units for microprocessor systems are based on this standard.

The IEEE 754 Floating-Point Standard not only covers the format of number representation, but also several other topics; such as conversions between different floating-point formats, conversions between these formats and integers or BCD numbers, the results of arithmetic operations and exception handling.

A.   FORMATS

Four basic formats exist, which are divided into two groups: basic and extended formats. Each group includes a single and a double-precision format. The basic formats are composed of a sign bit, s, a fraction, f and an exponent, e. Although e can be positive or negative, it is represented by adding a bias to the actual value, so that the value of e is never negative.

The extended formats depend on the implementation and comprise a sign bit, s, an integral part of the significand, j, a fractional part of the significand, f, and an exponent, represented as in the basic format.

Single-basic format   This format includes a 1-bit sign, an 8-bit exponent and a 23-bit fraction, as shown in Figure 2.4(a). The value v of the number is determined as follows:

- if $e = 255$ and $f \neq 0$, then $v = $ NaN (NaN or *N*ot a *N*umber is a

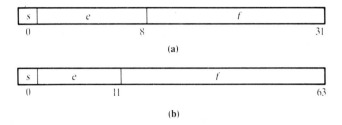

Figure 2.4 Standard floating-point formats: (a) single-basic format; (b) double-basic format.

symbolic entity encoded in the floating-point format);

- if $e = 255$ and $f = 0$, then $v = (-1)^s \infty$;
- if $0 < e < 255$, then $v = (-1)^s 2^{(e-127)}$ $(1.f)$;
- if $e = 0$ and $f \neq 0$, then $v = (-1)^s 2^{-126}$ $(0.f)$;
- if $e = 0$ and $f = 0$, then $v = (-1)^s 0$ (zero).

Double-basic format This format includes a 1-bit sign, an 11-bit exponent and a 52-bit fraction, as shown in Figure 2.4(b). The value v of the number is determined as follows:

- if $e = 2047$ and $f \neq 0$, then $v = \text{NaN}$;
- if $e = 2047$ and $f = 0$, then $v = (-1)^s \infty$;
- if $0 < e < 2047$, then $v = (-1)^s 2^{(e-1023)}$ $(1.f)$;
- if $e = 0$ and $f \neq 0$, then $v = (-1)^s 2^{-1023}$ $(0.f)$;
- if $e = 0$ and $f = 0$, then $v = (-1)^s 0$, (zero).

Single-extended format This format includes a 1-bit sign, a 1-bit integer, at least a 31-bit fractional part and an exponent ranging from a minimum $m \leq 1022$ and a maximum $M \geq 1023$. The value v of the number is determined as follows:

- if $e = M$ and $f \neq 0$, then $v = \text{NaN}$;
- if $e = M$ and $f = 0$, then $v = (-1)^s \infty$;
- if $m < e < M$, then $v = (-1)^s 2^e$ $(j.f)$;
- if $e = m$ and $j = f = 0$, then $v = (-1)^s 0$ (zero);
- if $e = m$ and $j \neq 0$ or $f \neq 0$, then $v = (-1)^s 2^{e'}$ $(j.f)$, where e' may be selected by the implementor to be either m or $m + 1$.

Double-extended format This format is the same as the single-extended format, except that the exponent range is from $m \leq -16\,382$ and $M \geq 16\,383$, and the number of bits of the fractional should be at least 63.

B.   ROUNDING

The rounding operation takes a number regarded as infinitely precise and modifies it to obtain a number that fits into the destination format. A signal is also produced to indicate whether or not the result is correct.

The IEEE 754 Standard includes a default rounding mechanism and three selectable rounding methods. The default mechanism rounds the format to the nearest representable value. If there are two possible values, the format is rounded to an even value. In such cases, the error is on half of the least significant digit position.

The three selectable rounding mechanisms are as follows:

(1)   round towards $+\infty$;

(2)   round towards $-\infty$; and

(3)   round towards 0 (truncation).

The first type of rounding produces a value for the format (including $+\infty$) closest to and not less than the given number. The second type of rounding works in a similar way, since it produces a value closest to and no greater than the given number. Truncation, in comparison, yields a value closest to and no greater than the given number in magnitude.

The rounding operation is applied to the destination format, but in double or extended formats the standard allows the user to specify whether rounding should be performed in the single-basic format. In this way, it is possible for a machine allowing only double-basic and extended formats to emulate the single-basic format.

C.   SPECIAL VALUES

The standard floating-point representation supports infinity arithmetic under two user-selectable modes: **projective** and **affine**, the former being the default. Affine infinity is defined by the following relation:

$$-\infty < (\text{every finite number}) < +\infty$$

Projective infinity, on the other hand, always compares equal numbers, regardless of sign. The standard defines a set of operations such that the use of an ∞ operand does not lead to wrong results; thus, no special trap is required to detect this case, while all the other exemptions discussed later remain valid also for computations on ∞.

NaN is also a special value, introduced to signal invalid operations or operations producing invalid results with a special value. Trapping and non-trapping NaNs are also defined by the standard. The former activate an exception when an operation is performed on them, while the latter produces a non-trapping NaN for operations involving at least one NaN input operand, and set the appropriate error flags.

D. OPERATIONS

The operations defined in the standard are the basic arithmetic operations: addition, subtraction, division and multiplication; finding square roots and remainders of a division; converting between floating-point formats, integers and BCD numbers (except for extended to *BCD* conversion); and comparing floating-point numbers.

The last of the operations just listed deserves some explanation because the use of infinity and NaNs leads to some peculiar situations. The relations allowed are: 'less than', 'equal to', 'greater than' and 'unordered'. The last case arises when at least one operand is NaN and ∞ is compared, in projective mode, with a non-infinite number. The relation 'unordered' affirms both the predicate 'unordered' and the predicate '$\neq$', but denies all the others. If it is necessary to test whether a number has a NaN value, it is not possible to check the equality between a NaN constant and the number because the result will always be false, since the relation is always 'unordered'.

E. EXCEPTIONS AND TRAPS

The IEEE 754 Standard also defines the exceptions that should be detected and the information to be passed to the trap handler for finding such exceptions. The implementation of the standard should also provide a flag for each type of exception. The default response to an exception should be to proceed without activating the trap.

Invalid operation This type of exception can be subdivided into two classes: invalid operand and invalid result exceptions. In both cases, if a trap is not activated, the result should be set to a non-trapping NaN.

The following events give rise to an operand exception:

- an operand is at least a non-trapping NaN and no trap is enabled or activated;
- one of the following operations is executed: $(\infty) + (\infty)$ (projective mode), $(+\infty) + (-\infty)$ (affine mode), $(\infty) / (\infty)$, $0/0$ and $0 \times \infty$;
- when in the operation x REM y, either x is infinite or y is zero;
- when the square root is applied to a negative number;
- conversion from floating point to integer or BCD, when overflow, infinity or NaN preclude a correct conversion;
- comparison using the predicates $<$, $>$ or their negations, when the relation is 'unordered', and no operand is 'unordered'.

Invalid result exceptions are raised when the result of an operation is not correct for the destination format.

Other exceptions   Other standard exceptions are as follows:

- division by zero;
- overflow;
- underflow;
- inexact results, raised when no other exception is generated and the rounded value of the result overflows without a trap.

Trap parameters   The traps corresponding to each exception can be disabled and enabled by the user. When enabled, the exception causes the control to be transferred to a user- or system-provided trap-handling routine. Such a routine should be provided with the following information:

- the type of exception that occurred;
- the kind of operation that was being performed;
- the format of the destination;
- a correctly rounded result – in the case of overflow, underflow, inexact and invalid result – in addition to other information that does not fit the destination format;
- the operand values, in the case of dividing by zero and invalid operand exceptions.

2.3   Interrupts

An interrupt is caused by some event outside the CPU, normally an I/O operation. The effect of an interrupt is to suspend the execution of the running program and transfer the control to a specific routine called an **interrupt handler**, which then performs the actions required to cope with the external event associated with the specific interrupt received.

Interrupts improve the use of the CPU, since they allow users to execute I/O operations in parallel with CPU activity. For example, it may be necessary to output a block of data using a peripheral device, while executing some other computation. Figure 2.5 shows the operations performed. The CPU sends the first datum to the peripheral device and enables the interrupt from it. It then resumes other computations while the peripheral device starts the output operation. When the output halts an interrupt request is sent to the CPU, which temporarily suspends its activity and sets the handler to test whether or not the data block has terminated. If it has not, another datum is sent to the peripheral device and the interrupt is left enabled. After execution of the interrupt-handling routine, the activity suspended when the interrupt occurred is

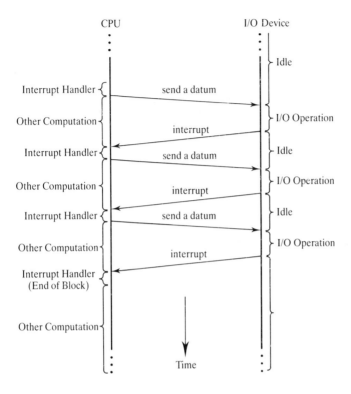

Figure 2.5 Use of an interrupt to overlap I/O and CPU operations.

resumed. When the handler is activated and no more data is transferred to the peripheral device, then the interrupt from that device is disabled. It should always be possible to send a signal to each peripheral, normally by writing into one of its control registers, to enable or disable the interrupt request from that device, since not all the interrupting devices may be used at the same time in interrupt mode.

2.3.1 Types of interrupt

Four classes of interrupt are generally used in microprocessors:

(1)   **vectored interrupts**;
(2)   **non-maskable interrupts**;
(3)   **non-vectored interrupts**;
(4)   **restartable interrupts**.

A. VECTORED INTERRUPTS

Since several external devices can send interrupt requests to the CPU, it is necessary to identify the specific interrupt source to select the handling routine to be activated. This is done by performing a special cycle, called an **interrupt acknowledge cycle**, on the external bus. This cycle does not perform a memory or I/O operation, but rather it addresses the interrupting device, which should provide the CPU with an identification code. The code read during the interrupt acknowledge cycle is used by the CPU as an index for an array in memory, where the information required to start all the interrupt handlers in the systems is stored. Once the proper element is selected, the corresponding handler is activated.

Vectored interrupts are, in general, maskable. In other words, it is possible to ignore the request for a vectored interrupt using suitable instructions, so that the running program cannot be suspended by an interrupt request. The interrupts are, however, disabled when it is necessary to perform an operation more important than any external interrupt.

Only one physical signal needs to be used to receive vectored interrupt requests, since the subsequent interrupt acknowledge cycle is used to obtain the interrupt code.

B. NON-MASKABLE INTERRUPTS

This type of interrupt is not subject to the masking operation described for vectored interrupts; hence, whenever activated, a non-maskable interrupt causes the interruption of the running program regardless of the operations performed by the CPU. This means that the external events leading to a non-maskable interrupt request are more important than any possible operation performed by a program. Therefore, only particular (often catastrophic) events are allowed to generate such an interrupt. Typical examples of such events are when the system detects that the power supply is failing, or that there are errors in a memory cycle, providing no other special interrupt is used for this purpose.

To receive non-maskable interrupt requests a separate input signal is required, since it is necessary to indicate that the request arriving via such a special input must not be masked. When a non-maskable interrupt request is received, most microprocessors perform the same actions as for vectored interrupts, including the same interrupt acknowledge cycle; however, this cycle is used just to inform the external device that its request is now being serviced by the CPU. No data is read, since the information on the handling routine is stored in a reserved position within the vector of interrupts.

C. NON-VECTORED INTERRUPTS

Basically, a non-vectored interrupt has the same effect as a non-maskable interrupt. As the information on the interrupt handler is located in a reserved position within the interrupt vector, no external code is provided. Non-vectored interrupts are also maskable. A separate CPU input should generally be provided to receive this type of interrupt.

D. RESTARTABLE INTERRUPTS

When an interrupt request is received for servicing, it is necessary to suspend the program running on the CPU, saving the minimum amount of information required to resume its execution later. The suspension of a program should be performed when an instruction has just been completed, to minimize the effort involved in saving the state of the computation. Consequently, almost all interrupt requests are sensed and acknowledged by the CPU only at the end of an instruction. However, when an interrupt request is generated due to a situation preventing the correct execution of the instruction itself, the interrupt should be serviced immediately, before the end of the instruction. A typical example is an interrupt activated when some error is found during the execution of a memory cycle – a parity error, for example. Since this type of interrupt suspends the running program in the middle of an instruction, all the information required to resume the instruction has to be saved. Alternatively, instructions should be designed so that it is always possible to re-execute them correctly, even though they have been partially executed. In the first case, all computations already performed are saved, while in the second case less effort is needed to save the computation. The latter case also requires that either no partial result (except for the program counter, which is always incremented) will affect the register contents, or that all the operations already completed will be undone.

As the detection of possible transient errors in memory or I/O transfers is one of the commonest uses of restartable interrupts, some microprocessors – the MC68000, for example – provide a special interrupt which repeats the last bus cycle automatically, rather than activating an interrupt handler.

2.3.2 Latency time

Interrupts signal the occurrence of external events requiring some action by the CPU as a response to their occurrence. In the case of data output to a peripheral device, the event is the completion of a single output operation, and the response is the new datum sent to the peripheral device, or the interrupt disable signal, when the transfer is terminated.

The speed of the CPU in providing a suitable response to an

interrupt request is important in a microprocessor: it is not possible to handle interrupts (and hence peripherals) with a minimum interval between two consecutive requests shorter than the time required to serve each of them. The time taken to service an interrupt depends on the operations performed to respond to the associated external event plus the delay between the request activation and the beginning of the interrupt-handling routine. The first depends on the specific interrupt, while the second is a characteristic of the microprocessor and is referred to as the interrupt **latency time**.

To determine the latency time, it is necessary to examine the sequence of operations performed to switch the execution from the running program to the interrupt-handling routine. Although this sequence may depend on the actual microprocessor, the following operations are always performed, not necessarily in the order listed:

- the program counter and the flags are pushed on to the stack;
- an interrupt acknowledge cycle is performed and the interrupt vector index is read, in the case of vectored interrupts;
- the new program counter and flags are read from the interrupt vector, causing a jump to the beginning of the interrupt handler.

These operations are those strictly required to start the handler. In many cases, however, the first action performed by the service routine is to save the contents of the CPU registers, in addition to performing other housekeeping operations. The true latency time therefore should also include the delay caused by these initializations.

2.3.3 Priorities

As several interrupts of different types can be allowed in a system, each one associated with a different event, it is possible for more than one interrupt request to be active at one time. It follows, therefore, that some mechanism must be provided to solve the contention for service from the CPU, by associating a different priority with each interrupt. Such an interrupt-priority mechanism is also used to decide whether or not it is possible to service an incoming interrupt request when a program is executed. The general rule is that an interrupt can suspend the execution of a program only if its priority is greater than that of the operation being performed by the CPU. Interrupt requests with a low priority can therefore be delayed longer than higher priority ones, because the associated handler is prevented from commencing when higher priority requests are being serviced. The actual execution time of the handler can also be stretched by the occurrence of higher priority interrupts during its execution.

The basic criterion used to assign priorities to the different interrupts is therefore based on the response speed required by the associated events: the higher the priority, the faster the response. The order generally used to decide interrupt priority when multiple requests have been submitted to the CPU is as follows:

(1)   restartable interrupts: these interrupts have the highest priority since they are associated with events that cannot wait until the completion of the current instruction to be serviced;

(2)   non-maskable interrupts: interrupts in this class have higher priority than vectored and non-vectored ones, since the associated events need such an urgent service that it is not possible to mask them;

(3)   vectored interrupts;

(4)   non-vectored interrupts.

Vectored interrupts represent a different class of requests, requiring different types of responses, although their requests are sent to the same CPU pin. The specific event generating a vectored interrupt is distinguished by the vector index, read during the interrupt acknowledge cycle. Thus, it is necessary to introduce another priority order within the class of vectored interrupts, and this priority rule should be enforced by an external circuit, since the CPU provides a single input for all the requests of the same type.

A special **interrupt control unit** (**ICU**) is provided by each microprocessor family to arbitrate between different vectored interrupt requests. These circuits, which are shown in Figure 2.6, receive individual interrupt requests from the peripheral devices and associate a specific priority with each input request. When an interrupt acknowledge cycle is performed, an output signal (INTAi) indicates which request should be serviced according to the priority rule. The INTAi signals, when enabled, allow the selected device to put its own interrupt vector index on the bus during the interrupt acknowledge cycle, so that the corresponding handler will be activated by the CPU.

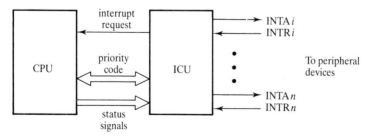

Figure 2.6   Interconnection between the CPU and the interrupt control unit.

When the number of interrupting devices is larger than that capable of being handled by the ICU, it is possible to connect a device to the same interrupt request and interrupt acknowledge lines, implementing a structure called a **daisy chain**, which is shown in Figure 2.7 for a single line only. With this circuit, it is possible to have different priorities for each input of the ICU, and different priorities within each class. This is illustrated by the circuit in Figure 2.7: a device with a pending interrupt request prevents all following devices in the chain from receiving the INTAi signal. The first device with an interrupt pending is enabled to send its interrupt vector index, so that its request will be serviced. Hence, the priority is determined by the logical position in the chain – the closer to the CPU, the higher the priority.

Another important feature of the ICU is in disabling all the maskable interrupts that have a priority lower than or equal to a priority code associated with the running program. This has the effect of stopping the delay of urgent activities that would be delayed by an interrupt occurrence. For example, if a handler of an interrupt with priority i is executed, it would not be possible for a request with priority j, where $j \leq i$, to be serviced, until the priority of the program running on the CPU falls below j. This masking mechanism is implemented either in the ICU or in the CPU; however, in both cases, it is necessary for a priority code to be exchanged between the two units. The program priority is sent

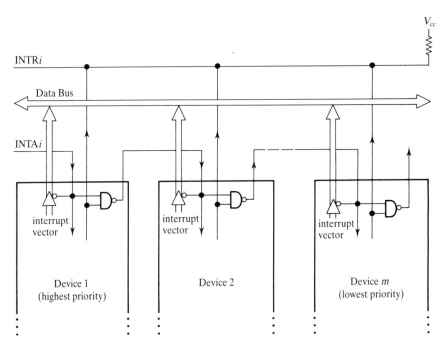

Figure 2.7 Interrupt priority implemented using a daisy-chain connection.

to the ICU, if it implements the masking circuit, or the highest priority of pending interrupt requests is sent to the CPU, if the masking mechanism is implemented there.

2.4 Traps

Another mechanism causing an automatic procedure call is the **trap**. Unlike an interrupt, a trap is activated, explicitly or implicitly, by an action performed by the running program. Traps are used to handle exceptional and often anomalous conditions arising during the execution of a program, or to activate some special procedure, such as operating system routines.

The exceptions generated by the external memory management and floating-point units should be considered traps, although the CPU has dedicated external signals to detect such situations, as with interrupts. With traps, though, these external signals are activated by error states caused by the program itself, either in the memory management or floating-point units.

There are three types of trap:

(1)   traps always enabled;

(2)   program enabled/disabled traps;

(3)   traps explicitly requested by the program.

The first of these is activated by an error event, regardless of the type of operation performed by the CPU; therefore, there is no means of disabling such traps. Typical examples of events always trapped are attempts to execute a non-existent instruction, or to execute an instruction reserved for a high privilege state in a low privilege state. It is also possible to include exceptions generated by the memory management unit in this class, although it is possible to disable the whole unit, so that the corresponding exceptions are no longer generated.

Examples of the second type of trap include those events that may or may not represent an exceptional or anomalous condition, according to the specific actions performed by the program. For this reason, their activation can be enabled and disabled by the program itself, according to whether it is necessary to detect such situations. For example, the IEEE 754 Floating-Point Standard (see Section 2.2.2) prescribes that the exceptions generated by a floating-point operation or conversion can give rise to a trap only if they have been enabled by the program. Another example of this type of trap is that used to detect an attempt to execute a floating-point instruction, when the arithmetic co-processor does not exist in the system. In this case, the trap must be disabled if the hardware configuration includes the floating-point unit.

The third type of trap is not normally used to detect anomalous conditions, but represents a means of activating the execution of special routines – in particular operating system functions. These are often organized so that they can be activated as a consequence of specific trap occurrences. Special instructions are devoted to this operation, which are often called system-call instructions, since their commonest use is to activate operating system routines. When one of these instructions is executed, a corresponding trap is activated. To allow different traps to be activated by the same type of instruction, a parameter is provided that identifies the specific trap handler to be initiated.

2.4.1   Trap handling

The actions required to handle a trap activation are similar to those performed when an interrupt occurs: first the program counter and the flags are saved on to the stack, then a jump is performed to a suitable trap-handling routine. Information on trap handlers is normally stored in a vector in a specific memory area, as with the interrupt vector, and in some cases both traps and interrupts share the same vector.

Those traps that are always enabled or are enabled by the program each have a specific element of the trap vector associated with them, as they correspond with events defined *a priori*. The third type of trap uses this associated parameter as a vector index to identify the associated handler, because the program itself associates a specific meaning to these traps.

Traps used to detect anomalies also push information on the specific condition causing the trap on to the stack. This helps the handler to diagnose and recover from the error state.

The trap handler is often executed at a higher privilege level than the program causing the trap for the following reason. Microprocessors providing a double-stack pointer, one for the normal and the other for the system state, use the system stack to save all the information related to trap handling. Consequently, a simple return-from-interrupt instruction can correctly terminate the trap handler and return control to the program.

2.4.2   Priority

The occurrence of several different traps and interrupts during the execution of a single instruction gives rise to the problem of selecting which interrupt or trap should be serviced first.

Traps, like interrupts, are normally serviced at the end of an instruction, but some traps require immediate attention, to allow correct execution of a program. A page fault trap (see Chapter 4), for example, must be serviced immediately, interrupting the current instruction, because it is necessary to bring a new piece of program into the main memory. Thus, some traps must be restartable, like interrupts.

Although each microprocessor adopts its own priority rules according to which traps are implemented, it is possible to extrapolate the following basic criteria for trap priorities:

- restartable traps have the highest priority, as with restartable interrupts;
- the other traps are generally more privileged than maskable interrupts, since they are used to detect errors and anomalies and require prompt attention;
- the non-maskable interrupt can interrupt the execution of interrupt and trap handlers.

Note that no external circuit is necessary to determine trap priority.

2.5 Debugging supports

Most people with some experience of program development understand that all non-trivial programs, however carefully written, initially contain some errors or **bugs**. These should be located and corrected, or debugged, in a sequence of subsequent trials. This task is normally performed by constructing one or more hand-written examples and checking whether the results obtained by running the program match those calculated outside the computer.

It would be very difficult to find bugs if a program could not be broken down into smaller blocks, whose inputs and outputs could be checked against those of the hand-written example. A set of three basic debugging tools are thus used to help the programmer to locate program errors:

(1)   step-by-step execution;
(2)   breakpoints;
(3)   program trace.

The first mechanism allows programmers to run the program, stopping its execution after the completion of each instruction. In this way it is possible to examine the state of the CPU and memory after each step in the program, and any departure from the expected results can be located immediately.

Breakpoints are used to stop the execution of the program under test when specific instructions are reached. This allows programmers to execute whole blocks of a program and to stop the execution at some specific point, where the intermediate results may be checked.

A program trace, in comparison, is a record of all the instructions executed by the program since the last stop, and is used to check *a posteriori* whether the flow of the instructions is correct.

All three debugging tools are supported by the following hardware mechanisms implemented in modern microprocessors.

2.5.1   Trace trap

A specific trap, referred to as a **trace trap**, is implemented in most modern microprocessors to support both step-by-step execution and program tracing. This trap may be enabled and disabled by setting or clearing a dedicated flag, depending on whether program tracing or stepping are required.

When activated, the trace trap starts the execution of the corresponding handler after the last completed instruction; of course, the trap is automatically disabled during the execution of the handling routine, otherwise the completion of the first instruction would cause a new jump to the trap handler, leading to an infinite loop on the first instruction of the trap handler.

The service routine of the trace trap implements a command decoder to allow the user to request the display of some subset of the CPU or memory states. The handling routine can also include a procedure for storing data about the instruction just executed in a suitable trace buffer.

2.5.2   Software breakpoint

Stepping through a program is useful in the early debugging stages, but it can become very time consuming when whole blocks of program have already been corrected. A more useful tool is the **breakpoint**, which allows stops to be inserted in the program. This is accomplished by selecting instructions that block execution when the CPU attempts to execute them. The breakpoint can be implemented by using a specific trap instruction, whose length is the minimum allowed for an instruction.

This requirement can be understood by considering the operations performed to obtain the breakpoint. Figure 2.8(a) shows the operations performed when the breakpoint is set, as specified by the user. The instruction whose execution should cause the program to stop is saved in a special memory area and is replaced by the breakpoint instruction. For this reason, it is necessary that the trapping instruction is no longer than the one it replaces, otherwise it is not possible to make the substitution without altering other instructions. When an instruction is called from the breakpoint address, the new trap instruction is executed, activating the corresponding handler that in turn displays the internal system state at the user interface.

It is possible to resume the program execution after a stop at a breakpoint, but the original instruction must be copied back from the

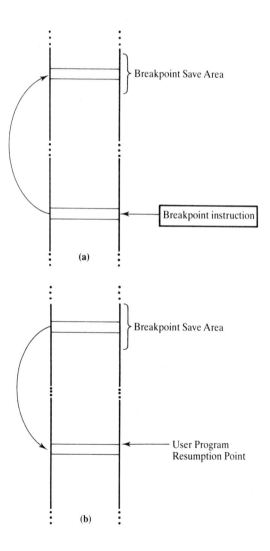

Figure 2.8 Operations connected with software breakpoints: (a) operations to set a breakpoint; (b) operations to resume the user program.

save area into its original location before the handler terminates and the program execution is resumed. This operation is shown in Figure 2.8(b).

2.5.3   Hardware breakpoint

The software breakpoint mechanism does not allow the user to program a breakpoint other than on the execution of a specific instruction, and it is not possible to stop the program accessing any operand stored in any location. This problem is overcome in microprocessors implementing the so-called hardware breakpoint.

A hardware breakpoint is implemented by the memory management unit (MMU), which holds registers used to store the memory addresses causing a program stop. Whenever an address is received, and the breakpoint mechanism is enabled, the MMU, in addition to its normal operations, checks the address against those stored in the breakpoint registers. If it finds a match it issues a trap signal. In this way, any access to the memory locations specified in the breakpoint registers cause the suspension of the program and the activation of a specific trap handler.

Software and hardware breakpoint mechanisms are often found in the same microprocessor. The software mechanism allows a program to have a large number of breakpoints active at the same time, since this number is limited only by the constraints on the size of the save area; in contrast, the number of hardware breakpoints is limited by the number of breakpoint registers implemented in the MMU.

2.6   Conclusion

The architectural features examined in this chapter, unlike those of Chapter 1, are not explicitly intended to support the execution of programs written in high-level languages, although floating-point arithmetic provides the implementation for real numbers and the register organization influences the program execution speed.

Nevertheless, these features are important, as they define other microprocessor mechanisms relevant in typical implementations. For example, the type and speed of the interrupt mechanism defines the responsiveness of the microprocessor to external events, which is an important parameter for real-time applications. Moreover, it will be shown in the following two chapters that such mechanisms are essential prerequisites for the implementation of complex operating system functions, such as memory management, protection and multiprocessing.

EXERCISES

2.1 Translate the following simple Pascal statements into the assembly languages used in Table 2.1:

> $s := 1; i := 1$
> **while** $i <= 2$ **do begin** $s := s * i; i := i + 1$ **end;**

Why, in this case, does the stack machine require more memory cycles than a machine with general-purpose registers? (*Hint*: See how many expressions are evaluated at each step.)

2.2 What is the range, and the absolute and relative precisions of the two basic formats of the IEEE 754 Standard if only normalized numbers are considered? What are the differences if non-normalized numbers are also considered?

2.3 What is the result of the comparison $a = b$, if both a and b are NaN?

2.4 Which of the following operations give rise to an operand exception?

- $(\infty) + (\infty)$ (projective mode);
- $(\infty) + (\infty)$ (affine mode);
- $0/0$;
- $0/\infty$.

2.5 What is the meaning of an incorrect result exception?

2.6 Which conversions between number representations, other than floating-point, are defined by the IEEE 754 Standard?

2.7 Assume that a microprocessor has the instruction INDEX A, B, C, performing the operation $C := A * B + C$, plus the check that the value of A is not negative and less than B. Write a small program to compute the offset of an element in a matrix with five subscripts: the subscripts are stored at the locations $A1...A5$, while their bounds are stored in the locations $B1...B5$. (*Note*: Also use the instruction **DJNZ reg, label**, which decrements **reg** and jumps to **label** if not zero.)

2.8 In a microprocessor with a non-maskable interrupt and 256 vectored interrupts, how many inputs are required to receive the interrupt requests?

2.9 Compute the upper bound for the frequency of occurrence of an interrupt, given that:

- the time required to acknowledge the request and start the handler is 2 µs;
- the time required to save or restore the registers is 13.5 µs;
- the actual handler operations require 80 µs;
- no other interrupts occur.

2.10 Solve Exercise 2.9 assuming that a second interrupt of higher priority occurs; this second interrupt requires 70 µs of CPU service and occurs every 200 µs. (*Note*: Consider the worst case.)

2.11 What is the limiting factor for (a) the number of software breakpoints and (b) the number of hardware breakpoints?

2.12 What is the relationship between the instruction length and the size of the breakpoint trap instruction?

References

[1] W. A. Wulf, 'Compilers and Computer Architecture', *Computer* **14**(7), July 1981, pp. 41–48.

[2] IEEE/ANSI Standard 754, *Standard for Microprocessor Floating-Point Numbers*, Academic Press, 1983.

[3] D. Stevenson, 'A Proposed Standard for Binary Floating-Point Arithmetic', *Computer* **14**(3), March 1981, pp. 51–62.

[4] D. Hough (1981), 'Applications of the Proposed IEEE 754 Standard Floating-Point Arithmetic', *Computer* **14**(3), March 1981, pp. 70–74.

[5] J. T. Coonen (1981), 'Underflow and the Denormalized Numbers', *Computer* **14**(3), March 1981, pp. 75–87.

Further reading

M. Hasegawa and Y. Shigei, 'High-Speed Top-of-Stack Scheme for VLSI Processors: Algorithm and its Analysis', *Proceedings of the 12th Annual Symposium on Computer Architecture*, June 1985, pp. 48–54.

C. Y. Hitchcock, III, H. M. Brinkley and Sprunt, 'Analyzing Multiple Register Sets', *Proceedings of the 11th Annual Symposium on Computer Architecture*, June 1985, pp. 55–63.

J. R. Goodman and W.-C. Hsu, 'On the Use of Registers vs. Cache to Minimize Memory Traffic', *Proceedings of the 13th Annual Symposium on Computer Architecture*, June 1986, pp. 375–384.

T. Lang and M. Huguet, 'Reduced Register Saving/Restoring in Single-Window Register Files', *Computer Architecture News* **14**(3), June 1986, pp. 17–26.

The register set organization is one of the topics investigated in the field of reduced architectures, and other references may be found in Chapter 10. A continual source of papers on this topic is ACM *Computer Architecture News*, and by the series of Proceedings of the Annual Symposium on Computer Architecture.

CHAPTER 3

MULTIPROGRAMMING AND MULTITASKING

OBJECTIVES

This chapter is devoted to the illustration of the basic mechanisms used to implement **multiprogramming** and **multitasking** in microprocessor systems. In particular, the following concepts are covered:

- mutual exclusion;
- process synchronization;
- process communication.

The hardware mechanisms needed to implement these concepts are also discussed, for both mono- and multi-microprocessor systems.

3.1 Introduction
3.2 Processes and processors
3.3 Interleaved process execution
3.4 Process switching

3.5 Mutual exclusion
3.6 Synchronization
3.7 Process communication
3.8 Processor scheduling
3.9 Conclusion

3.1   Introduction

CPU time has always been regarded as one of the most important resources in a computing system – the word 'computer' itself implies that the major function of the system is to perform computations as fast as possible. To obtain the maximum computing time from a computing system the CPU should be kept as busy as possible – each idle CPU period is equivalent to loss of computing time.

The techniques developed for achieving better CPU utilization are non-naive, and the basic concepts can be best introduced by considering some examples of their use. One example is from a real-time application field that has used microprocessors ever since their first appearance on the market. Another example is from a rather more recent application – namely multi-user time-sharing systems – made possible by the increasing computing power of CPUs. This property of CPUs has also paved the way for the development of single- as well as multi-user personal or small microcomputers.

3.1.1   Multiprogramming in time-sharing systems

In a multi-user system, the CPU is required to execute several programs, written by different programmers, to achieve different goals. A naive CPU management system would lead to the situation shown in Figure 3.1(b) and (c). The three programs A, B and C are executed sequentially, since each of them cannot begin its execution as there is another program initiated but not yet completed. The activities taking place in the system during program execution may be grouped into two classes: CPU and I/O activities (the time dedicated to these two kinds of operation has been differentiated in the figure for ease of reference). To keep the figure simple, the time periods have been made longer and fewer than in a real system. The total time required to complete all three programs is 340 time units, while the total CPU time required for performing the corresponding computations is 210 time units; hence, the CPU has been used for only 62% of its potential. In this case, the 38% of unused computing power has been wasted by the CPU waiting for the completion of I/O operations. But could this time not be used to perform useful computations during I/O activities?

The answer to this question can be found in Figure 3.1(c), where the three programs are executed using an **interleaving** method. In this case, as soon as the CPU becomes idle, because the program in execution has entered an I/O activity period, another program (not in an I/O phase) is executed by the CPU. The first program is resumed as soon as it has completed its I/O operations and the CPU enters a new idle period. In this CPU management system, the time required for performing the whole work is 240 time units; thus, the CPU is now used at 87.5% of its

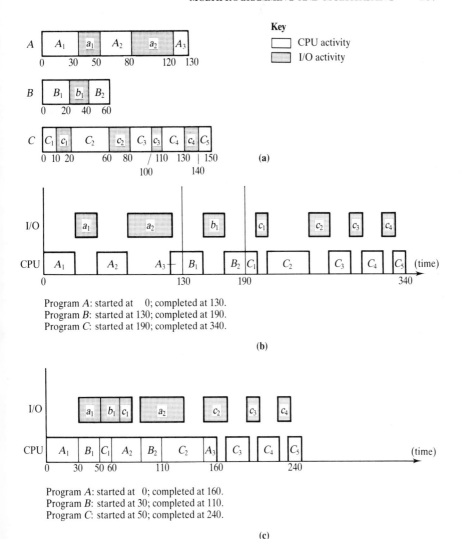

Program A: started at 0; completed at 130.
Program B: started at 130; completed at 190.
Program C: started at 190; completed at 340.

(b)

Program A: started at 0; completed at 160.
Program B: started at 30; completed at 110.
Program C: started at 50; completed at 240.

(c)

Figure 3.1 Program execution on (b) monoprogrammed and (c) multi-programmed systems.

maximum power. It is worth pointing out here that the time required to run each program is longer in the case of Figure 3.1(c) than in Figure 3.1(b); hence, while the overall time required to perform the whole task is shortened, a single user can and does experience a certain increase in system response time. However, this effect is not as pronounced in a multi-user system as it does not cause large delays.

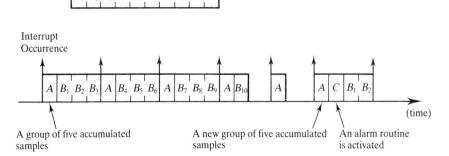

Figure 3.2   Execution of different tasks in a real-time control system.

3.1.2   Multitasking in real-time applications

A different situation occurs in real-time systems, where some tasks cannot be delayed beyond a prescribed deadline. Another important difference is that the tasks to be performed by the system are all coordinated to implement a specific set of features. Despite these differences, however, the two systems need common basic support for the interleaved execution of different programs.

Interleaving is quite a normal occurrence in real-time systems, since the interrupt mechanism itself provides a method for alternating program and interrupt handler executions. Consider a system designed to read samples of a signal at constant intervals by means of a D/A converter. Each time a new sample is read, the routine handling the interrupt from the converter (A) has to check whether the sample value falls within a specified range; if so, the value is stored in a buffer and passed to a routine B when five samples are accumulated. This routine performs some long numerical processing on the samples: when a sample value is out of range, a short alarm routine (C) is activated, which does not stop the other activities. Figure 3.2 shows a possible arrangement of the computations. It can be seen that the execution of routine B is interleaved with the execution of the two other programs, to catch all the signal samples.

3.1.3   Supports for multiprogramming

The two preceding examples show that the efficient execution of different programs in the same system requires the availability within the system of the following basic mechanisms:

(1)   saving and restoring of the status of the programs, to allow the interruption and the correct resumption required by interleaved executions;

(2)   mutual exclusion, which allows users to share a resource among several programs, avoiding the problems arising from multiple possession of the resource;

(3)   synchronization, to coordinate the activities of interacting tasks (for example, the interrupt handler and the alarm routine of the second example);

(4)   activation and deactivation of tasks, to start or stop the operation of a specific task.

The implementation of these mechanisms in microprocessor systems is discussed in the next section.

3.2   Processes and processors

All the basic mechanisms required for efficient execution of different programs in the same system cannot be programmed by the application programmer, since they deal with events that are unpredictable at compile time. These events include the occurrence of an out-of-range sample or the number and characteristics of other programs, whose execution is interleved with the program. Therefore, the operating system should provide basic operations for the correct and easy implementation of multiple execution. The whole software structure is represented in Figure 3.3, where the Operating System Kernel (OSK) is a collection of procedures implementing the four basic operations, which can be used by the other tasks shown in the figure to achieve coordination among their operation. However, not all these tasks are necessarily devoted to the implementation of application activities. Some of them form part of the operating system (such as the file manager and the electronic mail system), and so these tasks can be further subdivided according to their use. Nevertheless, both system and application tasks use the same functions and are not distinguishable (except for their priority) by the OSK.

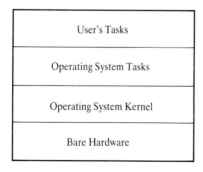

Figure 3.3   Operating system structure.

The tasks shown in the figure are usually referred to as **processes**. Each process is composed of three main parts:

(1)   A database, usually stored in main memory, containing all the data values and memory space needed to represent the program variables used in the program, as well as the other variables needed to carry out the required computation.

(2)   The code implementing the algorithm to be performed by the process.

(3)   The environment where the process has to be executed. The term 'environment' is used to indicate a set of process attributes, often managed by the operating system alone, which are required for correct execution. Typical examples are the descriptors of the memory areas reserved for the process with the access rights for each of them (for a clearer explanation of these terms see Chapter 4).

Several different processes may have parts in common; the most frequent cases are those of processes sharing the same code or part of their databases. An example of the first type of sharing is found in multi-user systems where several users can request the use of the same compiler at the same time. In such cases, a single copy of the code is loaded into memory, while a different data area and environment are set up for each user, avoiding replication of the compiler code. When several processes share the same code, they are called 'instances' of the same program. Data sharing among processes is needed when the user wants to implement process-to-process data transfers through a set of variables visible to all the communicating processes. This is similar to global variables in a Pascal program, which are seen and can be used by all the procedures declared within the same program. In this case, however, the binding of common variables is performed by the operating system with the help of some programmer's directive.

3.3   Interleaved process execution

The instructions composing the code of a process are executed serially, one at a time, in the order specified in the program. However, unless the interrupts are disabled, the execution of the current process could be interrupted at the end of each machine instruction and the CPU switched to the execution of another process. Hence, instructions from other processes may be executed between two consecutive instructions of the same process.

The effect of this interleaving of the execution of different processes is that at a macroscopic level the computing system seems to perform the operations required by all the processes in parallel. However, as seen in Section 3.1, by observing the system with a finer time scale – in microseconds – the CPU only executes one process at a time. This leads to the name 'pseudo-parallelism', which has been used to designate such systems.

More recently, several commercial microcomputers that are designed to be used in the multiprocessor configuration shown in Figure 3.4 have been put on the market [1 – 2]. Such systems, with several CPUs, allow the implementation of real parallel processes (as opposed to pseudo-parallel ones), as each processor can execute a process concurrently with other CPUs. However, synchronization and mutual exclusion problems still need to be solved. Moreover, even in multi-microprocessors, considerations of CPU utilization lead to the implementation of pseudo-parallelism between processes within the same set assigned to a processor, in addition to real parallel execution between different sets of processes assigned to different processors.

Since the conventional mono-microprocessor and the multi-microprocessor with a single shared bus are the commonest system configurations, only these two architectures will be considered in this chapter.

3.4   Process switching

3.4.1   Process state

Switching the CPU between two processes is a basic operation implemented to obtain pseudo-parallelism. It is constituted by two symmetrical phases: the saving of the status of the interrupted process,

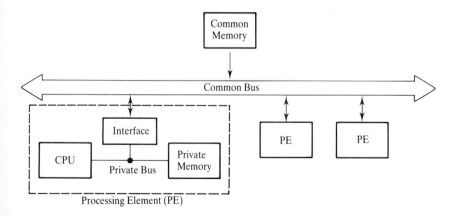

Figure 3.4   Multiprocessor system based on a single shared bus.

and the restoration of the status of the process after the interruption. A crucial implementation issue is the definition of the status of a process, which is constituted by all that information required to resume the process operations correctly later, when the CPU is assigned again to the suspended process.

When defining a process, three components were indicated; hence, it is natural to divide the information composing the status of the process into three categories:

(1)   Data values to be saved: these are usually stored in some 'unsafe' current memory and are in general the values stored in the CPU registers. They are saved because the code of the process to be resumed might use the registers, destroying the old values. These registers include the stack pointer and the ALU flags.

(2)   A program counter, pointing to the first instruction of the code to be executed when the process is resumed.

(3)   All the registers containing the information describing the execution environment of the process, including the registers of external devices, such as the external MMU and floating-point co-processor (if any).

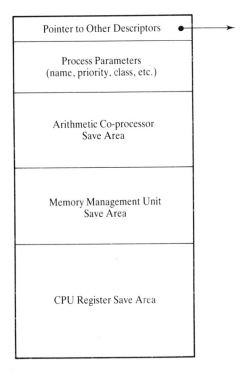

Figure 3.5   Example of format of a processor descriptor.

All such information must be saved in a dedicated memory area reserved for this purpose and for each process. The contents of this area describe the state reached by the associated process when it has been suspended; hence, when it is necessary to resume its operation, a simple reloading of the information into the registers they were copied from will allow the correct process to resume.

The information saved during a suspended process constitutes a description of the process status; however, more information is needed to describe the process state fully in a multitasking environment. A common technique groups both the register contents stored during the last suspended process and the additional information needed to identify the process itself, and to provide process parameters for implementing a scheduling strategy for the CPU, in a single memory area. All this information is called the **process descriptor**, since it describes all the relevant process characteristics and the status reached by the associated computations. A possible layout for a process descriptor is shown in Figure 3.5. Note the presence here of pointers to other process descriptors, which implement linked data structures to be used by the scheduler and all the other process management components.

3.4.2 Register up/downloading

Process switching (also referred to as **context switching**) is a very elementary operation, but it is an important component of more complex primitives devoted to multitasking management; hence it is often executed during the operations of a multi-user system. This implies that the speed of context switching is a major factor influencing the effectiveness of the system, especially in real-time applications where the operation may be performed quite often.

The major fraction of the time spent on this operation comes from the downloading and uploading of the registers to and from the process descriptors. However, there is a tradeoff between the need for fast execution of the process code and the need for quick process switching.

If a CPU has many registers, then the execution speed of a single process will be boosted by the large register set, since it will be able to keep a significant set of the variables to be manipulated by the code in the internal registers. Thus, most of the instructions will be executed between registers with a remarkable speed enhancement. On the other hand, if the same processor is shared between several processes, then context switching becomes a fairly complex operation due to the large number of registers to be dumped and loaded to and from the main memory.

The alternative – a CPU with operands and results in memory – is not truly viable because context switching will be fast, but the performance penalties on the execution of a single process are fairly large.

The usual solution is to have a moderate set of general-purpose registers (8 to 16), which can all be stored or loaded with a single instruction, saving a substantial amount of operation time.

3.5   Mutual exclusion

Parallel or pseudo-parallel execution of several processes necessarily leads to contention for system resources, which may be required by more than one process to complete the tasks assigned to them. While this phenomenon may be easily understood for real parallelism where several CPUs are used and a single common resource is shared among them, contention for common resources in pseudo-parallelism is not straight-forward, because the CPU only executes one process at a time.

3.5.1   Contention in psuedo-parallelism

Consider two processes, A and B, which need to acquire a system resource whose free/busy state is stored in the memory location X; $X = 0$ indicates the free resource. Each process employs the following code, written in the assembly language of a hypothetical machine:

test X;   *set the flags according to the value stored in* X
bne after; *branch to* **after** *if the resource is busy*
set X;   *set the contents of* X *to 1s to signal that the resource is now busy*

Of course, it is assumed that the resource cannot be granted to more than one user, because some resources tend not to support multi-user operations – magnetic tapes, for example.

Bearing in mind the fact that CPU switching between processes takes place after the execution of each machine instruction, consider what will happen in the following possible execution of the two processes, A and B, which try to acquire at the same time the resource whose state is represented by X, initially set to 0.

process A	process B	value read or written
test X		*0*
bne after		
(A is suspended and B activated)		
	test X	*0*
	bne after	
	set X	*all 1s*

.

.

.

(*B* is suspended and *A* activated)

set *X*   *all 1s*

Note that in this implementation, with no control on the use of *X*, it is possible that both processes consider that the resource is free and so the resource will be incorrectly used. Thus, both processes believe themselves to be the only owner, while, in fact, they are actually using the same resource in parallel.

This example shows that some mechanism is needed to control the access to critical resources. The solution to the mutual exclusion problem must satisfy the following criteria:

(1) only one process at a time can use the resource in question;

(2) when several processes are trying to acquire a resource simultaneously, then the control mechanism must grant the resource to only one of them, in a finite time;

(3) when a process 'owns' a resource, it must use it for a finite period, and then it must release the resource;

(4) processes waiting for the availability of a resource should not waste CPU time (that is, they should be suspended).

The specification, in (2) and (3), of a finite completion time is not strictly related to the mutual exclusion problem, but is introduced to avoid the possibility of deadlock. It will be shown later that (4) can be satisfied only partially, so it should be considered as a recommendation, rather than mandatory.

3.5.2 Critical regions

All the preceding problems were caused by the interleaved execution of instructions of the two processes when they were manipulating the critical data structure *X*. If, when a process is using a resource, no other process can access that resource and its associated data structures, the mutual exclusion problem is solved. A classical construct used to implement mutual exclusion is the **critical region**, proposed by Dijkstra [3].

A set of statements and a variable common to all the processes wishing to use a resource are associated with a critical region. All the critical regions referring to the same common variable are executed in mutual exclusion.

The properties of a critical region are as follows:

(1)   at most, one process should execute the statements associated with the critical region;

(2)   a process wishing to execute the statements associated with the critical region should be able to do so in a finite time;

(3)   a process should execute the statements of a critical region in a finite time.

The operations occurring when a process needs to execute a critical region are very simple. First, it is necessary to test the value of the common variable, to determine whether the same region is currently executed by another process. Then the variable is set to indicate a busy region. If the region is free, then the requesting process begins its execution, which must terminate in a finite time. At the exit from the critical region, the process modifies the value of the common variable associated with the region, so that its new value will allow other processes to accede to the code in the region. If the region is busy, the process must wait until it can execute the code within the region. Although no assumption is made about the behaviour of the waiting processes, criterion (4) suggests that the waiting processes will be blocked and awakened whenever the region is released. Since more than one process may be waiting in front of the region's entry point, a scheduling policy must be adopted. Once again, the concept of a critical region does not include any specific priority algorithm; however, the algorithm must be fair in order to allow a finite waiting time for each of the waiting processes.

3.5.3 Indivisible test-and-set

The description just given shows how each critical region includes another, smaller critical region. Testing the common variable linked to a region is an operation performed in mutual exclusion, as shown by the example in Section 3.5.1; hence, it must be a critical region itself.

At the lowest level, the problem in the example shown is the one to be solved, to implement more complex critical regions by using the mutual exclusive update of a single variable. But trouble arises due to the possibility of having a process switch during the variable update sequence. In pseudo-parallelism, the only way to switch is on the occurrence of an interrupt, because this is the only event able to provoke a non-programmed (or asynchronous) jump to another routine.

As it happens, the mutual exclusive update of a variable can be implemented in a monoprocessor system by not acknowledging interrupts during this operation. Two methods are possible, depending on the instruction set of the specific microprocessor used. The first possibility refers to those microprocessors (8-bit ones, for example) where no special instruction is provided for handling this case:

di; *disable the execution of any interrupt routine*
move *A, X; copy the value of X in to the variable A*
set *X; set the value of X to all 1s*
ei; *enable the execution of interrupt routines*
test *A; test the value of the variable A*

Note that the test on the value of X has now been moved outside of the critical region to shorten the period of interrupt masking; thus, the variable X can be set before the test because its final value does not depend on its initial value.

The second method takes advantage of a special instruction present in different forms in all the instruction sets of new microprocessors. This instruction, referred to using the generic name of **test-and-set** (**tas**), is able to perform both the copy and the set operation of the previous solution in a single machine instruction as well as the test on the old value of x. Since interrupt requests are sensed only at the end of each machine instruction, the test-and-set operations cannot be interleaved with interrupt service routines. In this case, the indivisible operation is implemented by the following code:

tas *A, X; test-and-set X with copy of the old value in A*

Another possible source of trouble is due to the presence of DMA processors, since they can access memory interleaving cycles with those of the CPU, even within the same machine instruction. For this reason, the test-and-set instruction execution automatically disables the DMA cycles. However, the DMA processors do not usually cause too many problems, because they write to memory with data from peripherals, so it is easy to avoid having I/O buffers that include shared variables manipulated by the processes.

3.5.4 Test-and-set in a multiprocessor

More complex situations arise in multi-microprocessor systems with a common bus. To illustrate the problems it is necessary to look closely at certain operations, and in particular at the common bus connecting the CPUs to the memory where the shared variables are stored.

The common bus is shared by the processors according to some arbitration or contention policy, which grants bus usage to one of several requesters. Since the bus can be used by only one CPU at a time, it is a critical region itself. The access (that is, the possibility of using the bus) is controlled by a concentrated or distributed arbitration circuit, which notifies the chosen requester that it can take control of the bus as soon as the current user releases it.

In general, all the multiprocessor buses [4 – 6] have a signal whose status is controlled by the interface of the current user of the bus, indicating whether or not the bus is busy. Normally, the bus can be kept by a single user for the time needed to perform a single memory cycle, then it is released. With this allocation scheme, some error situations may arise, even if the **tas** instruction is used, because two memory references (in addition to instruction fetch) are necessary to complete the operation: a memory read, to copy X into A, and a memory write to set X to all 1s. Figure 3.6 shows what could happen on a common bus when two processes, executed in CPU1 and CPU2, perform a test-and-set instruction on X. A low voltage level on the signal $\overline{\text{BBUSY}}$ notifies other interfaces that the bus is busy. When this signal goes up, a new bus master can take control of the bus. The memory cycles required to complete the test-and-set instruction may thus be interleaved with the cycles of other instructions, leading to the same problems arising with instruction interleaving in the case of monoprocessor systems.

The solution, of course, follows the same path, avoid interleaving bus cycles during critical operations. In particular, keeping the bus busy from the beginning of the read cycle, which copies X into A, until the completion of the write cycle, which sets X to all 1s, avoids interleaving. Figure 3.7 shows the effect of this choice on the situation in Figure 3.6; now CPU2 cannot interrupt the test-and-set operation performed by CPU1.

Since read–modify–write cycles differ from normal bus cycles, the bus interface needs to know whether the operation requested by the local CPU is a normal one. This information may be provided by the CPU

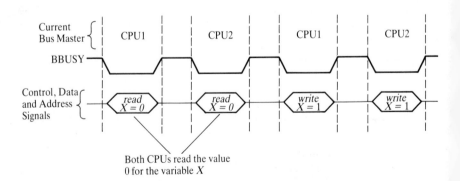

Figure 3.6 Possible sequence of cycles on a common bus when different processes on different CPUs perform a non-indivisible test-and-set operation on X.

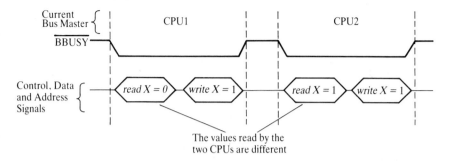

The values read by the
two CPUs are different

Figure 3.7 Execution of an indivisible read–modify–write operation on the common bus.

itself in different ways, through a special signal or through the combination of status signals output when a read–modify–write operation is required. This special condition may be associated with a specific instruction, whose execution causes its activation, or it may be linked to a set of instructions, where a specific flag within the opcode causes the activation of the special code signalling indivisible operation. A third mode, to signal indivisible read–modify–write cycles to the interface, has to be used in microprocessors without support in their instruction set for this operation. In this case, the instruction to be executed without interleaving is enclosed between two instructions, which respectively set and reset a particular interface flag. In this method, the common bus is kept busy for longer than necessary, and thus leads to some inefficiency in bus usage.

3.5.5 Implementing larger critical regions

So far, the behaviour of the processes which, attempting to execute a critical region, find it busy, have been unspecified. This is important since the criteria for a reasonable solution of the mutual exclusion problem prescribe finite waiting times and a minimum waste of CPU time. A possible solution is to leave the process looping around the same test until it succeeds, when the region is free. However, the CPU will be kept busy executing unsuccessful loops while its time could be better employed running other processes not blocked in front of a critical region. Moreover, this solution does not guarantee any finite waiting time. For example, consider A and B, which compete for the execution of the region associated with X, which is currently executed by C. The following is a possible sequence of instructions executed by the CPU:

        tas A, X
        bne *loopa*

tas *A, X*
bne *loopa*

(process *A* is suspended and *B* activated)

tas *B, X*
bne *loopb*
tas *B, X*
bne *loopb*

(process *B* is suspended and *C* activated)

clear *X*

.

.

.

(process *C* is suspended and *B* activated)

tas *A, X*
bne *loopb*

(process *B* enters critical region)

It is worth noting here that process *A* has been overtaken by *B*, which arrived after *A* in front of the critical region. This is caused by the fact that the critical region scheduling relies on the same scheduling algorithm used for alternating the processes on the CPU. While this algorithm can be fair for CPU usage, it may lead to situations where a process has to wait for a long, possibly infinite time. Thus, it is necessary to provide specific scheduling mechanisms for critical regions, which should be able to avoid wasting CPU time (**busy waiting**) and non-finite waiting times (**process starvation**).

3.5.6   Conditional critical regions

To achieve this goal, the database associated with a critical region is modified so that a list of descriptors (see Section 3.4.1) of the processes waiting for the critical region, are ordered in the list according to some priority scheme. When the region is freed by its current user, the first descriptor of the list (if any) is extracted and passed to the CPU scheduler. That process can now continue its execution since the region is free. All other processes whose descriptors are in the list associated with the region cannot be executed, therefore, because they are waiting for the critical region. Because of this, the CPU does not execute all the unsuccessful loops of waiting processes, and the access to the critical region is regulated by an explicit scheduling algorithm, which can be selected according to a programmer's needs.

However, this implementation still contains busy-waiting and process starvation phenomena, because the insertion and extraction operations on the list of process descriptors are critical regions themselves. It is possible to allow busy waiting and process starvation in these smaller regions, since the short time required to execute them will not delay more than a few processes waiting for the critical regions. Longer critical regions, however, would lead to severe problems if their access was not regulated by some explicit scheduling mechanism.

3.6 Synchronization

In mutual exclusion, different processes compete for the use of a specific resource (that is, the critical region), and the nature of the interaction allows the processes to be implemented with no knowledge of other processes, which run in parallel. This is possible because the process tries to acquire the resource, whatever its competitors.

Another class of interaction is **process cooperation**, which is required to implement a complex task. Here, all the processes belonging to the task force need to have some information about the state of the other processes they have to interact with. Each process has to be designed and implemented taking account of the number and type of possible interactions with other specific processes. This arises from the fact that the processes are now cooperating rather than competing.

3.6.1 Semaphores

The simplest type of information exchanged between two processes is a synchronizing signal. These signals are needed because the relative speed of two processes is generally unknown. The execution time of a piece of code depends, in a system with concurrent processes, on the number and characteristics of the other processes running concurrently. Alternatively, it may depend on some external event, which may occur at times unpredictable by the programmer.

A classical solution to the problem of synchronizing the operation of two or more processes, without data exchange, is based on the use of **semaphores**. They were introduced by Dijkstra [3] and they have been investigated by several other researchers [8 – 9].

Basically, a semaphore is a variable x with the two following procedures associated with it:

$P(x)$ and $V(x)$

(Other authors refer to the same pair of procedures using the names 'signal' and 'wait', respectively [9].) Another characteristic of a semaphore is the maximum number $c(x)$ of signals sent to the semaphore and not yet extracted.

The correct behaviour of a semaphore is regulated by rules called **communication invariants**. If $s(x)$ and $r(x)$ are the number of signals sent to and received from the semaphore x, then the following relations must hold in order to have a correct behaviour:

$$0 \leqslant r(x) \leqslant s(x) \leqslant r(x) + c(x)$$

In some cases it is useful to allow an initial value $i(x)$ to be assigned to a semaphore before the synchronization operations between processes are started. In this case, the communication invariant must be rewritten in the following form:

$$0 \leqslant r(x) \leqslant s(x) + i(x) \leqslant r(x) + c(x)$$

The operation of the two associated procedures P and V must satisfy the following rules, defining how a semaphore can synchronize process execution:

(1)   A V operation performed on a semaphore where $r(x) < s(x) + i(x)$, just increments $r(x)$. In addition, if $s(x) + i(x)$ is equal to $r(x) + c(x)$, and some processes are waiting at the semaphore, then one waiting process is enabled to continue and $s(x)$ is incremented. If the procedure is performed when $r(x) = s(x) + i(x)$, then the process is suspended and inserted in a waiting queue associated with the semaphore.

(2)   A P operation performed on a semaphore where $s(x) + i(x) = r(x) + c(x)$ causes the process suspension and insertion in a waiting queue associated with the semaphore. If $s(x) + i(x) < r(x) + c(x)$, then $s(x)$ is incremented. In addition, if some processes are waiting at the semaphore, then one of them is allowed to continue and $r(x)$ is incremented.

3.6.2   Semaphore operations

To implement the synchronizing rules a single integer variable $n(x) = s(x) + i(x) - r(x)$ is needed. It is possible to derive from the communication invariant that $n(x)$ must satisfy the following relations:

$$0 \leqslant n(x) \leqslant c(x)$$

In addition, the initial value of $n(x)$ must be set to $i(x)$ to have correct operations; this rule can be derived from the definition of $n(x)$, by imposing $s(x) = r(x) = 0$. Since waiting queues are devised in the synchronization rules, some provision for implementing these queues must be put in the data structure used by the P and V procedures.

Two types of queue are necessary: one for the processes delayed while performing a P operation, and one for the processes delayed while performing a V operation. Although logically distinct, the two queues can be implemented by using a single structure, since it is easy to prove that if $c(x) \neq 0$, then it is impossible to have processes waiting in both queues simultaneously. Thus a single data structure can hold either all the processes delayed during a P operation, or all those delayed during a V operation, the type of waiting process being determined by the state of the variable $n(x)$. The proof is based on an analysis of the conditions regulating the insertion and the extraction of the processes in the queue. First, the two queues are initially empty, and they remain so until $n(x)$ becomes equal to either 0 [that is, $r(x) = s(x) + i(x)$] or $c(x)$ [that is, $s(x) + i(x) = r(x) + c(x)$]; in the former case, all the V operations performed will delay the corresponding process, while P operations will not. If processes are waiting because they performed a V operation, then the value of $n(x)$ must be 0, because each P operation will increment both $r(x)$ and $s(x)$; thus, only when all the waiting processes have been enabled to continue can the value of $n(x)$ be incremented by P operations.

With similar arguments it is possible to show that processes delayed by P operations can exist only when $n(x) = c(x)$. A situation where the processes waiting at the semaphore have been delayed by either P or V operations is impossible because the counter $n(x)$ would have to assume two different values, 0 and $c(x)$, at the same time. Since only one class of process can be waiting at the semaphore at a given time, it is not necessary to allocate two different parts of the data structure in the semaphore implementation. Figure 3.8 shows a data structure suitable for the implementation of a semaphore, but note that only one list for the processor descriptors is used, for reasons already discussed. The field $c(x)$ is set when the semaphore is created, since it is never modified from then onwards.

The two operations, P and V, used to define a semaphore, must be inserted in a critical region, since the uncontrolled manipulation of the

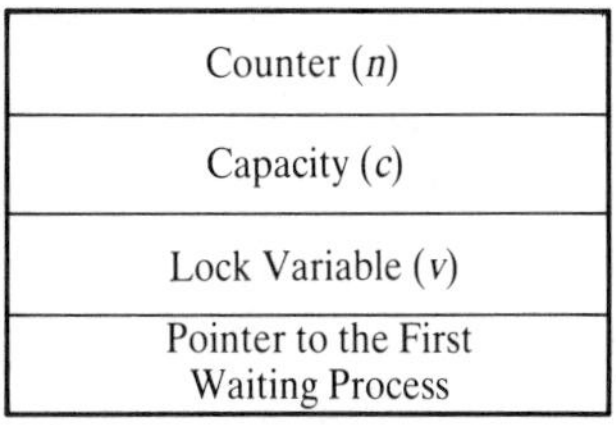

| Counter (n) |
| Capacity (c) |
| Lock Variable (v) |
| Pointer to the First Waiting Process |

Figure 3.8 Example of data structure to be used for semaphore implementation.

field $n(x)$ would lead to the situation illustrated in Section 3.5.1 for free-access shared variables. Since such operations are not as simple as the setting of a variable, it is wise to control the access to the semaphore critical region by means of test-and-set operations on a single variable, v, and to implement a queue of processes waiting for access to the semaphore operation. This mechanism is the same as suggested in Section 3.5.3 for implementing non-elementary critical sections.

A process attempting to perform a semaphore operation may be delayed twice: the first time because the semaphore critical region is occupied, the second time because the state of the semaphore causes a process delay. However, since the first delay is caused by other semaphore operations in progress it is rather short, because the P and V operation are rather simple.

3.6.3   Implementing a semaphore

To show a possible implementation of the P and V operation, it is assumed that the **entercr** (enter critical region) and **exitcr** (exit critical region) procedures are available. Once called, the former terminates its execution only when a successful test-and-set operation has been performed on the variable passed as a parameter. It is possible, within this procedure, to implement all the mechanisms needed to avoid process starvation and busy waiting. The **exitcr** procedure simply resets the variable passed as a parameter.

The data structure of Figure 3.8 is assumed to be declared as follows in the following Pascal-like procedures:

> **type** *semdata* = **record**
>   *v:*   *lockvar;*
>   *n, i:*   *integer;*
>   *waitqueue:* ↑ *processdescriptor;*
>   **end;**
> **var** *x : semdata;*

With the above declaration, the P and V operations may be implemented by the following procedures:

> **procedure** $P(x : semdata);$
> **begin**
>   **entercr***(x.v)*
>   **if** *x.c* = *x.n*
>   **then**
>   **begin**
>   *extract the current process descriptor from the set of*

```
          processes to be executed;
          insert it into the waiting queue;
          exitcr(x.v);
          re-assign the CPU usage
        end
    else if x.n = 0 and x.waitqueue <> nil
        then
          begin
              extract one process from the waiting queue;
              exitcr(x.v);
              put descriptor extracted in the set of processes to be
              executed;
              re-assign CPU usage (if necessary)
          end
        else
          begin
              x.n = x.n + 1;
              exitcr(x.v)
          end
end;
procedure V(x : semdata);
begin
  entercr(x.v);
  if x.n = 0
    then
      begin
          extract the current process descriptor from the set of
          processes to be executed;
          insert it into the waiting queue;
          exitcr(x.v);
          re-assign the CPU usage
      end
    else if x.c = x.n and x.waitqueue <> nil
        then
          extract one process from the waiting queue;
          exitcr(x.v);
          put descriptor extracted in the set of processes to be
          executed;
          re-assign CPU usage (if necessary)
        else
          begin
              x.n := x.n - 1;
              exitcr(x.v)
          end
end;
```

Note that when a process is extracted from the waiting queue as a consequence of a *P* or *V* operation, the scheduling algorithm for the CPU is executed to decide whether the extracted process has higher priority than the process that extracted it. If so, the process performing the *P* or *V* operation is suspended and the one extracted is executed. Therefore, even when the process signals or receives correctly at the semaphore, it may be suspended because it activates a higher priority process. However, it is worth noticing that the latter type of process delaying is quite different from the delaying caused by receiving from an empty semaphore or signalling to a full one. The difference is that a process blocked because it finds a particular state of the semaphore will not be allowed to be executed until the semaphore changes its state, while a process delayed because it unblocks another process will be resumed as soon as the CPU is available.

3.7   Process communication

3.7.1   Mailboxes

In some cases, the process interaction requires that data are exchanged between cooperating processes, in addition to synchronization signals. A classical structure used to solve this type of problem is the **message buffer**, also called a **mailbox**. The mailbox is an extension of the semaphore because it is able to associate a set of data, referred to as a message, with each signalling operation.

Except for the addition of messages, a mailbox behaves in the same way as a semaphore; thus, the same synchronizing rules and invariants are still valid for the mailbox. The operations should however be changed to take account of the messages to be sent or received. The new operations are **send**(x, m) and **receive**(x, m), which correspond to *P* and *V* respectively; in this case x is the mailbox identifier and m is a message identifier.

When a send operation is performed, the message is inserted into the mailbox, provided that it is not full. When a receive operation is performed, then the first message in the mailbox is extracted, provided that the mailbox is not empty. It is usually assumed that message ordering within the mailbox is FIFO; that is, the receive operation always extracts the message that has been waiting for the longest time. Other priority rules are also possible, such as message ordering based on priority.

3.7.2 Implementing mailboxes

The implementation of a semaphore should also accommodate messages, which makes it a mailbox. A possible data structure for the mailbox implementation is as follows:

mailbox = **record**

v :	*lockvar;*
n, i :	*integer;*
buffer :	↑ *message;*
waitqueue :	↑ *processdescriptor;*

end;

The send and receive procedures are obtained from the *P* and *V* procedures of Section 3.6.3 as follows:

```
procedure send(x : mailbox; m : message);
begin
   entercr(x.v);
   if x.n = x.c
     then
       begin
         insert the message m into the buffer;
         extract the current process descriptor from the set processes
         to be executed;
         insert it into the waiting queue;
         exitcr(x.v);
         re-assign the CPU usage
       end
     else
       begin
       if x.c = 0 and x.waitqueue <> nil
         then
           begin
             extract a process descriptor from the waiting queue;
             associate the message m with the extracted process;
             exitcr(x.v);
             insert the process descriptor into the set of processes to
             be executed;
             re-assign the CPU usage (if necessary)
           end
         else
           begin
             insert the message m into the buffer;
             x.c := x.c + 1;
             exitcr(x.v)
           end
       end
   end;
```

```
procedure receive(x : mailbox; m : message);
begin
entercr(x.v);
if x.c = 0
  then
    begin
      extract the current process descriptor from the set of
      processes to be executed;
      insert it into the waiting queue;
      exitcr(x.v);
      re-assign the CPU usage;
      {this is executed when the process is resumed because
      now there is a message}
      copy the message associated with the current process into m
    end
  else
    begin
      extract a message from the buffer and
      copy it into m;
      if x.c = x.n and waitqueue <> nil
        then
          begin
            extract one process from the waiting queue;
            exitcr(x.v);
            put descriptor extracted in the set of processes to be
            executed;
            re-assign CPU usage (if necessary)
          end
        else
          begin
            x.n := x.n - 1;
            exitcr(x.v)
          end
    end
end;
```

Note that in the send procedure, the message is inserted into the buffer even when the latter is considered full because the linked list structure allows no *a priori* limitations on the number of messages to be stored. Actually, the 'buffer full' condition is only used to synchronize the processes.

Another key point is that the send procedure is itself associated with a message to a process when it finds the buffer empty. This is because if the process waiting for a message is activated, it could actually be executed only a long time after, if its priority is low. In this case, it might happen that other send operations are performed in the meantime, and other processes with higher priority are activated and executed.

Therefore, the higher priority processes can extract their messages before the low priority processes activated first. In this way, the ordering of the message reception is saved, because the message is extracted when the waiting process is unblocked. To link the message and the process, a possible solution is the addition of a suitable pointer to the process descriptor (see Section 3.4.1).

3.7.3 Process synchronization

Consider a small production plant composed of two tool machines (machine1 and machine2) and a small buffer B with capacity c, placed between the two machines. The operation is organized so that machine1 receives a piece and processes it. When the operations of machine1 are completed, it puts the piece into the buffer, provided that the latter is not full, then machine1 gets a new piece, if available, and repeats the same operations. When machine1 attempts to put the piece in a full buffer its operations are blocked, because it has to wait until there is room in the buffer before it is allowed to leave the processed piece and continue its operations.

At the other side of the buffer, machine2 behaves in a similar way. First, it tries to get a piece to process from the buffer. If the buffer is not empty, machine2 starts to process the piece it received from the buffer, otherwise it has to wait until at least one piece appears in the buffer.

The two machines are controlled by two different processes, A and B respectively, executed by the same CPU. How can they synchronize their operations on the basis of the buffer contents?

In this case, since all the pieces are assumed to be identical, the state of the buffer can be conveniently represented by a counter showing the number of pieces stored. Since it is necessary to take account of the behaviour of the machines for the extreme values of the counter, a semaphore is the method best suited for synchronization. The skeletons of the two processes are given below in a pseudo-Pascal language, where x is a semaphore with capacity k, which has been initialized with the number of pieces stored in the buffer when the operations begin.

skeleton of process A

.

.

.

```
while true do
  begin
    get a new piece;
    work the piece;
    P(x);
    put the piece into the buffer;
  end;
```

.

.

.

skeleton of process B
.

.

.

while true do
  begin
    V(x);
    get a piece from the buffer;
    work the piece;
    put the piece in an output buffer;
  end;
  .

  .

  .

Note that the *P* operation will block the process *A* whenever it is performed with the buffer full, while the *V* operation will block the process *B* whenever nothing is in the buffer. On the other hand, *P* will start process *B* whenever the buffer is empty and *B* is waiting for something to work on. *V* will start process *A* whenever the buffer is full and *A* is waiting to store a piece in the buffer.

3.7.4   Process communication

By modifying the example in the previous section a situation can be shown where semaphores are no longer sufficient to implement synchronization simply. In the modified example, it is no longer assumed that the pieces are identical. Thus, the pieces are separated into four classes, identified by a number from 1 to 4. An additional requirement is that the pieces are processed in the same sequence by both machines.

This synchronization also involves a data exchange between the cooperating processes, since the information exchanged is not just a signal indicating that a piece has been inserted or removed, but that each insertion signal should carry data identifying the type of piece, which must be read when the piece is removed.

For these reasons, a mailbox should be used, where the messages are simply integers indicating the type of the associated piece. The skeletons of the processes *A* and *B* are modified as follows, with *x* now being a mailbox.

skeleton of process A

.

.

.

while true do
  begin
    get a piece and copy the type into m;
    case *m* **of**
    1: type 1 work;
    2: type 2 work;
    3: type 3 work;
    4: type 4 work;
    end;
    send(x, m);
    put the piece into the buffer;
  end;

.

.

.

skeleton of process B

.

.

.

while true do
  begin
    receive (x, m);
    case *m* **of**
    1: type 1 work;
    2: type 2 work;
    3: type 3 work;
    4: type 4 work;
    end;
    put the piece in an output buffer;
  end;

.

.

.

The synchronization is implemented in this example in the same way as the previous one, the difference being that now process *A* passes the information on the piece type to process *B*. Provided that the mailbox implements a FIFO insertion and extraction of the messages, the pieces are processed in the same sequence by both machines, because process *B* receives the messages in the same order they have been sent by *A*.

No assumption has been made on the relative speed of the two processes, or on the arrival process of the pieces at machine1, which regulates the whole production process. This means that the solution based on semaphores or on mailboxes is correct independently of the execution speed.

Another possibility is to extend the examples to cover the case where several identical machines perform the work of machine1 and put the processed data into the same buffer, B, that the data were extracted from, by several machines performing the operations of machine2. In this case, it is only necessary to have a process for each machine, executing the same code as process A, if controlling a machine like machine1, or the same code as process B, if controlling a machine like machine2. The synchronization can still be correctly implemented, either by the semaphore or the mailbox. Thus, semaphores and mailboxes may be used to implement many-to-many as well as one-to-one synchronization and communication (in the case of mailboxes).

3.8   Processor scheduling

The management of the CPUs in a system is the key to the operation of a multitasking operating system. The processor scheduling activity may be divided into two different classes: high-level or long-term scheduling and low-level or short-term scheduling. The former deals with the introduction of the user's job into the system and with the sequencing of the different processes comprising each job. As it can be implemented as a process itself (a system process rather than a user's process), its implementation is essentially in the software, and it will not be discussed further. Conversely, low-level scheduling is concerned with the sequencing of the execution of the processes present at a given instant in the system, and so is more closely allied with the hardware. In this section, only low-level scheduling will be considered, and the term 'processor scheduling' will refer only to short-term scheduling.

3.8.1   Scheduling states of a process

The commonest approach to the implementation of processor scheduling is based on the association of a particular state with each process in the system. Depending on the particular computer and operating system, there are different numbers of processor states as well as different definitions of these states. However, it is convenient to assume a specific state model to illustrate the scheduling operations. Figure 3.9 shows the model assumed here. The definitions of the process states are as follows:

- **Running:**   A process in this state is currently executed by the CPU or one of the CPUs in the system. It is therefore considered at a higher-priority level than other processes ready to run.

- **Ready**:   A process in this state is ready to run, but not currently executed, because its priority is lower than that of the running processes. In this state, all the parameters associated with the process that influence the scheduling decisions are known by the scheduler.

- **Waiting**:   A process in this state cannot be executed, because it is waiting for the occurrence of some special event in the system, whose occurrence will put the process in the ready or running state, according to the process priority.

- **Active**:   A process in this state cannot be considered for a possible execution, because it needs an explicit command to enter either the ready or running state, according to its priority.

- **Inactive**:   A process in this state cannot be scheduled, because although it is present in the system, it needs an explicit command from one of the executing processes, or from the scheduler, to enter the active state and have the scheduling parameters assigned.

Several events may cause a transition between process states and these events are reviewed here by examining the conditions leading a process to enter or leave each of the listed states.

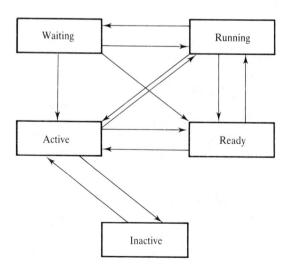

Figure 3.9   Process state diagram.

A. INACTIVE STATE

This is an interface state between long-term and short-term schedulers: a process is created by the long-term scheduler and put in the inactive state. A process can be removed from the system, by destroying it, when the long-term scheduler recognizes that the inactive process does not need to be processed by the system.

An inactive process can be activated and the parameters required by the short-term scheduling algorithm assigned to it. To obtain such a transition, the running process or the scheduler must issue an explicit request.

The opposite transition can be activated only when the process is in the active state. In this case, an explicit request for this operation is performed by the running process – some scheduling routine – and it is used to de-allocate all the control structures (such as process descriptor) used by the short-term scheduler.

In general, processes returning to the inactive state are removed from the system because they have reached successful or abnormal termination and need no further processing.

B. ACTIVE STATE

When a process is in the active state, all the information and control structures required by the scheduler have been allocated, hence the process is ready to compete for the CPU. However, it is necessary to perform an explicit command to put the process either in the ready or in the running state, according to whether the process priority is higher than the priority of the currently running process.

When a process switches from the active to the ready and then the running state, or directly to the running state, it is executed from the beginning; thus, for example, the program counter of the CPU will be initialized with the entry point address of the main program executed by the process. If a process competes twice for the CPU, then it is re–initialized each time it leaves the active state. This kind of switching to the ready or running states is different from that performed for processes leaving the waiting state, because in the latter case the process is not re-initialized – its execution is resumed, restoring the state of the computation reached when the process last left the CPU.

In addition to the use as transit state between the CPU contention and the outside world, the active state may be used to restart a process that incurred a recoverable error, or to execute processes that need more than a single execution.

C. WAITING STATE

The only possible way to enter the waiting state is to be in the running state and to perform some action leading to process suspension. The typical operations causing process suspension have been already encountered, and are summarized as follows:

- an attempt to enter a busy critical region;
- signalling to a full semaphore;
- sending a message to a full mailbox;
- receiving a signal from an empty semaphore;
- receiving a message from an empty mailbox.

All processes performing any of these operations cannot continue their execution until the entity (critical region, semaphore or mailbox) has changed its state so that the process is allowed to resume. The operations performed by the running process, which could switch a process from the waiting to either the ready or even the running state, are as follows:

- an exit from a critical region;
- signalling to an empty semaphore;
- sending a message to an empty mailbox;
- receiving a signal from a full semaphore;
- receiving a message from a full mailbox.

When one of these operations actually leads to a process extraction from the waiting state, the CPU control is passed to the scheduler, so that it can decide if the activated process has the highest priority. If so, the process leaving the waiting state is put directly in the running state, otherwise it goes into the ready state.

D. READY STATE

Transitions to the ready state are always an alternative to transitions to the running state (except that leading to the waiting state), because the difference between the processes in the two states is only a matter of priority. Thus, transitions between the ready and the running states are caused by modifications of the relative priorities of the executable processes.

The only major difference is that ready processes cannot modify their state by themselves. Running processes can, however, perform state transitions by executing suitable actions.

E.   RUNNING STATE

The processes in the running state are the only ones allowed to cause state transitions in other processes as well as for themselves. Hence, it is possible to leave this state as a consequence of an explicit, user-programmed operation, such as the normal completion of a process or temporary de-activation. It is also possible for a process to be forced to leave the CPU as a consequence of some program action, which was not explicitly intended to cause a process state transition. These actions may be subdivided into two classes: those causing a transfer to the waiting state and those bringing the current process into the ready state. The former have been discussed for the waiting state; the latter are those causing the activation or the resumption of other processes. As the activated process may have a higher priority than that just starting, a change may occur in the relative priorities of all the processes with the requisites to be run. When the latter situation happens, the process running is passed to the ready state.

A third type of event causing a process to leave the running state is constituted by actions fired by the occurrence of unusual external or internal situations, which are unpredictable by the programmer. Such events include interrupts and fatal exceptions occurring during the process execution. Both may be regarded as events activating special processes constituted by the corresponding handler routines. However, some differences exist between the two types of event. The handlers of fatal exception conditions – for example, overflow and protection violation – are executed whenever they are activated by the corresponding condition; hence, they always have higher priority than the process that generated them.

3.8.2   Scheduling with interrupts

Interrupts are used to notify the CPU of external events, which may have important effects on the system activity. For example, an interrupt indicating the completion of an I/O operation on a slow device has less stringent time requirements than another related to a faster device, so it is important that the former does not interrupt the execution of the handling routine of the latter.

Some mechanism must exist to allow the recognition of high-priority interrupts only. In other words, the general principle applied in this case is that an interrupt can be acknowledged only if its priority is higher than that of the running process. Since interrupts are external events and are usually managed by external hardware (the interrupt controller), it is necessary that whenever a new process is put in the running state on a CPU, its priority must be output to the interrupt controller to disable the interrupts with equal or lower priority.

If the installation of a new process causes the CPU priority to fall below the highest priority of the pending interrupts, then the most urgent interrupt handler routine is put in the running state, while the interrupted process steps back to the ready state. When an interrupt handler terminates, it returns to the inactive state, and it calls the scheduler to determine the next process to be executed. The scheduler decisions can be overruled by the interrupt mechanism if other high-priority interrupt requests are pending.

It is possible to consider the interrupt controller as a part of the scheduler itself, implemented in hardware. In the same way, the handlers of pending interrupts may be considered in the ready state, since their execution will begin as soon as the priority of the running process falls below theirs.

3.8.3 Scheduling in a multiprocessor

In a monoprocessor system, the scheduling mechanisms described in the previous section may be easily implemented by a software scheduler with the help of a suitable interrupt controller. In a system where more than one CPU exists the situation is more complicated.

In a multi-microprocessor system, each running process is assigned to one CPU and two possibilities exist for the way the processes may be executed by the system: all the processes can be run by any CPU, or the processes can be grouped into subsets, each one statically assigned to one CPU. The former case can be found in general-processing systems, where the system is considered as a whole; hence, there is a single group of processes for each of the possible states.

When a process is put in the running state, any of the CPUs in the system can be selected to execute that process. In general, however, the CPU running the lowest priority process is selected, and the interrupted process is put in the ready state.

The alternative multiprocessor system replicates the mono-processor situation on all the CPUs of the system for different groups of processes. Thus, each CPU has its own group of ready, inactive and waiting processes as well as a single running process. These systems are usually employed in real-time applications, where the I/O peripherals connected to each CPU dictate the execution place of each process. The difference between these multiprocessor systems and a set of independent multi-user but monoprocessor systems is that the processes running on different CPUs can synchronize, communicate and contend for shared resources.

In both types of system, an operation performed by a process running on CPU i can cause the CPU j to switch from the execution of process A to the execution of process B. The rescheduling of another

CPU needs some hardware support to propagate the information, from the CPU i to the CPU j, that a new situation requiring rescheduling has occurred.

Since the operation causing rescheduling occurs on a CPU different from the one to be switched between the two processes, this is an external event for the latter CPU, and therefore it is quite natural to implement this type of inter-process communication by means of interrupts.

Referring to the multiprocessor shown in Figure 3.4, several implementations have been used for the inter-processor interrupts. A possible solution is to implement special storage cells in the shared memory, each one generating an interrupt request for a specific CPU whenever they are written. In this way, it is possible to interrupt another CPU by performing normal write cycles at special addresses. Normally the data written in these cells are an indication of the origin of the interrupt.

Another solution is to implement a special set of lines on the shared bus, reserved for inter-processor interrupt generation. A particular case is represented by the use of a single broadcasting line, used to send interrupt messages, which are transmitted serially on the line. These messages include the origin and destination identifiers as well as data indicating the reason for the interrupt. This implementation is possible, though not officially indicated, in multiprocessor buses, such as the FutureBus (alias IEEE P896), VMEbus and Multibus II [7], which include a serial communication line.

3.9   Conclusion

This chapter has shown that the implementation of multiprogramming and multitasking in microprocessor systems is not just a matter of software, but also requires the implementation of a minimum of hardware supports. The minimal hardware requirements can be summarized as follows, according to the specific system configuration considered:

(1)   Monoprocessor systems
- possibility of enabling and disabling the interrupts (if the DMA activity is not considered);
- indivisible test-and-set instructions (if the DMA activity is considered).
- CPU and interrupt control unit able to dynamically mask the interrupts with priorities lower than the program executed by the CPU, to allow correct activity scheduling;

(2)   Multiprocessor systems
- the same features as for monoprocessors;
- external signals indicating that the CPU is performing an indivisible read–modify–write cycle, to lock the common bus, avoiding interleaved access to the same variable from two different CPUs;
- inter-processor interrupt facilities required to allow correct activity scheduling on different microprocessors.

In addition to these features, other mechanisms may be used to shorten the execution time required by some operations. One such support is given by special instructions able to save or restore the state of the computation of a processor. This operation is required to switch the execution between different processes. The state of the computation of a process may encompass the CPU register contents, as well as the state of the translation tables and access rights managed by the MMU (see Chapter 4). Hence, the hardware supports for fast process switching involve both the CPU and external units.

All modern microprocessors have these hardware supports, implemented in differernt forms. Some of them also implement more complex functions in the hardware. For example, in the Intel iAPX432 (see Chapter 9), where the **send** and **receive** procedures are implemented with a single machine instruction, the short-term scheduler is implemented in the hardware, and almost all the objects related to multitasking are recognized by the hardware. Other microprocessors, like the Intel iAPX286 (see Chapter 8), provide hardware mechanisms for manipulating some hardware-recognized data structures, such as process descriptors, to speed up the scheduling operations.

EXERCISES

3.1 Discuss the effect of multiprogramming in terms of system throughput and response time. Which parameters get better or worse in comparison with monoprogrammed systems?

3.2 Define the information that must be saved/restored in a process switching operation in a microprocessor system composed of a CPU, an arithmetic co-processor and a MMU, assuming that each one holds registers accessible to the programmer.

3.3 Almost all new microprocessor systems have some special mechanism to implement indivisible operations in multiprocessor systems.

Discuss whether such mechanisms are introduced merely to obtain better performances or whether they are mandatory, to implement indivisible operations. Why are such mechanisms not strictly needed for implementing indivisible operations in monoprocessor systems?

3.4 The Z80001 and 2 implement the instruction TST (equivalent to **tas**), which enables programs to avoid interrupts and DMA requests during their execution. Is this instruction sufficient to guarantee indivisible operations in multi- and monoprocessor systems?

3.5 Explain the advantages of conditional critical regions as compared with simple critical regions. Is it possible to totally eliminate the problem of process starvation and, if so, why?

3.6 Two processes, A and B, communicate – B sends messages to A, which prints them. Is it possible to implement a correct synchronization without using critical regions, semaphores or mailboxes? Does the answer depend on whether more than one process sends messages to B or more than one process is used to print the messages generated by A?

3.7 Discuss the advantages and disadvantages of using critical regions, semaphores or mailboxes in Exercise 3.6, including those cases that do not strictly need them.

3.8 Consider a multiprocessor system with a shared bus, implementing inter-processor interrupts by using reserved addresses, so that an interrupt is generated for the processor i whenever a write operation is performed at address $ad(i)$ on the shared bus. Since the interrupt also needs some information about the causes to be stored in a specific place in shared memory, discuss the opportunity of using critical regions, semaphores or mailboxes to control the access to the address $ad(i)$. Also examine the possibility of having a matrix, where each element $ad(i, j)$ is an address reserved for interrupts generated by processor j and sent to processor i.

3.9 What should the priority of the inter-processor interrupt be to obtain correct scheduling?

3.10 Assume that the running task in a system has a priority 4, while a process with priority 5 is waiting for a signal from semaphore A. Describe in detail the operations excuted when the running task signals at sempahore A. Also consider the case of an interrupt handler with priority level 6 performing a signal at *A* instead of the running process.

3.11 Discuss the implementation of a system that assigns fixed time slices to the running process, so that if it is still running when the slice expires, it must leave the CPU and be inserted at the end of the ready list. Assume that a real-time clock interrupt is available.

3.12 Real-time applications sometimes require that certain processes be activated periodically (with different periods). Extend the model of the short-term scheduler given in Section 3.8 to handle periodic processes.

References

[1] *Multibus OEM Products*, Intel Corporation, Santa Clara, 1984.

[2] *The VME Bus Buyer's Guide*, Ironoak Co, La Jolla, 1983.

[3] E. W. Dijkstra, 'Co-operating Sequential Processes', Technological University, Eindhoven, The Netherlands, 1965. (Reprinted in F. Genuys (ed.), *Programming Languages*, Academic Press, New York, 1986.

[4] A. N. Habermann, 'Synchronization of Communicating Processes', *Communications of the ACM* **15**(3), March 1972, pp. 171–176.

[5] P. Brinch Hansen, 'The Nucleus of a Multiprogramming System', *Communications of the ACM* **13**(4), April 1970, pp. 238–250.

[6] P. Brinch Hansen, *Operating System Principles*, Prentice-Hall, Englewood Cliffs, 1973.

[7] Micro Standards, *IEEE Micro* **4**(5), August 1985, pp. 82–89.

Further reading

P. Brinch Hansen, 'The Nucleus of Multiprogramming Systems', *Communications of the ACM* **13**(4), April 1970, pp. 238–241.

P. Brinch Hansen, 'Structured Multiprogramming', *Communications of the ACM* **15**(7), July 1972, pp. 574–578.

P. Brinch Hansen, 'Concurrent Programming Concepts', *ACM Computing Surveys* **5**(4), December 1973, pp. 223–245.

P. Brinch Hansen, *The Architecture of Concurrent Programs*, Prentice-Hall, Englewood Cliffs, 1977.

H. M. Deitel, *An Introduction to Operating Systems*, Addison Wesley Publishing Company, Reading, 1984.

E. W. Dijkstra, 'The Structure of the T.H.E. Multiprogramming System', *Communications of the ACM* **11**(5), May 1968, pp. 341–346.

A. N. Habermann, *Introduction to Operating System Design*, Science Research Associates Incorporated, Chicago, 1976.

C. A. R. Hoare, 'Towards a Theory of Parallel Programming', in *Operating System Techniques*, Academic Press, New York, 1972.

C. A. R. Hoare, 'Communicating Sequential Processes', *Communications of the ACM* **21**(8), August 1978, pp. 666–667.

D. Knuth, *The Art of Computer Programming*, Volume 1, Addison Wesley Publishing Company, Reading, 1969.

P. C. Treleaven, 'Exploiting Program Concurrency in Computing Systems', *Computer* **12**(1), January 1979, pp. 42–50.

CHAPTER 4
MEMORY MANAGEMENT

OBJECTIVES

Memory organization and protection are covered in this chapter. The major points discussed are as follows:

- hierarchical organization of memory;
- simple memory management organizations that do not require special hardware features and are already in use in micro-computer systems;
- virtual memory management techniques;
- protection of objects stored in memory against unauthorized use, by means of capability list checks;
- protections implemented by privileged machine states;
- error detection and correction, and reconfiguration of memory systems.

The memory management mechanisms will be illustrated, pointing out the requirements of each of them, in terms of hardware support.

4.1 Introduction
4.2 Program locality
4.3 Virtual and physical addresses
4.4 Memory hierarchy
4.5 Simple management mechanisms
4.6 Swapping
4.7 Segmentation
4.8 Paging

4.9 Principles of memory protection
4.10 Closed environments
4.11 Multiple domains
4.12 Privileged machine states
4.13 Supports for capability checking
4.14 Hardware memory protection
4.15 Conclusion

4.1 Introduction

The increased computational power and address space of new advanced microprocesors has extended their possible applications, reaching fields such as time-sharing multi-user systems, once reserved only for mainframes or minicomputers. Dealing with these sophisticated applications means that memory management should not be left in the hands of a single programmer any longer, as happens in 8-bit microprocessor systems. Instead, automatic management of memory resources should be performed by a suitable operating system, and this can achieve a better space utilization.

The basic ideas underlying the implementation of memory management are not new, but rather they are borrowed from the solutions adopted in mainframes and minicomputers. However, such ideas are rather new in the field of microprocessor-based systems, and so this chapter is devoted to the description of the commonest techniques used to achieve the goals of good memory utilization, and its protection against unauthorized and mistaken accesses.

Good memory utilization is achieved by taking advantage of the following considerations:

- There are several kinds of memories with different speeds and cost per bit (for example, semiconductor and magnetic memories). In general, the capacity of fast memories is limited by cost or technological capabilities, while cheap memories have long access times.

- In a complex system, such as a multiprogrammed time-sharing computer, it is not necessary to store all the programs in the primary memory at the same time, as only a subset may be ready to run, while others may be waiting for the completion of I/O operations or be temporarily blocked because the user is considering the next command to be issued.

In general, it is convenient to implement the whole memory system by means of several subsystems having different access times and capacities. In such an arrangement the memory management mechanisms will scatter the information all over the different kinds of memory, trying to keep the data and code that are most likely to be accessed in the fastest one, and placing other information in slower memory.

Of course, memory allocation is not static, since eventually the system will process all the information stored in its memory. Hence, data and code will be moved around the different memory subsystems. The flow of this information can be controlled by the programmer, the operating system, the hardware, or by some combination of these. Each is capable of managing a particular type of memory subsystem, as will be discussed in Section 4.4.

4.2   Program locality

An example of the allocation of information under explicit program control is represented by register management performed by an assembler programmer. The CPU registers are the fastest memory in a computer system, but their capacity is not large enough to store all the data manipulated by a program. Hence, a wise programmer uses the registers to hold the data most frequently accessed in a piece of code. Furthermore, since the set of such variables may change during the execution of a program, the programmer will change the register usage, so that variables not used so frequently in the next piece of code are moved back to primary memory, while those that are frequently called are brought into the registers.

In this example, the management of a small and fast memory is based on knowledge of the program structure; thus, such a technique is not suitable for storage management by hardware mechanisms or the operating system, which do not have such knowledge. However, a number of experiments and measurements performed on real systems have shown that the following principle holds. It is called the **Principle of Program Locality**, the term 'principle' being used to indicate that this result has not been obtained from a formal derivation, but it is confirmed by experience rather than theory.

Principle of Program Locality

If a memory address x is accessed at time t, then there is a high probability that an address $x + \Delta x$ will be referenced between t and $t + \Delta t$, with relatively small values for x and t (the principle is also valid for $\Delta x = 0$).

In other words, the principle says that the pattern of memory references generated by an executed program can be divided into **phases**. During each phase, the memory references are directed only to a relatively small subset of the whole program memory space, and this accessed memory is almost all concentrated in a few contiguous memory blocks. Only when the program moves from one phase to the next, does the memory reference pattern become irregular, until the new phase is reached, and the references generated are clustered around a different set of memory blocks.

The mechanisms for the automatic management of memory space can use the program locality to keep the subset of the program memory space most frequently used during the current phase in the fast memory; the crucial point is marked by the detection of the transitions between phases and the identification of the memory locations used within each phase. The following sections will be devoted to illustrating the commonest solutions for these problems.

Finally, the joint automatic and user management of the memory space requires that the programmer provides information about the program structure, so that the automatic mechanism can move the information between the different memory subsystems according to the information given by the programmer.

4.3   Virtual and physical addresses

Organizing the memory into several different subsystems has important implications on addressing. Since memory allocation is dynamic, it is best if the program (hence the CPU) does not make direct use of the addresses of the actual memory location, where the accessed information is stored, since it would be necessary to relocate the program each time a subset of it is moved within the memory. The solution usually adopted is to assign the program its own address space, which differs from the actual address space implemented within the system. Then, the mapping between the program (virtual) address and the machine (physical) address is performed at run time, using suitable hardware supports.

Since the virtual and physical address spaces are independent, their sizes may also differ. The virtual address space may therefore be larger than the primary memory size, in which case some subsets of the program must be stored on mass storage devices. However, the program locality allows such a program to be executed efficiently if suitable subsets of the program are stored in primary memory.

As it is possible to have a different function for mapping virtual to physical addresses for each program, more than one virtual address space may exist. This solution complicates the mapping operation, but avoids any address clash with other programs, which might occur if the virtual space is unique.

4.4   Memory hierarchy

The principles of memory management outlined in Section 4.1 lead to a hierarchical organization of the different memory subsystems. The smallest and fastest memory is at the top of the hierarchy, while the largest and slowest is at the bottom. In general, data transfer can only occur between memory subsystems occupying contiguous levels in the hierarchy.

Since memory organizations based on the program locality have often achieved good cost/performance ratios, this idea is even more widely used in new microprocessors. However, the memory hierarchy in these systems is composed of a greater number of levels than in the previous models.

	Data	Code	Memory Management (MMU) Information
Level 0 (registers)	CPU registers	instruction register	MMU registers
Level 1 (on-chip cache)	data cache	instruction queue (or cache)	MMU internal memory
Level 2	on-board cache		
Level 3	primary memory		
Level 4	mass storage		

Figure 4.1 A general model for memory hierarchy.

Figure 4.1 shows a possible organization of the memory hierarchy for a system based on an advanced microprocessor. This memory organization includes the most usual and recent hierarchy levels. Not every system will include all the levels shown in Figure 4.1, though this could be achieved.

The principle of program locality is valid for any kind of memory reference. However, at different hierarchical levels, the instructions, data and information needed for memory management are handled in different ways, and this distinction between the different memory references is illustrated in Figure 4.1.

It is important to note that while the term **virtual address** may be used to indicate the address manipulated by the user programs, the term **virtual memory** is used to indicate a memory where part of the program executed is stored on fast mass storage devices, regardless of the other levels implemented in the memory hierarchy.

4.4.1 Registers

Internal CPU registers are the fastest and smallest memory in the system since they are directly connected to the different processing subunits within the CPU, such as the ALU, the instruction decoder and the arithmetic unit for address calculation.

General-purpose registers are the level 0 memory for data (including the program's addresses) and the instruction register is the level 0 memory for code. The novel feature of some 32-bit micro-processors, such as the iAPX286 (see Chapter 8), is that they have a few registers dedicated to holding temporarily information used for memory management. These registers may be partially under (privileged) program control but, in general, they are managed by the CPU itself.

4.4.2 On-chip caches

The continually increasing processing speed of new microprocessors requires even faster memory systems. Since the access times of the memory chips are steadily decreasing, the total response time is affected to a noticeable extent by the interfacing delays, including the time penalty due to the transmission across chip boundaries.

In the light of this technological situation, it makes sense to introduce a new hierarchical level composed of a memory not directly connected to the processing subunits, but implemented on the same chip as the CPU. Although this level 1 memory will be slower than registers, it will require some interface circuitry; however, it will be faster than memory implemented outside the chip. At this level, there is still a distinction between data, code and information for memory management. On-chip caches for code are sometimes organized as FIFO buffers, with the head represented by the instruction register. This simple organization is possible because the reference pattern for fetching instructions is almost linear, with jumps corresponding to the execution of explicit jump instructions. Thus, there is a high probability that the next word of code to be fetched is at the next address.

Jump instructions empty the FIFO buffer as they destroy the linear path through addresses. Therefore, the on-chip cache effect disappears for a short time after the execution of these instructions, since the new

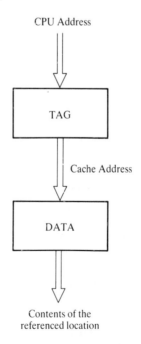

Figure 4.2   General cache organization.

word of code must be fetched from outside memory. However, since the instructions also comprise a period of internal data processing, the management unit of the instruction buffer refills the queue more quickly than the CPU empties it by fetching new instructions; hence, the effect of the on-chip instruction queue re-appears after a few fetches following the execution of a jump instruction.

A conflict can arise between the CPU, which needs to perform a bus cycle for reading/writing some data, and the instruction buffer management unit, which needs to perform a bus cycle for filling the instruction queue. In such a case, the bus cycle required for data processing always has higher priority.

As the references for accessing data are generated following a more unpredictable pattern than that for fetching code, the corresponding on-chip cache is organized as a random access memory composed of a data part and a tag part, as shown in Figure 4.2. In general, both TAG and DATA parts are composed of the same number of words; DATA holds the data values and TAG holds the corresponding information about the CPU address used to access the data. When the CPU emits an address, the cache controller performs the operations shown in Figure 4.3. This type of cache organization used for on-chip cache is called 'fully associative', because the TAG memory is addressed by its contents.

The implementation of on-chip data caches incurs a number of architectural problems. First, the TAG memory is larger than the DATA memory, thus a considerable chip area is consumed by cache management. Second, some simulation studies [1] have shown that the introduction of on-chip data caches increases rather than decreases the

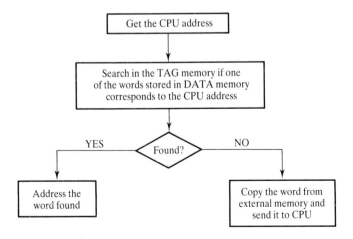

Figure 4.3 Operations of the cache controller.

speed required for transmission across chip boundaries. However, a few implementations of on-chip caches do exist, such as the Zilog Z80000 [2]. Real on-chip caches are now limited to instructions, as they do not give rise to memory consistency problems, and represent an enhancement of the instruction queues, since it is possible to hold the whole code of small loops in an on-chip memory, delaying the code fetch from external memory. Instruction queues, on the other hand, must be reloaded with the same piece of code every time the loop is executed. However, the cost of an instruction queue is much smaller than that of an instruction cache.

Finally, the cacheing technique is also used to store the most frequently used information for memory management in the same chip as the CPU or a special MMU. This small cache is usually managed according to the least recently used (LRU) policy, which replaces the least recently used information with the new data requested by the CPU and copied from off-chip memory. Not all the management mechanisms for on-chip caches are not under program control, but they are implemented in the hardware, and their presence tends to be transparent to the programmer.

4.4.3   On-board caches

The same reasons that merit the introduction of on-chip caches are valid for implementing a cache memory on the same board as the CPU. Indeed, the delay introduced by the interfacing circuitry, and by the transmission and settle times of the signals on the backplane bus, often require the introduction of one wait cycle for the fastest microprocessors, when they address off-board memory locations. Moreover, although on-board caches are implemented using semiconductor memories as the memory in the next hierarchical level (primary memory), there are always semiconductor memories with different speeds. Hence, on-board caches make it possible to obtain a memory system with access times close to those provided by the fast semiconductor memory (cache) at a cost close to that of the larger and slower memory (primary memory).

There is an additional reason for introducing caches in multi-processor systems. In these systems, delays caused by the contention between CPUs and primary memory for channels increase the average access time.

Cache management requires certain hardware. The cache organization shown in Figure 4.2 is still valid for an on-board cache, but since the cache is larger, other management mechanisms are needed to keep the size of the TAG memory as small as possible.

The requirements of these additional mechanisms have been studied and to illustrate them further the following cache parameters must be introduced:

- **Cache size**: Dimension of the DATA memory, expressed in terms of the smallest piece of memory addressable by the CPU.

- **Block size**: Dimension of the smallest piece of memory manipulated by the cache control mechanisms. Each access to a memory location within a block is seen as a reference to the block. Furthermore, any transfer to and from the primary memory consists of a whole block (in general, the block size is a power of two).

- **Set size**: Number of different places in the DATA memory where the cache organization allows any given block of primary memory to be stored (in general, the set size is also a power of two).

Figure 4.4 shows a possible way of translating the address issued by the CPU into a DATA memory address. Let n be the number of address bits of the CPU and $k < n$ the number of bits necessary to address the DATA memory.

Given a block size $B = 2^b$, the b least significant address bits are copied from the CPU into the DATA memory address, since the offset within a block is not considered by the address translation mechanism.

If the set size is $S = 2^s$, the CPU address may be translated into one out of S possible DATA memory addresses. Therefore, s bits of the cache address are obtained by real mapping through the TAG memory, while the remaining $x = k - s - b$ bits are determined uniquely by the CPU address, then they are copied. Since the x bits, shown in Figure 4.4, determine the set of possible blocks within the data memory, and the exact location within the set is not constrained by the other address bits, the mapping of the most significant $n - b - x$ bits of the CPU address

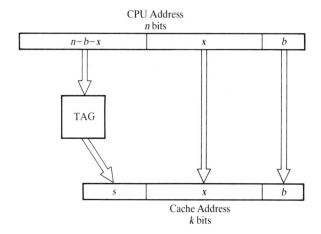

Figure 4.4   Address mechanism translation for caches.

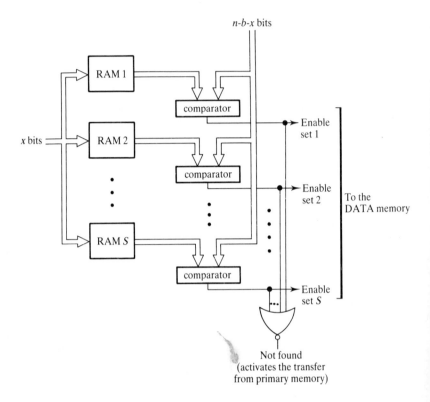

Figure 4.5 Implementation of the TAG memory for set associative caches, without using associative memories.

into the s most significant bits of the cache address should ideally be performed by a set of associative memories (one per set). An alternative solution is shown in Figure 4.5, where only RAM memories are used. In this case, the number of TAG memory bits used are given by the following formula:

$$2^{(k-b)} \times (n - k + s) \tag{4.1}$$

which relates the cache size (2^k), the block size (2^b), the set size (2^s) and the CPU address space size (2^n). By varying the value of s, the following three classical organizations are obtained:

(1) $s = 0$ (**indexed organization**):   Each block in primary memory can be mapped on to a single cache block.

(2) $0 < s < k - b$ (**set associative organization**):   Each block in primary memory can be mapped on to a limited set of cache blocks.

(3) $s = k - b$ (**fully associative organization**):   Each block in primary memory can be mapped on to any cache block.

From Equation (4.1) it follows that the larger the value of s, the larger the size of TAG memory. On the other hand, several experimental results [3] have made it clear that increasing the set size leads to an improvement of the probability of accessing a location whose contents are already stored in the cache. However, the same studies have shown that, in general, a set size of two or four leads to performances very close to fully associative caches.

Hence, the preference of system designers is for set associative caches with a small set size. For example, the VAX 11/780 has a cache of 8 Kbytes with set size two and block size eight.

4.4.4   Primary memory

The primary memory is the largest memory subsystem directly address-able by the CPU. All programs (data and code) to be run should be stored in the primary memory, as well as the information needed for memory management. However, not all programs are ready to run in parallel and, even when a program is executed, it uses only one subset of its address space during each phase.

The techniques for managing the contents of the primary memory need some hardware support, but the algorithms are implemented in software; hence, a variety of solutions is possible.

It is worth noting that primary memory and registers are the two hierarchy levels already present in a system, while the others may or may not be implemented.

4.4.5   Mass storage

The information not immediately needed by the CPU (programs not ready to run or subsets of the memory address space not used in the current phase, for example) is stored in magnetic devices that provide a large amount of memory at a low cost per bit and access times two or three orders of magnitude larger than primary memory.

4.4.6   Cost and performance considerations

The success of hierarchical memory organizations is due to the effectiveness of this approach in terms of both cost and performance, since the cost per bit is close to that of the slowest memory in the hierarchy, while the performances obtained approach those offered by the fastest memory.

Table 4.1 illustrates the characteristics of the different types of memory used for the different hierarchical levels, which help to evaluate the cost and performances of a hierarchy of memories. In particular, the cost per bit of the memory is given by the following formula:

$$\frac{\sum_{i=0}^{4} m_i \, c_i}{\sum_{i=0}^{4} m_i} \tag{4.2}$$

where m_i is the size of the ith level in the hierarchy and c_i is the corresponding cost per bit. From Table 4.1, it can be seen that the size of the whole memory is largely dominated by the size of the highest (slowest) levels. Hence, the cost per bit approaches the cost per bit of the cheapest memory.

Table 4.1   Characteristics of the different levels in the memory hierarchy.

Name	Typical Size	Typical Access Time	Typical Transfer Time
Registers	16–32	0.1 ns	0.1 ns
On-chip cache	256–1K	10 ns	10 ns
On-board cache	1K–8K	50 ns	50 ns
Main memory	64K–16M	300 ns	300 ns
Disks	10M–1000M	1 ms	1 μs

The performances depend on the location of the accessed memory address in the hierarchy. Since each level has its own access and transfer time, it is possible to evaluate the memory speed only in terms of average access time, which can be expressed by using the following formula:

$$T = \sum_{i=0}^{4} p_i \, T_i \tag{4.3}$$

where p_i is the probability of finding the accessed location in the ith level of the hierarchy, while T_i is the time required to accede the required data. Note that the higher levels are managed on a per block basis, especially for magnetic storage devices that show transfer times close to retrieve times. This implies that a whole block is transferred to the bottom levels when a reference to a memory location stored in the upper levels occurs. Therefore, the value of T_i should also take account of the time needed to perform the whole block transfer.

The final value of T depends greatly on the values of p_i: the larger the values for small i, the smaller the value of T. Experience with hierarchical memory organizations has shown that values of T close to the access time of the on-board cache memory are possible (no results are now available for on-chip caches as only a few new systems adopt this solution), since a high probability of finding the location in the cache can be obtained with reasonable costs.

4.4.7 Memory hierarchy in multiprocessor systems

A hierarchical memory organization has several advantages, but it can give rise to problems in multiprocessor systems, since the hierarchy concept often contrasts with the need to perform multiple read and updates of the memory correctly. The major problem in using a memory hierarchy in multiprocessor systems is that several copies of the same virtual location may exist in different hierarchy levels, and so it is necessary to update all such copies to maintain a consistent state of memory.

The following example clarifies the types of problems introduced by memory hierarchy in multiprocessors. It is assumed that a system is composed of several microprocessor boards, each with a private memory, connected to a shared memory through a multiprocessor bus, as shown in Figure 4.6. The memory is organized in a hierarchy whose bottom levels are implemented in the private memories, while the upper levels are in the shared memory. This organization is also shown in Figure 4.6 by indicating the level number, according to the model in Figure 4.1.

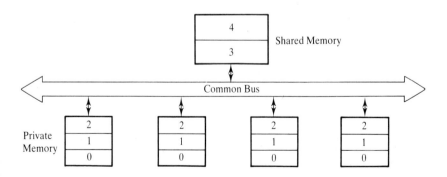

Figure 4.6 Example of hierarchical memory organization in a multimicroprocessor system.

If a program running on the processor i accesses the location x, this is copied in to the private cache at location x'; then the contents of x' are modified so that the value of x and x' are no longer identical. If a second program, running on the processor j, needs to use the contents of location x, it will read from processor j a value that differs from that read by a program running on the processor i, though the same virtual address is used.

The solution to this kind of problem depends on the hierarchy of levels involved. The problem of private caches has been extensively studied [4–6], whereas the same problem applied to on-chip cache is still open. Consequently, this has delayed the introduction of such caches on advanced microprocessors for read/write data, while on-chip caches for storing program code are used in some cases (see Chapter 6), since the read-only nature of programs avoids any inconsistency problem.

4.5   Simple management mechanisms

This section illustrates simple memory management techniques not requiring hardware support, but providing poor flexibility for a user's space management. These methods provide examples of memory management under full or partial program control and show the advantages offered by other techniques possible with new microprocessors.

4.5.1   Memory with extra banks

The first technique is typical of microprocessor systems, since it was conceived to extend the addressable memory beyond the limits imposed by the number of address signals (16, in general) used by 8-bit microprocessors. The basic idea is to expand the system addresses by adding extra bits; however, since the CPU is able to manipulate and only issue a subset of the new address, the remaining address bits must be issued with a separate operation.

The hardware organization of the memory is shown in Figure 4.7. Note that the selection of the different banks is performed on the basis of the contents of a small register R holding the most significant bits of the address, the least significant one being issued by the CPU. Once the contents of R are set to select a specific bank, it is possible to access data and code stored there by using only the address subset issued by the CPU. Whenever it is necessary to refer to a location in a different bank, the contents of R are changed to perform a bank switching. It is then possible to address the location by using the address subfield manipulated by the CPU.

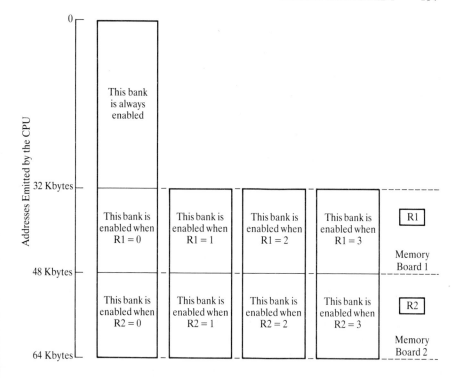

Figure 4.7 Memory implementation and addressing with switched banks.

This technique does not require any special hardware support as all the management functions must be performed by the programmer. These management operations are as follows:

- partition data and code of the program so that each piece fits into one of the memory banks and the bank switching operations do not occur too often;

- writing the program taking into account the possible bank switching operations required to access the operands, since they require the insertion of a suitable portion of code used to modify the contents of the external register R.

Note that the last operation here can be performed if the program is written in assembler language, while high-level language programs need special compilers and linkers able to cope with bank switching. Unfortunately, such program developing tools are not commonly available, complicating the software development for systems adopting such a memory organization.

An additional drawback of this technique is the static allocation caused by the fact that the program must be aware of the allocation of both data and code. This prevents any possibility of performing automatic relocation to achieve better memory use when the system state requires memory re-assignment.

4.5.2   Overlay

The second technique discussed here has been widely used in mini-computer systems, such as DEC PDP11 models without demand paging, and is still used to run large programs on microprocessor-based personal computers. In this technique, the program is partially resident in main memory and partially stored on disks. When part of the program on disk is required, it is brought into memory and loaded in the same locations occupied by another part of the program not currently needed. Since different subsets of the program space can be loaded in the same memory area, there is an overlap of such subsets; hence, this memory management technique is called **overlay**.

Since it is essential to avoid situations where two different and overlapping parts of the same program are both required in memory to execute the program, it is necessary that the overlay of the different program subsets is performed by programmers, since they know how the program evolves and which portions need to be resident in memory at the same time.

This partitioning can generally be performed by structuring the whole program into a tree of modules, where all the related modules in the tree overlap. This overlay tree can be constructed following the tree of procedure calls; thus, the root is represented by the main program, which always resides in main memory, and all the procedures directly called by the main program can overlap, because they are called one at a time and do not require each other's presence.

Unfortunately, the construction of the overlay tree might not be a trivial task for several reasons. First, it is necessary to obtain overlapping modules of approximately the same size, so they all fit in the same memory space, as shown in Figure 4.8, where both the tree and the positions occupied by the different modules are shown. Another problem arises due to the necessity to minimize the operations for swapping the modules in and out, since the larger this number, the poorer the performance; hence, it is wise to avoid small modules. On the other hand, small modules allow the programmer to exploit more overlapping and to decrease the memory used. Thus, when preparing the overlay tree, the programmer should balance memory against performance require-ments.

In addition to the problems connected with the preparation of the overlay tree, the programmer can rely on software development tools for preparing the final task, since some linkers able to cope with overlay do

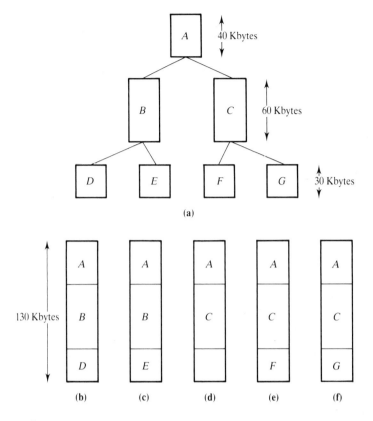

Figure 4.8 Example of memory allocation using overlays: (a) an overlay tree; (b) initial memory allocation; (c) allocation after a call to module E; (d) allocation after a call to module C; (e) allocation after a call to module F; (f) allocation after a call to module G.

exist. When executed, an overlaid program performs operating system calls whenever it is necessary to call a procedure not currently resident in main memory. The implementation of the overlay technique does not therefore require any special hardware support – except fast disk units for quick swapping. The program addresses generated by the compilers do not depend on the structure of the overlay tree, since the calls to external procedures can be resolved by the linker, either in the normal way or by inserting an operating system call.

The overlay technique is a typical example of those techniques where the programmer's knowledge of the program behaviour is combined with automatic memory swapping to implement memory management. The major drawback of this technique is represented by the problems connected with the preparation of the overlay tree, and by the need to load a whole module when only a part of it is required, leading in some cases to poorer performances than other fully automatic management techniques. On the other hand, it allows to run programs larger than the physical main memory implemented in the system.

4.6 Swapping

In a multiprogrammed machine, several programs may be executed concurrently, so using the primary memory to store only the programs ready to run is a wise decision.

According to the swapping policy, a program waiting for completion of I/O operations, which will take some milliseconds, is swapped out of memory. When it is again ready to run, the system tries to find some space in the primary memory to swap in the program; if there is not enough space available, the program is placed on a swap list, waiting for memory availability. Each time a swap-out operation takes place, the memory management routines try to re-use the memory space, to swap in programs in the list.

The translation from virtual to physical address in primary memory is performed by adding the virtual address to the starting address of the memory area where the program has been loaded. Since this relocation operation must be performed for each memory cycle, special hardware is required to speed up the relocation, so that no time penalty is incurred by the swapping policy. This special hardware, often implemented in a single chip, is called the **memory management unit** (MMU), and can be considered as an extension of the CPU, which performs memory management tasks requiring high processing speed. Different memory management techniques require different kinds of MMU; however, multiprogrammed systems always require such special hardware.

Every time a new program is started or resumed, a special register of the MMU must be loaded with the base address of the memory area where the program is stored. In addition to the base address, the size of the program is also stored in another register, so that during the address translation the MMU can check whether or not the program is accessing a memory location within its own memory space. This simple check assures that a program cannot access information outside its own area and also protects each program against mistakes or malicious actions of other programs.

Swapping is a memory management technique that can be implemented simply, but it has some important drawbacks. In the situation shown in Figure 4.9, PROG2 should be swapped out, releasing the corresponding memory area. However, there is no room to 'swap in' any program in the swap list, although the amount of free memory is $1000 + 2000 = 3000$ words, which would be sufficient to hold PROG7. Since the swapping technique considers a program as a whole block to be

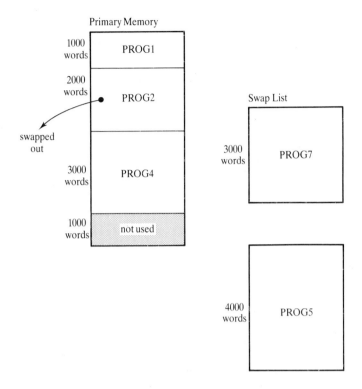

Figure 4.9 A typical situation where the swapping technique fails to obtain the best memory utilization.

allocated in a contiguous space, it is not possible to use small fragments of free memory space, which may become significant after several swap operations. This effect is called **memory fragmentation** and can be lessened by using segmentation instead of swapping.

4.7 Segmentation

The process of segmentation involves breaking the program down into several segments that need not to be stored in adjacent memory areas, though each one requires a contiguous block of memory. Hence, the problems of fragmentation are lessened, since it is possible to utilize smaller contiguous areas.

Segments correspond to logical subsets of the program – for example, an obvious division is between a code segment and a data segment. However, it is possible to have a larger number of smaller segments, each one including one or a few subroutines or one or a few data structures.

The address translation mechanism involved in segmentation is quite complex as the operating system needs to maintain a table of segment descriptors for each program. Each entry in this table is composed of:

- a base address;
- a segment size;
- attributes (used to check whether or not the access performed is correct).

The algorithm for address translation is shown in Figure 4.10. A subset of the virtual address is used to identify the accessed segment, whose descriptor is extracted via a lookup operation in the segment descriptor table. The translation then occurs as for the swapping technique.

The relocation is critical as regards system performance, since it must be performed in each memory cycle. Hence, if the segment descriptor table is to be stored in primary memory, a memory cycle is needed to perform address translation, doubling the time needed to perform a memory cycle.

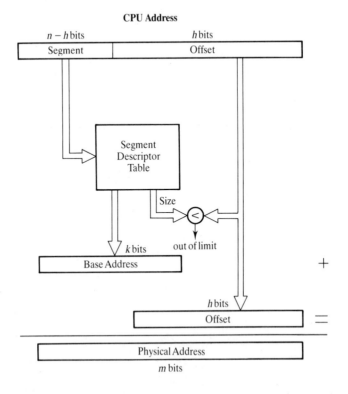

Figure 4.10 Address translation scheme required by segmentation.

To overcome this problem, the segment descriptor table is stored in a small but very fast RAM implemented within the MMU. However, given the limited size of this special memory, the segment descriptor table of one or several programs needs to be swapped in and out between the MMU and primary memory.

Another problem arises when the number of segments is larger than the RAM in the MMU. In this case, the fast memory inside the MMU can be used as a cache, where the most recently used segment descriptors are stored. When the address translation begins, the MMU searches for the segment descriptor in its internal memory; if it is not there, the descriptor is read from primary memory and copied into the internal memory. As the program locality leads to a high probability of finding the descriptor in the internal memory of the MMU, the additional cycle needed to read the descriptor from primary memory should seldom be performed, and so it does not greatly influence the overall performance.

Another key point as regards the relocation delay is the speed of the addition shown in the lower part of Figure 4.10. The m-bit physical address is obtained by adding a k-bit ($k \leq m$) left-justified base address and an h-bit ($h \leq m$) right-justified offset. First of all, the number h determines the maximum segment size, because it is not possible, within a given segment, to access any information with an offset larger than $2^h - 1$. The least significant $m - k$ bits are not really added, but are copied from the virtual to the physical address; hence, the addition is performed only on k bits (provided that $k + h > m$). Since the larger k is, the longer the addition delay, performance considerations would lead to small k. On the other hand, it can be seen that the base address can be placed only at 2^{m-k} boundaries, so only small values of k will again give rise to fragmentation problems, since it will be possible to load a segment only in a limited number of positions. In general, the solution adopted represents a compromise and typical values for $m - k$ are from 4 to 8.

4.7.1 Segmented virtual memory

In Section 4.1, which discussed the program locality concept, it was pointed out that program executions evolve through a sequence of phases, and the address space accessed during each phase is smaller than the whole program space. If the segments accessed in the current phase are stored in primary memory, the program is executed almost as fast as if all the segments were stored in primary memory, because almost all the accesses are directed to segments already present. However, when a reference to an absent segment is generated, a segment fault occurs and the accessed segment is brought into primary memory, eventually replacing some other segments.

This mechanism implies that the MMU will check that the accessed segment is present by testing a suitable bit in the corresponding descriptor; this bit is set when the segment is swapped in and reset when it is swapped out. Swapping out is performed more quickly if the segment has not been modified since being copied into primary memory, because it does not need to be copied into mass storage (this is normally valid for code segments). Hence, in general, a modified/non-modified flag is included in the attribute field of each segment descriptor for this reason. The flag is initially cleared and it is set by each write operation on a location within the segment.

Another important feature essential in the hardware of a system employing this segmentation technique is the ability of the CPU to interrupt the execution in the middle of an instruction and then resume the same instruction exactly where it was interrupted. The classical interrupt and trap mechanisms are not sufficient in this case, as their activation is sensed only at the end of an instruction, and so they are not suitable for handling segment faults, because these may occur anywhere within an instruction. The instruction cannot therefore be completed before the segment fault occurs because the instruction would already have executed some invalid and non-recoverable operations.

Although the latest version of the segmentation technique has several advantages – programs larger than the primary memory space can be run, for example – it also suffers from some important drawbacks. The most important is caused by the variable length of the segments, which complicates the management of the memory space, because when a program segment needs to be copied into the primary memory, it is not always possible to find room for it, because the segment it swapped out was shorter, hence the memory released is too small. This implies either the need for some complex replacement algorithms or the continuous presence of unused memory space. Paging is a technique that overcomes these problems, by subdividing the program space into fixed-size subsets.

4.8   Paging

Partitioning the whole program space into pieces of equal size, referred to as pages, avoids some memory allocation problems arising when variable length segments are used.

This solution also has important consequences for the programmer's view of the virtual address space, because with paging there is no relation between the logical organization of the program and the pages. The memory management mechanisms are the only system components aware of the partition of the program space into pages. Analogously, the physical memory is seen as a set of blocks, each with the size of one page, so that it is possible to store one page into one memory block. As for segmentation, contiguous pages need not be allocated to contiguous blocks.

Figure 4.11 shows the allocation of a single program in the memory of a multiprogrammed system. Pages, like segments, may be partially stored in the primary memory; when a reference for a virtual address belonging to a page not present in memory is generated, then the paging mechanism copies the whole page containing the address into a block. This mechanism is referred to as **demand paging**, since the pages are brought into the memory when needed by the program.

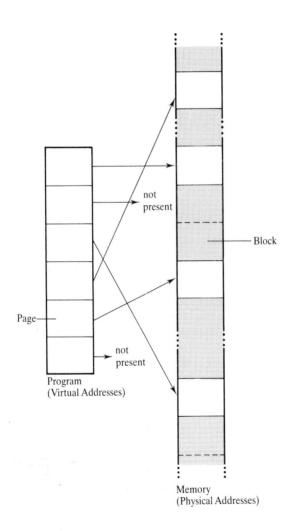

Figure 4.11   Memory allocation in a system with paging.

A broad spectrum of different paging techniques have been developed over the years as a result of studies on paging. They fall into the following groups:

- Mechanisms to determine when a page should be copied into the main memory. Demand paging is the commonest technique, used by the MMU of some microprocessors illustrated in the following chapters. However, other techniques have been developed that try to foresee the program behaviour and put in the memory those pages that the program will use in the future.

- Mechanisms (or replacement techniques) that use an algorithm to select the page already present in the memory, and thus release the block occupied and swap it out to allow a new page to be copied into the memory.

- Mechanisms that use an algorithm to determine the increase or decrease of the number of blocks (hence the number of pages resident in the memory) dedicated to each program.

A detailed discussion of the different management techniques used in conjunction with paging is beyond the scope of this book, and the interested reader can find further information from the references and list of further readings at the end of this chapter.

4.8.1   Hardware supports for paging

The hardware mechanisms necessary for an efficient implementation of paging are very similar to those used for segmentation. The key feature is the possibility of checking the virtual address emitted by the CPU to determine whether or not the corresponding page is present in the memory.

This function may be implemented by using **page descriptors**, whose typical layout is shown in Figure 4.12. It is worth noting that the page descriptor is similar to the segment descriptor, the main difference being the absence of the limit field, since the pages have a fixed length usually equal to a power of two.

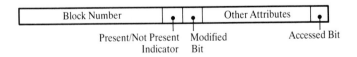

Figure 4.12   Example of page descriptor format.

4.8.2 Page tables

Virtual address checking and translation may be performed as shown in Figure 4.13. The virtual address is composed of a page number and an offset within the page. The page number may be divided into several fields, each one used as an index to address a descriptor in a tree-structured table, whose leaves correspond to page descriptors. The contents of the page descriptor are used to check for the presence of a page in the memory and to provide the most significant bits of the physical address, while the page offset gives the least significant ones.

One key parameter is the number of the tree levels of the addrës translation process, because the higher the tree, the longer the time spent to retrieve the page descriptor. On the other hand, a tree-structured table allows the system to implement more powerful and flexible memory allocation strategies; for example, it becomes simple to share the same subtree between different processes, so that shared data structures and procedures are implemented straight away. Because there is a single page descriptor for shared areas, updating their contents as a consequence of swapping in and out is no more complicated than for non-shared pages.

Although correct, this scheme needs additional modification to be suitable for an efficient implementation. The main problem is the size of the page table (PGT): if a separate virtual address space is implemented for each program, a separate PGT is required. Moreover, the virtual

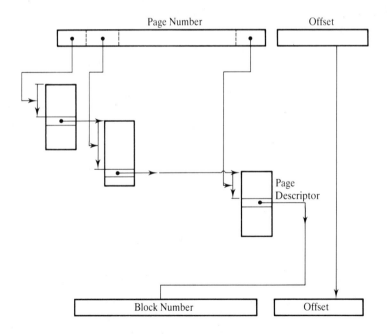

Figure 4.13 Address translation based on tree-structured page tables.

space size is normally far larger than the physical memory size, and so the number of pages and their descriptors is also large. Thus, it is not possible to implement a large and fast memory on the same chip as the MMU to perform the operations shown in Figure 4.13, without an unacceptable performance degradation.

The solution to this problem once again uses a memory hierarchy. A small and fast memory is implemented on the MMU chip, where only the descriptors of the most recently referenced pages are stored. During a program phase the references are clustered around a small set of pages, so the page descriptor corresponding to the address issued by the CPU will often be found in the MMU memory, and only seldom is it necessary to go to the main memory to retrieve a page descriptor in the PGT.

The small descriptor cache within the MMU is organized as a content-addressable memory (CAM), since the addresses of this memory are no longer related to the page number, as it stores the descriptors of the most frequently referenced pages.

Another implementation, often used in mainframe systems such as the IBM 370, is based on a larger CAM, with one word per memory block: each word of the CAM holds the descriptor of the page stored in the corresponding memory block or an indication that the block is empty. The page descriptor has the layout shown in Figure 4.14, where the base address field has been replaced by the page number field. In this figure, the page number issued by the CPU is used as input for the CAM storing the descriptors of the pages present in the memory; the output is the address of the CAM word holding the corresponding descriptor or an indication that the page is not present in memory. If a page is present, the output of the CAM gives the most significant bits of the physical address directly. Although faster, the latter solution requires a larger CAM; moreover, it is possible with this scheme to implement distinct address spaces for the different programs only if the CAM contents are saved/restored each time a process switching occurs. In the previous case, the cache management mechanism brings the descriptors into the cache as soon as they are needed.

4.8.3   Segmentation with paging

It has already been pointed out that many similarities exist between segmentation and paging. It is also possible to have a memory management technique that combines the characteristics of the two methods, and so obtain a technique with both the simple allocation scheme of paging and the protection features of segmentation (see Section 4.7). In such a case, the programmer divides the whole virtual space into segments reflecting the logical structure of the program, as with segmentation; then each segment is considered as being composed of

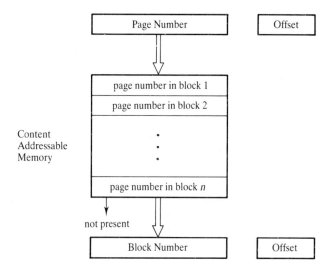

Figure 4.14 Address translation with associative memory.

several pages, as for paging, so that the memory allocation still works on fixed-length pieces. The hardware mechanisms required are the same as for pure paging; however, the memory fragmentation increases, because for pure paging there is only one page – the last – that is normally only partly used, while with a combination of segmentation and paging the number of partially used pages is equal to the number of segments, since no page can be shared between different segments.

4.9 Principles of memory protection

The need for protecting memory objects (that is, segments of code, data or a combination of the two) against misuse arises from the increased requirements for both reliability and privacy in multiprogrammed environments.

In a system implementing suitable protection mechanisms, the errors caused either by physical faults or by programming mistakes only propagate within the memory objects accessible by the process where the error first appeared. An attempt to access other objects, with the threat of a possible error export, is detected as illegal and is then blocked by the protection mechanisms. In this way, the failure of one or more processes does not cause the failure of all the processes in the system. Furthermore, the confinement of the errors is an important debugging tool, since it helps to point out where the error originated. This is also the basis for other mechanisms used to attain higher reliability, such as **categorization**, **recovery** and **restart**.

The same protection implemented for error confinement protects the information stored in the system against unauthorized use, provided that the operating system makes inaccessible all the objects that a process is not authorized to úse. It is possible to implement a finer protection mechanism allowing the system to specify the set of legal operations on an accessible object.

4.10   Closed environments

A key point in error confinement is the principle of **process isolation**, which requires that each process should have no capability beyond what is strictly required to perform its task. In this way, all the operations performed by each process on the objects are constrained to agree with the capabilities granted to it; any deviation from these predefined interactions is considered illegal. Since the capabilities of a process are themselves stored in the memory, it is necessary that such a table is also a special protected object.

The best way to implement the process isolation principle is to have a system with closed environments. In such a system, a process requiring an operation on an object must show, to the memory protection mechanisms, that an explicit capability for performing the required operation has been granted to it.

The overall situation of the access rights granted to the different processes for the different objects may be represented by the matrix shown in Figure 4.15, where each column is associated with an object and each row is associated with a process. The contents of the element (i, j) are the set of operations that can be performed by the process i on the object j.

		Resources				
		1	2	3	4	5
	A	—	arc (1)	arc (2)	—	—
	B	arc (3)	—	—	—	—
Processes	C	arc (3)	—	—	arc (5)	arc (6)
	D	—	arc (7)	—	arc (5)	—

arc (i): access right code
(different access right
sets corresponds to different
values of i)

Figure 4.15   Matrix representation for access rights.

There are two methods for representing the matrix of Figure 4.15: by row and by column. With the first method, a list of capabilities is linked to each process, eliminating all the empty elements corresponding to no capability. This list is also referred to as the **domain of access**, since each process is aware only of the objects it owns a capability for, while the other objects are hidden. When a memory reference is issued by the CPU, the capability owned by the process currently running on the CPU may be used to find the referenced object.

The second method links a list of access rights for the different processes to each object. When an operation on the object is required, the associated access list is considered and the access rights for the requesting process are checked.

The main difference between the two methods is the different costs of some typical operations performed to modify the contents of the matrix in Figure 4.15.

4.10.1   Capability lists

Capabilities are like keys and the owner is entitled to access the data whose access is protected by that key, just because it owns the key itself. This leads to simple protection checks and allows free circulation and copying of capabilities (though forging or enlarging a capability must be prohibited). If capability passing is a welcome feature, it creates problems when it is necessary to revoke capability; because that capability, originally granted to only one process, might be copied and passed to other processes, which in turn could pass it to others and so on. The problem is complicated by the fact that capabilities have a longer life time than the processes they belong to, and can be stored in long-term storage. To revoke capabilities complex operations are required to inspect all the capabilities associated with each process, active or not, wherever they can be stored.

An important reason supporting the use of capability lists is the possibility of storing the list of capabilities of the process currently running in a small and fast memory, to perform the access rights check quickly. If the same approach is adopted for the access list method, it is necessary to have all access lists of all the objects in the system in the fast memory, with the need to implement a larger fast memory than that required by capability lists.

4.10.2   Access lists

The access list approach provides some kind of centralized access rights directory associated with each object: whenever a process accesses an object, the associated checking mechanism retrieves the rights corresponding to the requesting process, and grants or refuses access to the object. Each operation involving either an object or the associated access rights must be performed through an object manager, which must check the validity of the operation. Therefore, all the operations, including capability passing, must follow the same route, leading to possible congestion problems. On the other hand, the access rights for a given object are stored in a single place, so it is simple to revoke capabilities. Since the legality of access is checked by the objects, the process knows the names of all the objects in the system, because this knowledge does not imply any access right. A characteristic of the access list method is that the identity of the requesting process must always be issued with the request and it must be controlled by the protection mechanisms. Hence, access list checking is intrinsically more time consuming than capability list checking.

Since both access list and capability list methods are different representations of the same database, they are functionally equivalent and provide the same degree of protection. However, since the capability list method implies a smaller number of implementation problems, it is the only one supported by recent microprocessor families.

4.11   Multiple domains

Sometimes it is necessary to assign different sets of capabilities to procedures of the same process. An example of this is the invocation of an operating system function: the invoked procedure has more privileges than the invoking one, since it can manipulate internal data of the operating system.

In this case, however, it is no longer possible to associate one access domain with a process, as it is necessary to have multiple domains. Each procedure has permanent capabilities on its local objects (that is, the objects private to the procedure), but, in addition, when called, it receives a set of capabilities on the non-local objects from the caller, as parameters of the procedure itself. This operation is called **pointer validation** because the capabilities may be used to address the objects; hence, they have a portion storing a pointer to the object.

The hardware for supporting multiple access domains should be able to recognize the need for changing the capability list associated with the running program and it should check that the capabilities passed by the caller are a subset of the owned capability. The latter check is necessary to avoid the improper enlargement of the capabilities, obtained by passing a copy of a capability with augmented access rights to a subroutine, so that the subroutine is now capable of performing those operations forbidden to the caller.

With a few exceptions, no special hardware support is provided by the MMUs of advanced microprocessors for implementing multiple access domains in its pure form. Instead, the MMUs are designed to efficiently support only access domains associated with processes. The same hardware can be used to implement multiple domains, with some performance degradation, because it would be necessary to alter the contents of the internal memory within the MMU whenever a procedure is called.

4.12   Privileged machine states

Another method of implementing multiple domains is based on the use of privileged machine states. With this approach, the CPU can, at each instant, assume one of n different privilege states. All the procedures are associated with one privilege state, so that when they start their execution, the CPU changes its state according to the privilege number associated with the procedure. A privilege number is also assigned to each object.

The access domain associated with each procedure is constituted by all the objects in the virtual space of the procedure, whose privilege number is greater or equal to the number of the current CPU state (if lower numbers indicate higher privileges). This mechanism is easy to implement because the privilege number is usually stored in the internal CPU status register, which is pushed on to the stack when a procedure is called, so that it is automatically restored when the procedure terminates. The privilege number can be determined by either specifying it in the call instruction or by reading it from a suitable procedure descriptor. The latter approach requires that the call instruction support such a feature, while an example of the former is found in the system call instruction of systems with a kernel/user mode that is used to cause kernel state switching.

Another hardware mechanism required to implement a privilege state machine is the possibility of checking if the references are directed to objects with a privilege number greater or equal to the CPU's. Although all new microprocessors implement different hardware-recognized states for the CPU, only a few (for example, iAPX286, see Chapter 8) provide hardware mechanisms for comparing the CPU state and the privilege number of the addressed objects. Hence, the privilege state mechanism only provides protection for a subset of special instructions and internal registers.

It is worth noting that the privilege state mechanism, even when fully implemented, violates the principle of the closed environment. This is because the procedures with lower privilege numbers often have more access rights than required to perform their own task, making it more difficult to detect errors caused by hardware faults, because their privilege level allows them to manipulate several objects they do not need to access. Furthermore, it is possible to enlarge capabilities by passing bad parameters (not pointers) to privileged procedures. For example, if a process invokes a **sendmessage** primitive passing the number of a mailbox not accessible to it, the result will be that it has been possible to append a message to a mailbox without owning a capability for doing this.

Another threat to system security is the possibility of calling a less privileged procedure. In this case, it would be possible to call a trusted routine and obtain some incorrect operation, since the trusted routine calls a less trusted procedure performing the erroneous operations. The final effect is that the user gets results whose level of reliability may be lower than believed, opening the door to the corruption of high-level software. Hence, while the objects accessible are only those with greater or equal privilege numbers, the callable procedures are only those with smaller or equal privilege numbers.

4.13   Supports for capability checking

The commonest method used to implement capabilities for memory objects in microprocessor systems attaches a set of flags, also referred to as 'rights', to the same object descriptor used for the virtual to physical address translation. With this approach, the MMU can find the rights associated with the addressed memory object in the same descriptor retrieved for address translation, so that both operations can be performed in parallel. As a consequence, the capabilities can only be associated with segments, if segmentation is used, or pages, if paging is used. However, an important difference exists between the two address translation methods from the point of view of memory protection.

Segments are program subsets visible by the programmer, who actually decides how the program is organized into different segments; hence, each segment may be chosen so that a specific capability is associated with it. On the other hand, the pure paging method does not allow the programmer to determine the organization of pages in the program; thus, the contents of each page has no relationship to the program's semantics and it can hold a mixture of information, which needs to be protected by different types of capabilities. For example, the same page can hold both data and code, where the code can be addressed only for fetching instructions, and the data can be accessed for operand read/write operations. Hence, it is not possible to protect the code portion against erroneous writes, since it is necessary to allow write operations on that page to access the data stored there. Therefore, segmentation is better suited for implementing capabilities effectively. However, since paging systems have important advantages for memory allocation, segmentation with paging seems to be a method that combines the features of both paging and segmentation.

Although capabilities have a long life time, this characteristic is difficult to implement in microprocessor systems, where the capability is stored in the same descriptor used for memory management. The problems arise when the programs are partially in main memory and partially on disks. In such a case, the fields of each descriptor used to compute the physical address change their contents each time the page or segment it refers to is swapped into the main memory. This makes it difficult to pass the capabilities by passing page or segment descriptors, because the contents of such descriptors could be invalid. Moreover, proliferation of descriptors gives rise to consistency problems between the different copies that must be invalidated when the segment or page is swapped out, and they must all be updated when the same segment or page is swapped in.

Finally, to conclude this section, a list of the most widely used right flags follows. Note that some of these cannot be set simultaneously because they indicate mutual exclusive rights.

- **execute only**:   If set, the only valid accesses are instruction fetches. This flag is used to protect the code areas.
- **read only**:   If set, the only valid accesses are data read and instruction fetch. This flag is used to protect memory objects that must not be modified.
- **no CPU**:   If set, the instruction fetches are considered illegal operations. This flag is used for identifying data objects.

4.14   Hardware memory protection

Capability and access lists are only a limited protection against corruption of the data and programs stored in the memory, since their action is limited to avoiding error propagation beyond the borders of the single access domain. Hence, other hardware-implemented protections are often used to achieve quicker error detection or correction of the memory contents.

The need for this kind of check derives from the steady increase in memory size, which leads to an increased contribution of the memory faults to the overall failure rate: this contribution has been estimated to be 60% to 70% of the total failure rate [7]. Moreover, the detection/ correction codes employed are not expensive in terms of additional memory and checking time required, and several integrated circuits are now available to perform the related coding/decoding operation, reducing the implementation cost of memory modules with fault detection/ correction capabilities.

This section illustrates common solutions adopted for three kinds of different problems: **simple error detection**, **error correction/detection**, **memory reconfiguration**.

4.14.1 Memory error detection

The simplest error detection technique is based on the **parity code**. Only one additional bit, referred to as a parity bit, is used. Its value is computed as the 'exclusive-or' or the 'exclusive-and' of all the bits constituting the data word. If the exclusive-or operation is used, then the parity is said to be 'even', since the code word composed by the data word and the parity bit is only allowed to have an even number of 1s. The use of the exclusive-and operation, on the other hand, yields the 'odd' parity code, which allows correct code words to have only an odd number of 1s.

When a data word has to be written into the memory, the associated parity bit is computed and stored along with the data. When the same memory word is read, both data and parity bit are retrieved; then a checking circuit calculates whether the whole code word is correct by testing if the number of 1s is even or odd. If the number is odd and odd parity is used, or it is even and even parity is used, then the code word is considered correct, otherwise a memory error detection signal is issued to the CPU. The operation required for checking the parity code words is the same as that used for generating the parity bit: for the odd parity, the exclusive-or of all the code word bits (data and parity bit) is 1 only if an odd number of 1s is found; for the even parity, the exclusive-and of all the code word bits (data and parity bit) is 1 only if an even number of 1s is found.

The checking mechanisms for parity codes implies that such a code is able to detect errors in the same code word as long as these errors transform the number of 1s from even to odd or vice versa, while if multiple errors occur such that the number of 1s is always even or odd, then they go undetected by this code. Thus, any combination of an odd number of errors is detected, while combinations of an even number of errors are undetected. Since the detection/correction capabilities of the different codes are indicated by the maximum number of errors detected/corrected in the worst case, the parity code issued is a single error detecting code.

Figure 4.16 shows a tree of exclusive-or gates that is the core of every even parity encoding/checking circuit (a tree of exclusive-and gates plays the same role for odd parity). The figure actually shows the checking circuit, since the parity bit is one of the inputs; however, the same circuit is able to compute the parity bit of the 8-bit data word if the input for the parity bit is tied to 0.

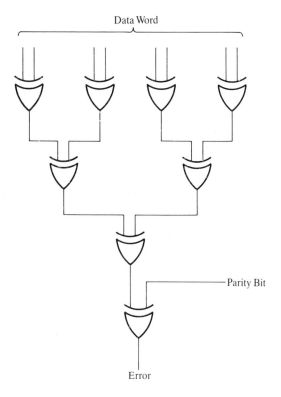

Data Word

Parity Bit

Error

Figure 4.16 Parity checker circuit for one byte.

The relative cost in terms of additional memory required to store the check bit is $1/n$, where n is the number of bits of the data word with an associated parity bit; hence, the larger n, the smaller the cost. On the other hand, the probability of having an even number of errors increases for larger values of n. A compromise between cost and protection could be the use of one parity bit per byte.

4.14.2 Error detection/correction codes

The advent of dense dynamic RAM chips has made it possible to implement large memory modules on a single board; hence, dynamic memories are increasingly used in microprocessor systems. Dynamic memories are denser, but also more error prone than their static counterparts: when an alpha particle, present in the atmosphere, crosses a dynamic memory cell, it can flip the value of the bit stored there, without damaging the circuit itself. Hence, even though the circuits are working properly, errors can appear in a dynamic memory module.

Redundant codes with error-correcting capabilities are commonly used to cope with errors in dynamic memory: when a memory word is read and a wrong bit is found, the bit is corrected and the word rewritten. If the error is caused by alpha particles, the correct value is restored in the memory array, since no damage to the circuits has occurred; if the error is caused by permanent damage to the circuits, the rewrite operation has no effect, but the correct value of the memory word can be delivered to the CPU.

The most widely used correcting code for dynamic memories is the single error correcting/double error correcting (SEC/DEC) Hamming code. This code requires a number of additional bits: k, for each n bit data word, so that a unique k bit pattern different from 0 can be obtained in correspondence of the isolated failure of each one of the $k + n$ bits received. Hence, the values of k and n must satisfy the following relation:

$$(k + n) \leq 2^{k-1} - 1 \tag{4.4}$$

A pattern of k check bits is appended to each data word before the whole $n + k$ bits are stored in the memory. When the memory is read, all the $k + n$ bits are extracted and a k-bit syndrome is computed: if its value is 0 the word is considered correct, otherwise its value uniquely identifies the wrong bit or signals the occurrence of a double error. The computation of the check bits requires the evaluation of the dot product between a $(k - 1) \times n$ Boolean 'parity matrix' A and the n bit data vector D to obtain the first $k - 1$ check bits of the vector C, according to the following formula:

$$d_1 a_{1,i} \oplus d_2 a_{2,i} \oplus \ldots \oplus d_n a_{n,i} = c_i \qquad i = 1, 2, \ldots, k - 1 \tag{4.5}$$

The last check bit is obtained as the parity bit (even) of the bit string composed by both the data and the previously calculated check bits.

The matrix A has a combination of $k - 1$ bits uniquely identifying each column; the combinations with a single 1 are not possible. The following example clarifies how the parity matrix is written and used.

d_1	d_2	d_3	d_4	
1	1	1	0	c_1
1	0	1	1	c_2
0	1	1	1	c_3

$$c_1 = d_1 \oplus d_2 \oplus d_3$$
$$c_2 = d_1 \oplus d_3 \oplus d_4$$
$$c_3 = d \oplus d \oplus d$$
$$c_4 = d_1 \oplus d_2 \oplus d_3 \oplus d_4 \oplus c_1 \oplus c_2 \oplus c_3$$

The syndrome is obtained by performing the dot product between a $(k + n) \times k$ matrix A', obtained by adding a row of 1s to A and concatenating the result with the $k \times k$ matrix, with 1s only in the first row and in the diagonal, and the vector of the data and check bits. The following example illustrates the syndrome computation for the same word as before.

d_1	d_2	d_3	d_4	c_1	c_2	c_3	c_4	
1	1	1	0	0	1	0	0	s_1
1	0	1	1	0	0	1	0	s_2
0	1	1	1	0	0	0	1	s_3
1	1	1	1	1	1	1	1	s_4

$$s_1 = d_1 \oplus d_2 \oplus d_3 \oplus c_2$$
$$s_2 = d_1 \oplus d_3 \oplus d_4 \oplus c_3$$
$$s_3 = d_2 \oplus d_3 \oplus d_4 \oplus c_4$$
$$s_4 = d_1 \oplus d_2 \oplus d_3 \oplus d_4 \oplus c_1 \oplus c_2 \oplus c_3 \oplus c_4$$

When the memory contents are correct, the syndrome is composed of 0s; if a single error is present, then s_4 becomes 1 and the other bits of the syndrome become 1 according to whether the erroneous bit is used to compute them. The final effect of a single error is that the syndrome assumes the same value of the column of the check matrix corresponding to the erroneous bit. If the bit s_4 is 0, while the syndrome is not 0, it signals that two or more errors have occurred, but no information on the location of the erroneous bits can be obtained in this case. Hence, this redundant code can correct any single error and guarantees the detection of any double error.

The relative additional cost of the SEC/DEC Hamming code is k/n; hence, the larger n, the smaller the additional cost per bit. However, once again the probability of having more errors than the code can correct or detect increases with n.

The cost in terms of memory controller circuits is now lessened by the availability of several chip sets designed to support all the encoding, correction and detection operations required by memory modules using SEC/DEC codes. These circuits are also designed to be used in memory modules with different word sizes, such as 1, 2 or 4 bytes per word, so that designers can select the amount of redundancy and protection they need.

Check bits can also be used to protect the memory against erroneous addressing; in this case, the check bits are computed taking account of both data and address bits. When a word is addressed for a read operation, the data and check bits retrieved in the memory array are concatenated to the address bits and the whole string is checked. This solution has a smaller additional cost due to the larger number of check bits, but gives some additional protection for the memory contents.

4.14.3 Memory reconfiguration

Error-correcting codes allow a memory module to behave correctly, even in the presence of a limited number of errors in the memory array, because the incorrect contents are modified so that outside the memory module it is seen as if it is correct. If the error is caused by a permanent fault, it can be corrected by the memory controller, but it can never be eliminated; hence, the number of these errors always grows, until it prevents correction by using check bits.

Spare memory bits can be used to enhance memory reliability. It is possible to consider the memory as a matrix, where each row corresponds to a word and each column is composed of the bits in the same order as all the words.

The spare bit technique employs a number (h) of additional columns, so that each word has h spare bits. The use of redundant columns rather than redundant rows is dictated by the organization of the memory chips, which tend to have many words with a small number of bits; hence, it is cheaper to implement additional columns. Moreover, a fault involving a whole memory chip will cause the occurrence of errors all placed in the same column; hence, it is more convenient to substitute the failed column with a spare.

To use the spare bits effectively it is necessary to have a redundant code to locate the column of the failed bits and a particular multiplexing circuit that should reconfigure the input and output connection with the bus, so that the spare column can be used as the replaced one, as shown in Figure 4.17.

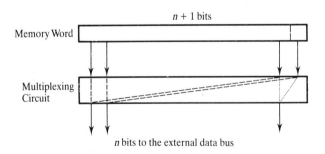

Figure 4.17 Circuit configuration for implementing a spare bit.

Since errors can occur in both the normal and the spare columns, the correcting code used must also encompass the spare bits, to avoid having a failed column replaced by another failed one.

4.15 Conclusion

The organization of the memory in microprocessor-based systems is approaching that of mini- and mainframe computers, given the increasing complexity of the application fields where microprocessors are used nowadays. Therefore, it is only natural that several models of memory organizations, developed for larger computing systems, are now also considered in the microcomputing field.

This chapter has illustrated the most important techniques for memory allocation and protection in microcomputers, paying particular attention to their potential advantages and disadvantags with respect to the specific characteristics of the microprocessing environment.

The first consideration of memory organization is that, thanks to program locality, a memory organized in a hierarchical model, with increasing capacities and access times, leads to an overall performance close to the fastest memory in the hierarchy with a cost nearly identical to the cheapest type of memory.

Hierarchy of memory subsystems also leads to the separation of the physical addresses, used to acccess the referenced memory location, and the virtual addresses, used by the user's program to indicate the memory location to be accessed, independent of the actual memory cell storing the necessary information. Of course, mapping is required to translate the virtual address into a physical address.

All the most popular methods used in microprocessors have been reviewed pointing out the hardware mechanisms required to implement each of them. In particular, it has been explained that the implementation of virtual memory requires the support of a trap able to interrupt an instruction amidst its execution.

Another important topic covered in this chapter is protection mechanisms, which arc rcquired to avoid incorrect use of objects stored in memory. In particular, capability list checking and privileged machine state mechanisms have been discussed, showing both their effectiveness and their costs in terms of execution speed and hardware.

Finally, the hardware mechanisms used to protect the memory contents against errors due to faults have been reviewed. The mechanisms presented are based on redundant codes, ranging from the simplest one (parity), with simple detection capabilities, to more complex codes (Hamming codes), with detection/correction capabilities. Memory reconfiguration has also been treated by outlining a technique based on spare bits.

EXERCISES

4.1 The DEC PDP11 minicomputer allows each program to use only 16-bit addresses, while the main memory physically present in the system can reach 256 Kbytes. Is the physical address space larger than the virtual address space seen by each program? Could this choice be considered optimal or not?

4.2 The operating system routines devoted to memory management in systems using swapping or segmentation must keep the allocated/free state of the different memory areas, to decide whether and where to swap in programs or segments. Study a suitable data structure for representing the memory allocation and write the routines that update it when a swap-in or swap-out operation is performed.

4.3 The following are two of the most used algorithms to allocate memory in systems using program swapping or segmentation:

- first fit: the program or segment to be loaded is placed in the first free memory block whose size is larger than the program or segment;
- best fit: the program or segment to be loaded is placed in the smallest free memory block whose size is larger than the program or segment.

Discuss the advantages and disadvantages of the two algorithms when the memory fragmentaton problem is considered.

4.4 Several replacement techniques for demand paging systems are based on the least recently used (LRU) algorithm to select the candidate page to be removed when a page fault occurs. Investigate the hardware support for an efficient implementation of a pure LRU algorithm, as well as an approximate form based on the use of an accessed bit, set in the page descriptor whenever the corresponding page is accessed.

4.5 Write a routine intended to perform the operations required to handle a page fault, assuming that all the page descriptors of the current process are stored in a dedicated table. (*Note*: Use a flag indicating whether the page has been modified.)

4.6 Discuss the possibility of implementing separate virtual address spaces with the different possible implementations of the translation mechanism using a CAM, illustrated in Section 4.8.2.

4.7 Five different segments exist in a system, and their use is as follows:

(a) a pure code segment;

(b) a segment holding a set of constants;

(c) a segment currently used as a buffer for fast I/O operations;

(d) a normal data segment;

(e) a stack segment.

For each of the segments listed, define which access rights must be enabled or disabled (use the set of rights defined in Section 4.13).

4.8 Assume that a system has five machine states to implement privilege levels (0 to 4; 0 being the most privileged). Which of the following operations should be avoided or detected in such a system:

- a program accesses data belonging to a level numerically lower;
- a program calls a routine with a lower privilege code;
- a program performs stack operations on a segment with a higher privilege code?

4.9 How many check bits need to be used to implement the SEC/DEC Hamming code for a memory with 32-bit words?

4.10 A memory system uses the SEC/DEC Hamming check bits for each 32-bit word, and it is also able to address whole words and single bytes. Describe the operations performed by the SEC/DEC checker when a single byte is written into the memory. (*Note*: The check bits must be updated even when only a portion of the data word is changed.)

References

[1] M. D. Hill and A. J. Smith, 'Experimental Evaluation of On-Chip Microprocessor Cache Memories', *Proceedings of the 11th Annual Symposium on Computer Architecture*, Ann Arbor 1984, pp. 158–166.

[2] Zilog, *Z80000 Architecture Reference Manual*, 1984.

[3] W. D. Strecker, 'Cache Memories for PDP11 Family Computers', *Proceedings of the 3rd Annual Symposium on Computer Architecture*, January 1976, pp. 155–158.

[4] R. H. Kats *et al.*, 'Implementing a Cache Consistency Protocol', *Proceedings of the 12th Annual Symposium on Computer Architecture*, Boston 1985, pp. 276–283.

[5] J. Goodman, 'Using Cache Memories to Reduce Processor-Memory Traffic', *Proceedings of the 10th Annual Symposium on Computer Architecture*, Stockholm 1983, pp. 124–131.

[6] M. S. Papamarcos and J. H. Patel, 'A Low-Overhead Coherence Solution for Multiprocessors with Private Caches', *Proceedings of the 11th Annual Symposium on Computer Architecture*, Ann Arbor 1984, pp. 348–354.

[7] D. P. Siewiorek and R. S. Swarz, 'The Theory and Practice of Reliable System Design', Digital Press, 1982.

Further reading

J. L. Baer, *Computer System Architecture*, Computer Science Press, Rockville, 1980.

C. Bell, J. Judge and J. McNamara, 'Computer Engineering: A DEC View of Hardware System Design', Digital Press, Bedford, 1978.

R. S. Fabry, 'Capability-Based Addressing', *Communications of the ACM* **17**(7), July 1974, pp. 403–412.

G. S. Graham and P. J. Denning, 'Protection Principles and Practice', *Proceedings of AFIPS*, 1972, pp. 417–419.

H. M. Deitel, *An Introduction to Operating Systems*, Addison Wesley Publishing Company, Reading, 1984.

P. J. Denning, 'Virtual Memory', *ACM Computing Surveys* **2**(3), September 1970, pp. 153–189.

P. J. Denning, 'Fault-Tolerant Operating Systems', *ACM Computing Surveys* **8**(4), December 1976.

J. J. Donovan and T. Madnick, *Operating Systems*, McGraw-Hill, New York, 1973.

R. W. Doran, 'Virtual Memory', *IEEE Computer Magazine* **9**(10), October 1976, pp. 27–37.

A. N. Habermann, *Introduction to Operating System Design*, Science Research Associates Inc., Chicago, 1976.

M. E. Houdek, F. G. Soltis and R. L. Hoffman, 'IBM System/38 Support for Capability-Based Addressing', *Proceedings of the 8th Annual Symposium on Computer Architecture*, May 1981, pp. 341–348.

J. K. Illiffe, *Advanced Computer Design*, Prentice-Hall International, 1982.

A. K. Jones *et al.*, 'StarOS, a Multiprocessor Operating System for the Support of Task Forces', *Proceedings of the 7th Symposium on Operating System Principles*, Asilomar, December 1979, pp. 117–127.

B. W. Lampson, 'Dynamic Protection Structures', in *Proceedings of the Fall Joint Computer Conference*, IFIPS 1969, pp. 27–38.

B. W. Lampson, 'Protection', *Operating System Review* **8**(1), January 1974.

T. A. Linden, 'Operating System Structures to Support Security and Reliable Software', *ACM Computing Surveys* **18**(12), December 1976, pp. 409–445.

M. V. Wilkes and R. M. Needham, *The Cambridge CAP Computer and its Operating System*, Elsevier-North Holland, 1979.

W. A. Wulf *et al.*, 'Hydra: The Kernel of a Multiprocessor Operating System', *Communications of the ACM* **17**(6), June 1974, pp. 337–345.

CHAPTER 5
THE ZILOG Z80000 FAMILY

OBJECTIVES

The aims of this chapter are as follows:

- to illustrate the basic organization of the Z80000 CPU and its interface to the external world;

- to introduce the main Z80000 characteristics concerning data types, addressing modes and instruction set;

- to show how the Z80000 architecture processes exceptional events, such as interrupts and traps, and how supports for exception handling have been incorporated in the CPU;

- to discuss memory management in the Z80000 system by illustrating the characteristics provided by the Z80000 on-chip memory management unit for virtual-to-physical address translation, memory protection and virtual memory organization;

- to show how the CPU can be used in conjunction with external special purpose co-processors;

- to analyze the main features of the Z8070 floating-point co-processor.

5.1   Introduction
5.2   CPU architecture
5.3   Cache memory
5.4   Basic data types
5.5   Registers
5.6   Addressing modes
5.7   Instruction set
5.8   Exceptions
5.9   Memory management
5.10 Co-processors
5.11 The Z8070 floating-point co-processor
5.12 Conclusion

5.1 Introduction

The Z80000 project has been aimed at the development of an advanced architecture for the latest generation of Zilog microprocessors. The design of the CPU and of the other units in the Z80000 family takes into account several requirements that emerged for implementing a modern system. While extending the characteristics and facilities of the Z8000 family, the Z80000 is also object-code compatible with its 16-bit predecessors, so that it can be seen as the 'natural' successor of the other Zilog CPUs.

The Z80000 has a true 32-bit architecture based on 32-bit data paths. Moreover, the CPU is able to directly address 4 Gbytes of external memory since it can drive 32 address lines. Support for memory management is integrated with the CPU or, in other words, no external MMU is needed to implement logical-to-physical address translation, memory protection and virtual memory systems.

Another characteristic typical of the Z80000 CPU is the presence of a small on-chip cache memory. It is worth noting that this cache, unlike those in other microprocessors, can hold both instructions and data, thus allowing very fast accesses by the CPU, both in fetching instructions and in reading/writing operands.

The introduction of some special features allows the system designer to extend the Z80000 architecture according to different needs, so that co-processors such as the Z8070 floating-point unit can be easily interfaced with the CPU. Flexible mechanisms have also been designed to simplify bus interfacing and control, and to support fast burst-mode memory data transfers.

5.2 CPU architecture

5.2.1 Internal organization

The Z80000 block architecture is shown in Figure 5.1. As it is easy to verify, three different units are used to carry out the CPU functions. These are the instruction decoding and control unit, the address arithmetic unit and the execution arithmetic and logic unit. The units work in parallel and their operations are extensively and carefully pipelined, so that the fetch and execution times of the overall instruction are significantly reduced. Moreover, the internal cache is connected to two different buses: the first is used for data, whereas the second is dedicated to instruction transfers.

Figure 5.2 shows the different stages comprising the instruction fetch–decode–execute pipeline – instructions pass through each pipe stage in sequence. First, the opcode is obtained either from the internal cache (Figure 5.1) or from the external memory. Then it is decoded by the

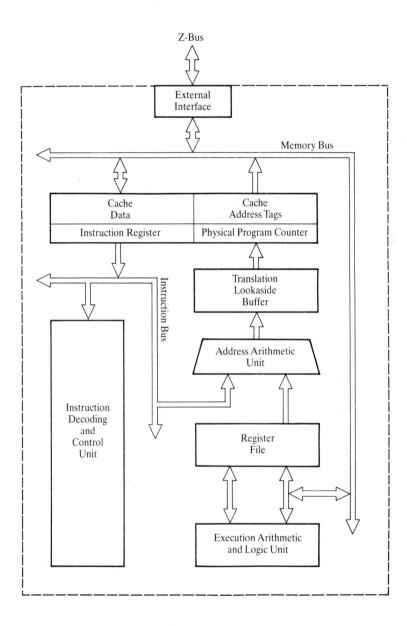

Figure 5.1 Z80000 internal architecture.

decoding and control unit (IDCU), which also sets up controls for the address calculation unit (ACU). The third stage in the pipe provides logical address evaluation and supplies the translation lookaside buffer (TLB) with the results of the computation. This buffer is a small fully associative memory that is used to speed up the logical-to-physical address mapping, since the most recently used translations are kept in the buffer. Hence, when an entry corresponding to the logical address supplied by the ACU is found in the translation lookaside buffer, the address translation operations are not executed and the corresponding physical address is immediately available, since it is read directly from the buffer.

In the fourth stage, operands are fetched either from the internal cache or from the main memory and are stored in the CPU working registers. Then, in the fifth stage, the instruction is executed, involving operations by the arithmetic and logic unit (ALU), which also loads the registers with the results of the computation. The final stage is responsible for writing the new operand values to the external memory and (possibly) into the internal cache.

Pipelining allows the different units in the CPU to work in parallel on different instructions so that, for example, a new instruction can be fetched while the previous one is being decoded and the results of an earlier computation stored in main memory. This usually causes overlapping in the processing times and an increased execution speed, so giving better performance.

5.2.2   CPU signals

Figure 5.3 shows the I/O lines included in the Z80000 architecture. There are 32 address/data signals and these are time multiplexed to reduce the number of I/O pins. They move data and addresses between the CPU and the external world. The bus status and timing group includes signals used by the CPU to perform asynchronous data transfers between the internal registers and the main memory and peripheral devices. Thus, strobe lines are provided both for addresses ($\overline{AS}$) and data ($\overline{DS}$). Moreover, a read/write ($R/\overline{W}$) output is used to select the transfer direction. The $BL/\overline{W}$ and $BW/\overline{L}$ lines are driven by the CPU to specify the size of the operand (byte, word, longword) involved in the transfer operations. Four status outputs (ST0–ST3) are used to encode the type of bus cycle performed by the processor. This information can then be decoded by external logic and used in a number of different ways; for example, to recognize an interrupt acknowledge cycle, to distinguish interlocked read–modify–write memory accesses, and so on. Table 5.1 shows the different kinds of bus cycle that can be performed by the CPU and the associated codes presented on the ST0–ST3 lines. The response inputs

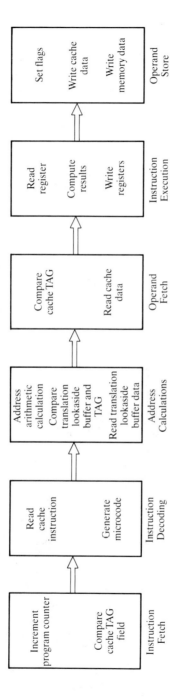

Figure 5.2 CPU six-stage pipeline for instruction fetching, decoding and executing.

(RSP0, RSP1) in Figure 5.3 are needed to return information to the microprocessor on the status (error, retry, wait, ready) of the bus cycle initiated by the CPU.

The burst transfer signals are used to support the fast transfer of blocks of contiguous data between the Z80000 and the main memory; the CPU supplies a single address strobe (for the address of the first datum in the block) followed by several data strobes, one for each operand in the block. External devices able to support burst transfer must notify the Z80000 by responding to the $\overline{\text{BRST}}$ signal by means of the burst acknowledge line $\overline{\text{BRSTA}}$. When no burst transfer can be performed, the CPU executes conventional bus cycles to move operands in a block one by one.

It is worth noting that the Z80000 supports separate address spaces for memory and I/O devices; the CPU notifies the external word that an I/O port must be accessed by suitably driving the status lines ST0–ST3. This information can be decoded by external logic and used to generate the correct chip-select signals to the peripheral devices.

The CPU architecture also includes signals for local and global bus control to be used in multiprocessor systems, or whenever other devices able to obtain the bus mastership are present in the system. The local bus group consists of a signal for requesting the bus control to the Z80000

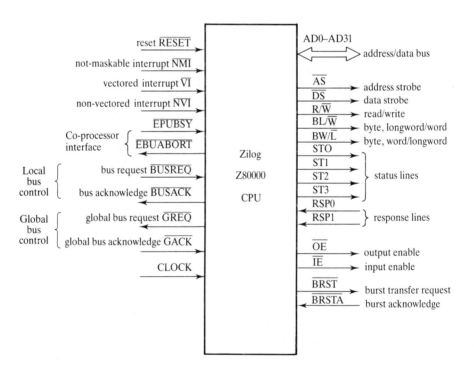

Figure 5.3 CPU interface signals to the external world.

Table 5.1 Z80000 bus cycle types.

ST3...ST0	Type of Transaction
0000	Internal operation
0001	Data transfer between CPU and EPU
0010	I/O
0011	Halt
0100	Instruction transfer between CPU and EPU
0101	$\overline{\text{NMI}}$ acknowledge
0110	$\overline{\text{NVI}}$ acknowledge
0111	$\overline{\text{VI}}$ acknowledge
1000	Data transfer between CPU and memory, cacheable
1001	Data transfer between CPU and memory, non-cacheable
1010	Data transfer between EPU and memory, cacheable
1011	Data transfer between EPU and memory, non-cacheable
1100	Instruction transfer between CPU and memory, cacheable
1101	Instruction transfer between CPU and memory, non-cacheable
1110	Reserved
1111	Interlocked data transfer between CPU and memory, non-cacheable

($\overline{\text{BUSREQ}}$) and an output from the microprocessor for the associated acknowledge ($\overline{\text{BUSACK}}$). On the other hand, the CPU can invoke the mastership of a global bus via the $\overline{\text{GREQ}}$ line and obtain the response of the bus arbiter by means of the $\overline{\text{GACK}}$ input.

Interrupts from external devices are sent to the Z80000 using the $\overline{\text{NMI}}$, $\overline{\text{VI}}$ and $\overline{\text{NVI}}$ lines. The first of these is associated with non-maskable interrupts, whereas the other two refer to vectored and non-vectored interrupts, respectively.

Finally, the $\overline{\text{EPUBSY}}$ and $\overline{\text{EPUABORT}}$ signals serve to simplify the interface between the Z80000 and the external co-processors.

5.3 Cache memory

To speed up CPU operations by avoiding repeated accesses to the external memory, the Z80000 architecture includes a small on-chip cache memory that allows a reduction in the number of machine cycles needed to perform a memory access from two (or more) to one. The cache is structured as shown in Figure 5.4. It contains 16 entries, each one consisting of a TAG field, some bits for validity checks and a data part. The data part is a block containing 16 consecutive bytes loaded from the external memory. The TAG field consists of 28 bits obtained from the most significant bits of the CPU physical address. When a memory access is performed, the Z80000 first addresses the internal cache, and the 28 most significant bits of the physical address are compared with the cache TAG field. If an entry that matches is found, the addressed data bytes are selected from the data part using the four least significant address bits. Note that some validity checks are performed in accessing the cache: first, the TAG field validity is verified by testing suitable bits contained in the TAG part of the cache entry. Then, when a match for a valid TAG occurs, other valid bits are checked corresponding to the data bytes to be accessed. In this way, a cache miss can be caused either by a TAG miss or by a data miss following a TAG match.

Cache misses cause a new entry to be loaded into the cache and a new data block to be read from the main memory. The CPU selects the entry whose content must be replaced using a 'least recently used' algorithm. In this way, due to the program locality principle (Section 4.1), very high hit ratios can be obtained and the external memory is seldom accessed.

The Z80000 internal cache can be programmed to store both instructions and data. When a read operation is performed, the cache is addressed – the external memory is not accessed unless a cache miss occurs. By contrast, when a write operation is executed the external

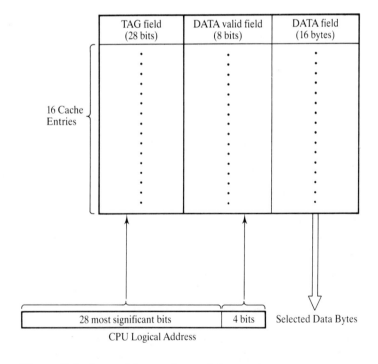

Figure 5.4 Internal instruction and data cache organization.

memory is addressed and updated even though a cache hit occurs. In fact, by writing to the external memory and to the cache at the same time, the Z80000 maintains the consistency of the two different data copies and avoids the possibility of obsolete data values being read from the main memory – for example, during a subsequent instruction.

There are a number of tools available to the system programmer to affect the cache working mode. The system configuration control longword register (SCCL), for example, contains two bits (CI and CD in Figure 5.6) that allow instruction and data cacheing to be enabled and disabled selectively. Moreover, cache entries can be 'frozen'; that is, their content is never replaced when a cache miss occurs. This allows references for strategic data and procedures to be permanently stored in the cache, so that critical accesses are performed as fast as possible. This mechanism is controlled by the CR bit in the SCCL.

A privileged instruction (PCHACE) is also provided to invalidate the cache's current content. This purge operation is particularly necessary when context switching operations must be performed by the operating system. In this case, cache entries associated with the suspended task must be discarded to avoid the CPU being able to use the old references with the new context.

5.4   Basic data types

The Z80000 is able to recognize and process several basic data types that can be operated on by a number of powerful machine instructions. Basic data types include integers, packed BCD digits, bits, bit fields, Booleans and strings.

- **Integers**:   Integer values can be either signed or unsigned. There are three possible lengths for integer data – byte, word (16 bits), and longword (32 bits) – while in some cases (that is, integer multiplication) quadword (64 bits) operands can also be used. The CPU considers the main storage as consisting of a sequence of bytes. Hence, when words and longwords are stored in main memory, the most significant byte in the operand is placed at the location with the lowest address.
- **Packed BCD**:   A pair of BCD digits can be packed into a single byte. The programmer can build extended precision decimal operands as strings of BCD bytes.
- **Bits**:   The Z80000 is able to access and manipulate individual bits stored either in main memory or in the CPU internal registers. Each bit operand address consists of two components – the base component, which specifies the byte, word, longword or CPU

register containing the bit, while the bit number allows the system to find the addressed bit inside the referred operand.

- **Bit fields**:   Unaligned bit fields can be read or written to by means of a single machine instruction working either on memory locations or on the internal registers. Bit fields can be up to 32 bits long. Moreover, a reference for a bit field consists of three basic parts – two are devoted to locating the base bit at the beginning of the field, while the third is needed to specify the field width. Bit fields are not allowed to span across longword boundaries.

- **Booleans**:   The Z80000 can manipulate byte, word and longword operands as logical values. In this case, only the least significant bit in the operand is affected by the CPU operations, while the remaining bits are not modified.

- **Strings**:   Unlike other basic operands, strings cannot be stored in the CPU internal registers. Strings are blocks of elements that have the same size (byte, word or longword) and are placed at consecutive addresses in main memory. Strings are processed by special machine instructions whose execution can be suspended when an interrupt occurs and resumed later, after the interrupt servicing, since long string processing can be very time consuming for the CPU.

5.5   Registers

5.5.1   General registers

The Z80000 register set includes both general-purpose and dedicated registers as shown in Figures 5.5 and 5.6, respectively. The general-purpose registers can be seen as a 64-byte array of very fast storage; hence, 16 registers (RR0, RR2...RR30), 32 bits long, are available to the programmer. Except for RR0, all these registers can be used to store long data, as index registers or to hold memory addresses, both in linear and in segmented mode (Section 5.6.1). The 32 least significant bytes in the array (RRi, $i = 0...1$) can also be accessed as 16-bit registers (Ri, $i = 0...15$); each Ri occupies the upper or lower word of a 32-bit register as shown in Figure 5.5 and, except for R0, can be used as an index register to store data words or memory addresses in compact mode (Section 5.6.1). In addition, R0–R7 can also be seen as 16-byte registers (RHi, RLi, $i = 0...7$) available as accumulators for byte data. Note that RHi corresponds to the upper byte in Ri, while RLi is associated with the least significant byte. Finally, 32-bit registers can also be paired to hold 64-bit data in operations such as multiplication, division and sign extension; thus, the programmer can consider the 64 bytes in the register array as organized in eight quadword registers RQ0, RQ4...RQ28.

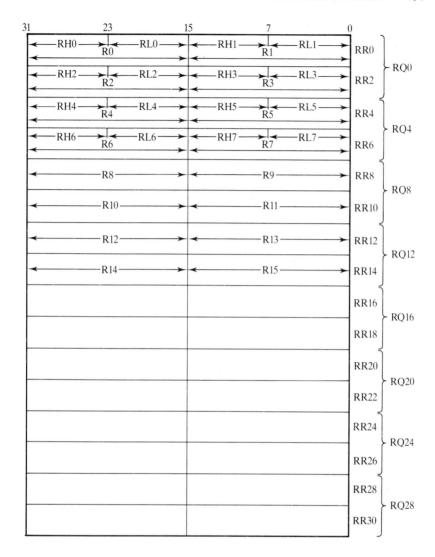

Figure 5.5 The Z80000 general-purpose register set.

Even though RR12 and RR14 can be used as general registers, a special meaning is assigned to them by the CPU. In fact, when linear or segmented addressing is selected (Section 5.6.1) RR14 is assumed to be the active stack pointer (SP) and RR12 works as a frame pointer register (FP). By contrast, in compact addressing mode, R15 is the stack pointer and R14 the frame pointer. The frame pointer register usually contains the base address, in the active stack, of the memory area for data and variables local to the procedure currently being executed. The stack pointer is implicitly accessed by the CPU when executing a procedure call or return instruction.

The Z80000 architecture supports two separate operating modes: system and normal. System programs can make use of the full instruction set, including privileged operations (such as I/O and control register manipulation instructions), while normal users are not allowed to execute protected instructions. Two different stacks are implemented (with dual stack pointers RR14) for user and system tasks, respectively. The active stack pointer is automatically selected when the operating mode is switched from normal to system and vice versa.

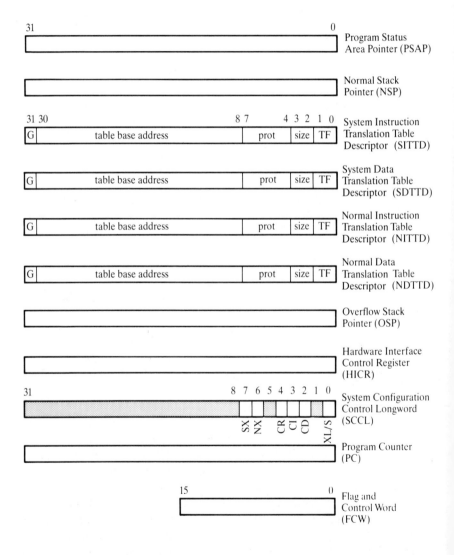

Figure 5.6   Special-purpose CPU registers.

5.5.2 Control registers

The Z80000 dedicated registers shown in Figure 5.6 include the following:

- program counter (PC);
- flag and control word register (FCW);
- program status area pointer (PSAP);
- normal and overflow stack pointers (NSP, OSP);
- four translation table descriptor registers for memory management (SITTD, SOTTD, MITTID, MOTTID);
- hardware interface control register (HICR);
- system configuration control longword (SCCL).

The last two registers are needed to inform the CPU about the system interface characteristics and hardware configuration, respectively.

The flag and control word register structure is shown in Figure 5.7. Its least significant byte contains the typical CPU flags (carry, zero, sign, parity/overflow, decimal adjust, half carry) and an integer overflow bit to enable the CPU trap mechanism when an overflow occurs during a computation. The most significant byte in the flag and control word register can be accessed only in system mode, since it contains CPU control bits that allow the programmer (a) to select the address representation format (Section 5.6.1), (b) to toggle the system/normal operating mode, (c) to notify the CPU that external co-processors are used in the system, and (d) to enable/disable vectored and non-vectored interrupts and the trace trap (Section 5.8).

The program status area pointer is a special register holding the memory base address of the system-wide table that contains the start address of the trap and interrupt-handling routines, as explained in Section 5.8.

5.6 Addressing modes

5.6.1 Address representation

As mentioned in the previous sections, the Z80000 can use three different representations for the logical addresses processed by the CPU. In compact mode, the address space is linear and addresses are 16 bits long. This is useful for applications requiring relatively small amounts of code and data. By contrast, in linear mode, addresses are 32 bits long, so programs requiring large memory areas can be easily implemented. The CPU can also work with a segmented memory space. In this case, the 32 address bits are organized in two subfields – the segment number and the

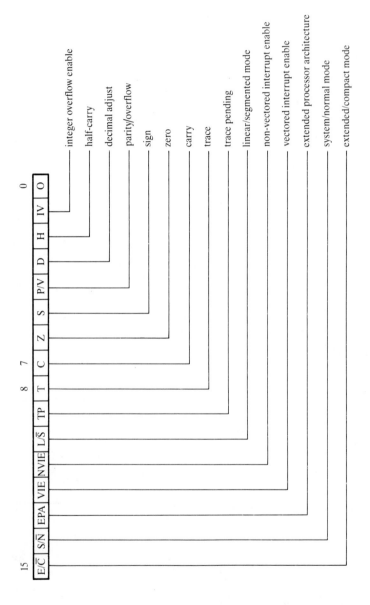

Figure 5.7 Flag and control register format.

offset within the segment, respectively. Moreover, there are two possible segment sizes; that is 64 Kbytes and 16 Mbytes to fit in with different users' requirements. In the segmented mode, address computations are performed only on the offset subfield and results are evaluated modulo the segment size. In other words, the offset cannot span segment boundaries during an address evaluation. The address representations available for the different modes are summarized in Figure 5.8. Note that segmented addressing with segment sizes equal to 64 Kbytes is fully compatible with the 16-bit Z80000 microprocessor family.

The address representation to be used is selected by the system programmer via the $E/\overline{C}$ and $L/\overline{S}$ bits in the flag control word (Figure 5.7). $E/\overline{C}$ is used to distinguish between extended and compact addresses, while $L/\overline{S}$ enables either the linear or the segmented address representation.

5.6.2 Operand addressing

The Z80000 architecture supports nine different addressing modes that can be used by the programmer to access program variables.

As in any microprocessor, data can be stored in the CPU registers (register operands) and in the instructions themselves (immediate

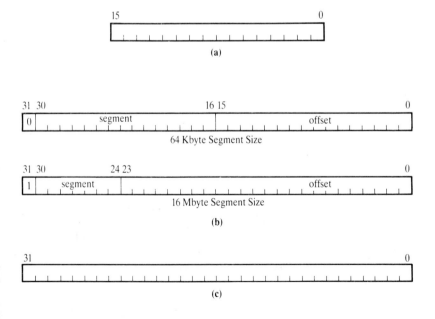

Figure 5.8 Different address representations in the Z80000 architecture: (a) compact; (b) segmented; and (c) linear.

addressing). Moreover, operands can be accessed by specifying their memory address directly in the instruction code (direct addressing) or by means of a register content (register indirect addressing).

In addition, five register indirect modes are available: index, base, base index, relative and relative index. However, no memory indirect addressing is possible. In practice, the Z80000 index and base addressing modes are two versions of base displacement indirect addressing introduced in Chapter 1. In both these cases, the operand address is always computed by adding a base address to a displacement/index component; however, index addressing uses a CPU register to specify the index part, while base addressing considers the register content as the base component. Z80000 base index addressing corresponds to base displacement index indirect addressing discussed in Chapter 1 with a scale factor equal to one. In the base index mode, two registers are added to a displacement component to form the operand address: one register is used to hold the base address, while the other contains an index value. When the base register is the program counter, addressing corresponding to the base and base index modes is called 'relative' or 'relative index', depending on whether an index register is or is not also used to compute the operand's final address.

5.7 Instruction set

The Z80000 instruction set contains operators that support efficient manipulations of the hardware-recognized data types, and easy data transfers between the CPU registers and the main memory or I/O devices. In addition, it allows users to control the program flow, and system programmers to affect the CPU working mode. Special-purpose instructions are included in the instruction set for transferring data to or from the I/O devices, since the Z80000 implements two separate address spaces for memory and I/O references, unlike other microprocessors that consider the I/O ports only as memory locations.

Finally, Z80000 instructions must be aligned at even-byte boundaries. When the CPU attempts to fetch an instruction code located at an odd address (that is, the program counter is loaded with an odd value) an 'odd-program counter' trap occurs (Section 5.8.2).

The Z80000 instructions are briefly discussed in the following sections. Since several operations are supported in three different versions, working respectively on byte, word and longword operands, the notation INST*i* is used. INST is the instruction mnemonic for word operands, while *i* is a suffix that can be equal to B or L depending on whether byte or longword operations are considered.

5.7.1   Data transfer instructions

The Z80000 supports register-to-register, register-to-memory and memory-to-register single operand transfers. Memory-to-memory data movements are obtained by using block and string manipulation instructions (Section 5.7.5).

Simple transfers are implemented by the load instructions, LDi and LDRi, the second being used only when an input operand is specified by means of the program counter relative addressing mode. On the other hand, format conversions can also be performed while transferring data to or from a CPU register. For example, the CVTij instructions ($i, j =$ B, W, L and $i <> j$) allow a signed byte, word or longword integer (the size is specified by i) to be converted to a different operand length (selected by j) while being transferred. Similarly, the CVTUij instructions allow format conversions and movements of unsigned data at the same time. Operand addresses can be loaded in the CPU general registers by means of the load address instructions LDA and LDAR. The first is used when the input operand is specified with a register direct or indirect addressing mode, while the second refers to program counter relative addressing. Immediate values that are constants can be loaded in the CPU registers by means of the LDK (for word operands) and LDKL (for longword data) operations.

Multiple register load-and-store operations can be implemented by means of a single instruction both for word (LDM) and longword operands (LDML). In addition, the content of a user-specified register can be exchanged with a memory operand using the exchange (EXi) instruction group.

The data transfer instructions also include the pop and push stack operations. Only word and longword operands located either in the CPU registers or in main memory can be pushed on to or popped from the current stack, by means of the PUSH, PUSHL, POP and POPL operators, respectively.

5.7.2   Integer and BCD arithmetic instructions

Integer arithmetic is supported by the Z80000 for byte, word and longword data. Thus, the basic operations such as addition (ADDi), subtraction (SUBi), negation (NEGi), increment (INCi), decrement (DECi) and sign extension (EXTSi) are available, in addition to the instructions for multiprecision computations that build up the 'add with carry' (ADCi) and 'subtract with borrow' (SBCi) groups. Signed division and multiplication are supported for word and longword operands by the DIV, DIVL, MULT and MULTL instructions, respectively. The same operations are available for unsigned arithmetic by means of the DIVU, DIVUL, MULTU and MULTUL operators.

The Z80000 does not support separate instructions for decimal arithmetic. However, BCD arithmetic computations can be programmed using the binary arithmetic instructions. The decimal adjust operator (DAB) allows the user to correct an operation result to the BCD representation when the result differs from the binary format.

Comparisons are implemented by the compare (CPi) and test arithmetic (TESTAi) instructions. The first performs a subtraction of the source operand from the destination and sets the CPU flags according to the result that is not saved, since the input operands are not modified. TESTAi allows only one input value to be specified, because the second is implicitly assumed to be zero.

The interlocked increment and decrement operators are particularly important. In fact, these are indivisible instructions executed by the CPU without releasing the bus mastership between the read and write cycles. Hence, they can be used to implement elementary critical sections (Section 3.3) where the mutual exclusion is granted at the hardware level. DECI, INCI, DECIB and INCIB can be used to increment and decrement word and byte operands indivisibly.

5.7.3 Logical and shift instructions

The logical group consists of the classical Boolean operators (ANDi, ORi, XORi), the complement operations (COMi) and some instructions that can be used to test operand values. The test condition code (TCCi) instructions, for example, allow the least significant bit of the input operand to be set or reset, depending on the value assumed by the condition code flag specified by the user. On the other hand, the TESTi group sets the condition code flags by executing the bit-wise OR operation between the input operand and the constant zero.

The Z80000 architecture offers the programmer a very rich set of shift and rotate instructions. The programmer is allowed to specify the number of positions to be rotated, the rotation direction and whether the carry flag must or must not be involved in the operation. Hence, the operators RLi, RLCi, RRi and RRCi are used for rotations to the left without carry, to the left with carry, to the right without and to the right with carry, respectively. The CPU also allows digit rotations to the left and to the right by means of the RLDB and RRDB instructions, which can be useful in decimal arithmetic computations. In this case, rotations occur on a digit basis, or four bits at a time.

The shift groups include static and dynamic arithmetic and logical shifts. In static shifts, the programmer is able to specify the number of bits to be shifted as a constant. Dynamic shifts allow the programmer to specify the number of positions by which data is to be shifted by means of a source variable. Arithmetic and logical dynamic shifts are implemented by the SDA*i* and SDL*i* operators, respectively. Static shifts to the left and to the right are obtained with the SLA*i* and SRA*i* (arithmetic) or SLL*i* and SRL*i* (logic) instructions.

5.7.4 Bit and bit-field instructions

Single-bit manipulations allowed by the Z80000 offer the programmer a number of instructions to test (BIT*i*), reset (RES*i*), set (SET*i*) and test-and-set (TSET*i*) bits located in memory operands or in the CPU registers. In particular, the BIT*i* group loads the complement of the selected bit in the zero flag, so that a conditional instruction can be immediately executed after BIT*i*, depending on the tested bit's value. Analogously, the TSET*i* instructions move the most significant bit of the input operand in the sign flag and load the operand itself with the signed integer value −1, thus setting the most significant bit.

Bit-field instructions consist of operators to extract a signed or unsigned field from a source operand (EXTR, EXTRU) and to insert a bit pattern into a destination variable (INSRT).

5.7.5 Array and string instructions

Array instructions supported by the Z80000 include operations to dynamically check the value of index operands and to compute and verify indices for multidimensional arrays. The CHK*i* group, for example, compares the input operand with the user-specified limits: if an 'out of bounds' result is obtained a trap occurs. CHK*i* instructions are useful for implementing run-time checks on array indices as required by advanced high-level languages such as Pascal and Ada.

Similarly, the INDEX and INDEXL instructions can be used in computing a single one-dimensional index for accessing multidimensional arrays. These instructions should be executed iteratively (one step for each array dimension except the first) and allow a single index to be obtained from the array dimension lengths and the values of the multidimensional indices.

String instructions allow efficient data-block manipulations in a variety of modes. For example, two strings can be compared by means of the CPSD*i*, CPSDR*i*, CPSI*i* and CPSIR*i* instructions. CPSD*i* and CPSI*i* perform a comparison step and set the condition code flags; then the input string pointers are decremented and incremented, respectively, while a user-specified step counter is always decremented. CPSDR*i* and CPSIR*i* work in a similar way, but repeated comparison steps are performed in this case, until the condition selected by the user is met, or the step counter reaches zero.

The instruction groups CPD*i*, CPDR*i*, CPI*i* and CPIR*i* correspond to CPSD*i*, CPSDR*i*, CPSI*i* and CPSIR*i*, respectively, but they are used to compare a string to a scalar operand stored in a CPU register instead of two strings. Strings can be copied step by step, or repeatedly with pointer increments or decrements, by means of the load string instructions (LDD*i*, LDDR*i*, LDI*i* and LDIR*i*).

Special instructions are also provided to allow string data translations. In this case, the values to be translated are used as indices to access a source table for obtaining the new element values to be stored in the translated string. Several variants of translation instructions are provided; for example, TRDB and TRIB perform a translation step and decrement/increment the destination address, while TRDRB and TRIRB perform repeated translation steps. Finally, four translation instructions (TRTDB, TRTDRB, TRTIB and TRIRB) allow single and repeated translation steps to be executed; however, in this case the translation result is saved not in a destination string but in the CPU register RH1. In addition, a test is also performed on the RH1 content and iterated instructions (TRTDRB and TRTIRB) are abandoned when RH1 is loaded with zero or the step counter reaches a null value.

5.7.6   Input/output instructions

Input/output instructions are privileged operations that allow data to be transferred to or from separate I/O address space. The Z80000 architecture, in fact, offers the programmer two mechanisms of accessing I/O mapped devices. The first is represented by the I/O instructions described here, while the second is based on the address translation support of the internal MMU, as explained in Section 5.9.1.

Input instructions allow data to be read from an input port and stored in a CPU register (IN*i*). Input operands can also be stored in main memory and the Z80000 provides instructions to automatically increment or decrement the user-specified memory pointer (INI*i* and IND*i*) and to perform repeated input steps (INDR*i*, INIR*i*) until a step count reaches the zero value.

A similar set of instructions is available for data output. Hence, OUT*i*, OUTD*i*, OUTI*i*, OUTDR*i* and OUTIR*i* can be used to perform single and repeated output operations.

5.7.7   Program flow and CPU control instructions

The program control instructions consist of operators that affect the program counter content in different ways. The Z80000 implements conditional and unconditional jumps (JP), and the programmer is also able to specify the jump address relative to the program counter (JR). Similarly, subroutine calls are possible by means of the CALL and CALR instructions, while returns from subroutines are performed by RET. Conditional jumps can also be executed by means of the 'decrement and jump if not zero' (D*i*JNZ) instructions; in this case, a jump occurs if a user-specified counter is not equal to zero after being decremented.

The ENTER and EXIT instructions deserve special attention. The first is used to set up the addressing environment for a procedure after its invocation, so that procedure activations, which often occur in programs written in high-level languages, can be efficiently mapped in a few machine instructions. Figure 5.9 shows the behaviour of the ENTER instruction. The programmer specifies two operands for ENTER: a register mask and a size. The mask is used to select the registers that must be saved in the stack by ENTER, while the size parameter allocates a suitable area at the top of the stack that will contain local variables and data for the invoked procedure. As depicted in Figure 5.9, ENTER

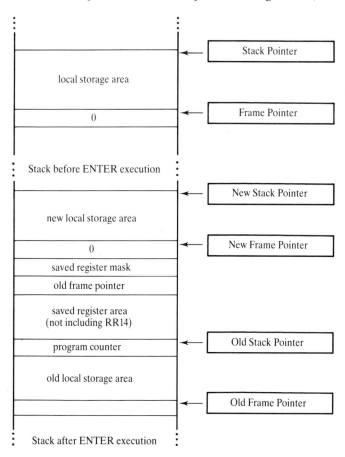

Figure 5.9 Behaviour of the ENTER instruction for high-level language procedure activations.

pushes the masked registers on to the stack together with the current frame pointer register, then the register mask is also saved to restore the registers correctly before the procedure returns. In addition, the frame pointer is loaded with the stack pointer value, so that the frame pointer is able to point to the base of the current local storage area. Then the content of the stack pointer is decremented by the 'size' parameter to allocate the requested memory words from the stack.

The EXIT instruction is similar to ENTER. The content of the frame pointer is moved to the stack pointer, thus releasing the local variable area, then the register mask, the frame pointer and the mask-specified registers are popped from the stack in order.

The program control instruction group also contains operators for the user-programmable exceptions. Thus, the SC and TRAP instructions can be used to cause a system call exception and a conditional trap, respectively (Section 5.8.2), while the breakpoint instruction (BRKPT) allows a breakpoint trap handler to be activated – for example, for debugging purposes, when the breakpoint instruction is reached.

The CPU control instruction group contains instructions to load (LDCTLB), set (SETFLG), reset (RESFLG) and complement (CMPFLG) the CPU flags that can be executed in user and in system mode. Other instructions are privileged and can be invoked only by system tasks. These include operators to load the CPU control registers (LDCTL and LDCTLL), operators to move data to or from the normal instruction and data address spaces (LDNIi and LDNDi) when the CPU is working in system mode, to load the program status register (LDPS), and to store the physical address of an operand located in the normal/system data/instruction space in a CPU general register (LDPNI, LDPSI, LDPND and LDPSD). Other instructions allow the programmer to enable and disable the interrupt mechanism (EI and DI) and to stop the CPU operation (HALT).

Finally, special operators have been introduced that affect the internal cache behaviour (as mentioned in Section 5.3) and the translation lookaside buffer content (Section 5.9.1).

5.8   Exceptions

The Z80000 can distinguish and process four different kinds of exceptions that can arise during the normal instruction execution cycle: reset, bus errors, interrupts and traps.

The CPU acknowledges an exception request, raised either internally (traps) or externally (interrupts or bus errors), by saving the current program status in the system stack, consisting of the program counter and the flag and control word. In addition, other information is saved in the stack, whose meaning depends on the particular kind of exception considered, to be used during the exception processing. Then the CPU obtains a new program status from a system table called the **program status area** and pointed by the program status area pointer register. Each entry in the program status table corresponds to a different exception and is used to obtain the starting address of the related service routine.

Exceptions are served by the CPU following a fixed priority scheme that orders the different events according to their urgency. Reset and bus errors have the highest priorities, whereas traps, non-maskable, vectored and non-vectored interrupts are served in that order. However, as in other microprocessors, the trace trap has the lowest priority and is processed after any other type of exception.

Reset and bus errors are hardware-generated events that cause the CPU to be initialized to the beginning state (reset) or to jump to a routine devoted to handle errors in bus transactions (bus errors), respectively. Note that while reset is usually not related to the instruction being executed, bus errors generally occur as a consequence of the current instruction processing. When reset, the Z80000 does not save the program status in the system stack, since this kind of exception is destructive (the interrupted task will not be resumed) and loads the new status (PC and FCW) from the physical address 2 in main memory. This is necessary since after a reset the system program status area and the internal MMU registers must be re-initialized by the system software; hence, they cannot be used immediately by the CPU.

5.8.1 Interrupts

External devices can request services to the Z80000 by driving the interrupt lines. The CPU is able to recognize three kinds of interrupt: non-maskable, vectored and non-vectored, issued respectively on the $\overline{\text{NMI}}$, $\overline{\text{VI}}$ and $\overline{\text{NVI}}$ lines shown in Figure 5.3.

Non-maskable interrupts are usually related to very high priority events (such as power failure) that must not be masked even though the interrupt mechanism is disabled. Vectored and non-vectored interrupts can be selectively disabled by suitably programming the VIE and NVIE bits in the flag and control word register (Figure 5.7). When the CPU acknowledges an interrupt request, it reads a data word supplied by the interrupting device by means of the standard address and data bus; the data word is saved in the system stack to be used during the interrupt processing. However, for vectored interrupts the least significant data byte is used as an index in the program status area to retrieve the starting address of the interrupt service routine. In this way, different software handlers can be provided for vectored interrupts, depending on the interrupting device, while a single entry point is supported for the non-vectored exceptions.

5.8.2 Traps

The Z80000 can recognize 12 types of trap that can occur during an instruction execution. They are due to errors met in the processing cycle, to co-processor operations or can be explicitly raised by the programmer. The Z80000 traps can be summarized as follows:

- **Privileged instruction**:   This exception is raised when the normal user attempts to execute a privileged instruction. Privileged instructions can be executed only in system mode.

- **System call**:   This trap is activated by the system call (SC) instruction. System calls are a means by which normal users can invoke privileged system services. When the system call instruction is executed, the associated trap-handling routine is activated and the CPU working mode is set to 'system' by forcing the $S/\overline{N}$ bit in the flag and control word register to one (Figure 5.7). In this way, normal users can access protected data and code areas in a controlled and safe way. During the execution of a system call, the instruction itself is saved into the stack, so that the service routine can use this identifier to distinguish between different system call types and hence between different service requests.

- **Conditional trap**:   This kind of trap is caused by the execution of a trap on condition code instruction (TRAP). The normal user can use this mechanism to activate system service routines depending on the current setting of the condition flags in FCW. As for system calls, the CPU saves the TRAP instruction code into the system stack so that it can be used as a trap identifier by the service routine.

- **Address translation**:   This trap occurs when an error is met during the logical-to-physical address translation, performed by the Z80000 on-chip MMU. Address translation traps can be caused either by true translation errors – that is, some invalid translation table entry is found during the translation algorithm (Section 5.9.1) – or by attempts to violate the access protection for a memory page. Address translation errors occurring when the system stack is accessed could result in fatal (non-recoverable) faults, since the CPU uses the system stack to save the program status information when an exception is acknowledged. For this reason, address translation traps caused by accesses to the system stack cause the CPU to save the status information in the overflow stack. The overflow stack pointer in Figure 5.6 always contains the physical address for the overflow stack, so that this address can be accessed without activating the translation mechanisms. In this way, translation errors for the system stack can be recovered by a suitable trap-handling routine.

- **Unimplemented instruction and odd PC:** These two exceptions are raised when the CPU attempts to execute an illegal operation code and when an odd byte address is loaded in the program counter, respectively. Z80000 instructions, in fact, must be aligned with even-byte boundaries.

- **Co-processor instruction:** This trap occurs when the CPU attempts to execute a co-processor instruction and the extended processor architecture (EPA) bit in the flag and control register is reset, thus meaning that no external co-processor is included in the system.

- **Integer arithmetic:** There are three traps that can be activated when integer arithmetic computations are performed by the CPU. The integer overflow exception, for example, is raised whenever an integer operation result overflows. This trap, however, can be disabled by resetting the integer overflow bit (IV) in the flag and control word (Figure 5.7). On the other hand, the limit check error and index error traps are related to array processing. The first occurs when an array index is detected to have fallen out of bounds by means of a check (CHK) instruction. The second is raised when an INDEX instruction is executed and one or more subscript operands is out of bounds.

- **Breakpoint:** This trap occurs when the CPU executes a breakpoint instruction (BRKPT). This can be used, for example, to activate a service routine automatically for debugging purposes. The Z80000 architecture allows users to distinguish between different breakpoints, since the breakpoint instruction code is pushed on to the system stack when the breakpoint trap is activated.

- **Trace:** The trace trap occurs at the end of each instruction execution when the trace bit (T) is set in the flag and control register. Since trace exceptions have the lowest priority, they are served after other exception requests submitted to the CPU at the same time. For this reason, some special mechanism must be provided to 'remind' the Z80000 whether the trace trap was already processed when returning from another exception service routine. As in other advanced microprocessors, the flag and control word register also includes a trace pending bit (TP in Figure 5.7) that is loaded with the trace bit content at the end of the instruction execution, and is cleared during the trace trap service. This allows instructions to be traced correctly only after they are executed.

5.9   Memory management

The Z80000 provides memory management support without any additional special-purpose external device. The MMU, in fact, is integrated with the CPU and offers the system programmer several basic mechanisms for performing the logical-to-physical address mapping, to implement virtual memory systems and to enforce memory protection.

5.9.1   Address translation

The Z80000 memory management is based on the paging approach. Thus, the physical memory is organized in pages whose size is equal to 1 Kbyte. The logical-to-physical address translation mechanism is shown in Figure 5.10(a). As it is easy to verify, the 10 least significant bits in the logical address are never translated and are used as an offset inside the

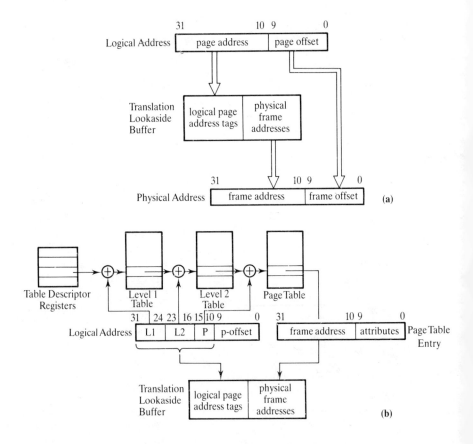

Figure 5.10   Logical-to-physical address translation performed by the Z80000 on-chip MMU.

page. In contrast, the other bits are organized in three different subfields involved in three translation steps. Each subfield, in fact, is used to access a translation table stored in main memory. Each table entry is 32 bits long and contains either a pointer to a next level table or a page base address when level 3 (page table) is considered. As depicted in Figure 5.11, table entries also contain protection and control bits used for access rights checks when pages are accessed. Figure 5.10(b) shows that the logical address level 1 subfield (L1) is added to the content of a table descriptor register to point to a level 1 table entry. In the same way, the level 2 and page subfields (L2, P) are used to access the level 2 table and the page table, respectively.

Since the Z80000 is able to support four physically separated address spaces for normal and system instruction and data, four different table descriptor registers are provided to allow a different translation path for each space considered. In other words, the CPU selects the

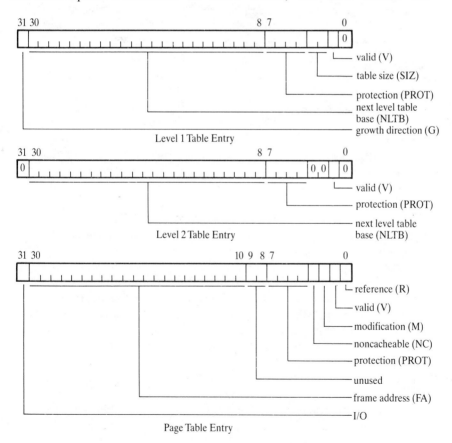

Figure 5.11 Translation table entry formats.

appropriate table descriptor register to be used in the translation, depending on the kind of memory access (system program, system data, normal program and normal data) to be performed. Obviously, two or more table descriptor registers must be loaded with the same value when separate address spaces are not implemented. (Figure 5.6 shows the format of each description register.)

Besides the next level table base address field, the register also contains bits needed to control the translation mechanisms. For example, the table format (TF) field allows the programmer to specify whether level 1 or level 2 or both must be skipped in the mapping process. Skipping a level reduces the logical address space size, but speeds up the physical address computations. Hence, small systems can benefit by drastically reducing the translation overhead. For example, level 1 and level 2 (that is the L1 and L2 logical address fields) can be ignored when the CPU is working in compact address mode, or L1 can be skipped when a 24-bit logical address size can be tailored to the user's needs.

The table size field (SIZE in Figure 5.6) allows the system to select the amount of memory allocated for a table among 256, 512, 768 or 1024 bytes, respectively. In this way, small tables can be constructed without wasting memory resources. Attempts to access entries outside a table are automatically detected by the CPU and cause an address translation trap to be initiated. The growth direction bit (G) in Figure 5.6 specifies the table direction with respect to the table base address; this allows memory areas to be efficiently allocated for tables from either upward- or downward-growing stacks. As Figure 5.11 shows, the G and TS fields are also present in the level 1 and 2 table entries; however, since the page table size is always equal to 1 Kbyte and page tables can only grow downward, these fields have fixed values in level 2 tables.

Each page table entry contains the physical base address for the corresponding page in main memory and other fields needed for control purposes and for implementing memory protection and virtual memory management. The valid bit is used to distinguish between valid and invalid table entries; an entry is invalid when the related page is not physically resident in main memory. For example, the operating system should clear this bit when tables and pages are moved or swapped out. In addition, an I/O bit is also provided (Figure 5.11) to allow easy mapping of the logical addresses to the separate I/O space. In fact, when the I/O bit is set, the corresponding physical page is placed in the separate I/O physical space; by testing the I/O bit the CPU is able to drive signals and status indications to address the external devices correctly. This mechanism is particularly useful since it also allows the use of logical addresses for accessing the I/O devices, so that programs can be developed with a higher degree of independence from the system hardware. For example, the operating system can map the I/O logical addresses used by the I/O handling procedure into different physical addresses, depending on the system configuration, with no changes in the running software. Moreover, the same protection scheme used for main memory is also available for the I/O locations.

5.9.2   Translation lookaside buffer

Since address translation introduces a large overhead in the program execution, a translation lookaside buffer (TLB) is included in the Z80000 to speed up the mapping process. This buffer is a fast, 16-entry, fully associative memory, available for the different separate address spaces (normal/system data and instructions) that contain the most recently used logical-to-physical address translations. When a location must be accessed, the TLB is addressed using the corresponding logical address. If an entry for that address is present in the TLB, the physical translation can be immediately obtained from the buffer, so avoiding any access to the tables stored in main memory. By contrast, when a suitable entry is not found in the TLB the translation algorithm is executed and a new entry containing the logical–physical address pair is stored in the translation buffer in Figure 5.10, possibly replacing another entry on a least-recently-used basis.

Since different tasks can be associated with the same logical address space some support must be provided to invalidate the TLB content when a task content switching occurs, so that translations concerning the suspended task cannot be used for the new running process. The privileged instructions, purge TLB (PTLB), purge TLB normal (PTLBN) and purge TLB entry (PTLBEND, PTLBENI, PTLBESD and PTLBESI), allow the system software to invalidate the content of the whole TLB or to delete selectively entries in TLB concerning normal data, instructions, system data and instructions, respectively.

The MMU incorporated in the Z80000 can be seen as placed between the conventional CPU circuits and the internal cache memory. In this way, once the physical addresses have been obtained from either the lookaside buffer or the translation algorithm, the external memory is or is not accessed, depending on whether a cache miss occurs.

In multiprocessor systems, shared variables cannot be stored in the CPU internal cache, since there is no way of maintaining the consistency of the different copies of the data owned by each CPU. In fact, when a change is performed on the shared data by a microprocessor, all the copies stored in the on-chip caches should be updated or, alternatively, the cache contents should be invalidated. If the system does not include special hardware support to perform this task (for example, by sending a sort of non-maskable interrupt to each microprocessor that will result in the cache content invalidation), the solution is to avoid shared pages being cached inside the CPUs.

Another example of non-cacheable data is represented by memory areas that can be written to by DMA devices, since these can modify the copy stored in main memory and the on-chip copies would not reflect the new data values. The non-cacheable bit (NC) in each page table entry (Figure 5.11) was introduced for this purpose. When NC is set, the Z80000 does not load the addressed data into the internal cache, but the external memory is always accessed.

The memory management mechanisms can be disabled by suitably resetting the SX and NX bits in the system configuration control longword register (Figure 5.6). SX is used to enable address translation for system accesses, while NX controls the mapping of the (normal) user logical addresses. When the memory management mechanisms are disabled, the logical addresses are the same as those used to drive the Z80000 address bus lines.

5.9.3   Memory protection

Memory protection mechanisms consist of access rights bits associated with the MMU translation and page tables. In particular, each translation table descriptor register and each table entry contains a protection field (PROT in Figures 5.6 and 5.11) used to encode the access type (read, write or execute) allowed to the user. Table 5.2 summarizes the possible values assumed by PROT and the related meanings both in system and normal mode. During the translation phase, the Z80000 checks the PROT field content at each step; the access rights are set to the first value different from 'next' found in a table entry, while all the PROT values met in the following steps are discarded. In this way, different tasks can have different access rights for the same physical page, even though their translation paths contain the same page table entry. In other words, the physical page protection can be inherited from a table entry at whatever translation level according to the designer's need. The protection bits are saved in the lookaside buffer when the translation algorithm is executed. This is necessary, since the CPU must be able to perform access rights checks even though the logical-to-physical address mapping is already contained in the translation lookaside buffer.

5.9.4   Virtual memory management support

The Z80000 also offers the programmer mechanisms intended to simplify the implementation of virtual memory management sytems. For example, when the accessed logical page is not present in main memory (that is, the valid bit in some table entry is reset), an address translation trap occurs. In this way, the program status information is saved into the stack so that the operating system is able to restart the suspended task correctly after loading the missing page in main memory.

Table 5.2 Access rights and memory protection codes in the Z80000 architecture.

Encoding	System	Normal
0000	NA	NA
0001	RE	NA
0010	RE	E
0011	RE	RE
0100	E	NA
0101	E	E
0110	R	NA
0111	R	R
1000	Next	Next
1001	RW	NA
1010	RW	R
1011	RW	RW
1100	RWE	NA
1101	RWE	E
1110	RWE	RE
1111	RWE	RWE

Notes: NA – no access is permitted; R – read access is permitted; W – write access is permitted; E – execute access is permitted; Next – use the protection field of the next level translation table; for page table entries, a PROT field of 1000 indicates no access is permitted.

The reference (R) and modification (M) bits in each page table entry (Figure 5.11) have been introduced to aid the memory management system in the page swapping operations. In fact, M is set by the CPU whenever the associated memory page is written, so that the system software can avoid having to copy pages, for which an updated copy already exists, back to the mass storage, when they must be swapped out. On the other hand, R is set when the associated page is accessed. In searching pages that can be replaced, the operating system is then able to detect those least frequently used by periodically clearing the R bit.

5.10 Co-processors

Advanced microprocessor architectures should include support to extend the CPU processing capabilities by means of special-purpose external co-processors. The Z80000 can be easily used in conjunction with other dedicated units, since some mechanisms were introduced implementing a standard co-processor interface.

The CPU can recognize up to four external co-processors present in the system. The presence or absence of any special unit in the system must be notified to the Z80000 by suitably programming the extended processor architecture bit (EPA) in the flag and control word register (Figure 5.7). When the CPU processes a co-processor instruction and the EPA bit is set, the instruction code is sent to the appropriate unit via the standard data bus. The instruction code also contains a co-processor identifier field. Each external unit compares this field with its own unique hard-wired identifier, and when a match occurs the instruction code is fetched from the data bus and stored inside the co-processor for execution.

The co-processor interface assumes that the external unit is not able to access the main memory directly; or in other words, co-processors are not DMA devices. For this reason, when memory operands are required for a co-processor instruction execution, the CPU performs memory accesses and data transfers to the external unit. In the same way, co-processor operation results can be stored in main memory under the CPU control: the Z80000 reads data from the dedicated unit and writes them in the destination memory locations. Data transfers can also involve the CPU general-purpose registers as source or destination. Moreover, the Z80000 flag bits can be automatically set at the end of a co-processor instruction to reflect the status of the external computation.

The two special signals $\overline{\text{EPUBSY}}$ and $\overline{\text{EPUABORT}}$ in Figure 5.3 are intended to synchronize the Z80000 and the co-processor operations. For example, an external unit that is busy processing an instruction can prevent the CPU from issuing other commands by driving the $\overline{\text{EPUBSY}}$ line; on the other hand, the CPU can abort the execution of an external unit command by means of the $\overline{\text{EPUABORT}}$ signal.

Co-processor instruction meanings are transparent to the CPU, since it is not concerned with data processing by external devices. The Z80000 architecture supports seven different classes of co-processor instructions, depending on the kind of data transfer to be performed. Six classes contain instructions for moving data from the main memory, CPU registers and CPU flags to the co-processor and vice versa. The seventh class of instruction is devoted to true co-processor operations depending on the particular kind of unit (that is, floating-point unit or signal processor, for example) being considered.

5.11   The Z8070 floating-point co-processor

Floating-point computation capabilities can be obtained in a Z80000-based system by using the Z8070 co-processor. In fact, the Z8070 implements the IEEE P754 Floating-Point Standard for data representation, operation set and the exceptions raised during the computations.

The Z8070 is interfaced with the CPU by the Z80000 standard co-processor interface and provides a number of data transfer and format conversion instructions, in addition to the conventional arithmetic operations.

Instructions are transferred from the CPU to the Z8070 and are immediately executed or queued by the co-processor if the unit is currently busy carrying out a previous computation.

The Z8070 supports three different floating-point data representations: the IEEE P754 single- and double-basic formats (Section 2.2.2) and an extended double format. The latter format uses 15 bits for the exponent, 63 bits for the operand fractional part and one bit for the integer part. In addition, the co-processor implements all the format conversions between the floating-point representations and the binary and decimal (BCD) integer formats. In the last case, integer operands consisting of up to 19 BCD digits can be accepted and processed.

The Z8070 converts all the input operands to the extended double format and each operation result is also produced using the 80-bit representation, thus assuring the highest precision in the computations. However, when data are moved from the CPU to the co-processor and vice versa, format conversions occur as specified by the programmer via the transfer instructions.

5.11.1 Registers

The Z8070 registers are shown in Figure 5.12. As can be seen, there are general data and special-purpose registers, the last being devoted to controlling and programming the co-processor's working mode. All the following registers, except for the system configuration word, can be accessed by normal users without any particular privilege.

A. FLOATING-POINT DATA REGISTERS

As shown in Figure 5.12, the floating-point unit contains eight data registers whose length is 80 bits. These registers can be used by the programmer to store operands and results that will be needed in following computations or that must be accessed as fast as possible.

B. FLOATING OPERAND REGISTERS

There are two 80-bit operand registers (FOP1 and FOP2), introduced for the purpose of trap-handling routines. FOP1 contains the input operand, while FOP2 usually holds the result of a computation. When a trap occurs, the trap handler can access both FOP1 and FOP2 in processing the exceptional event.

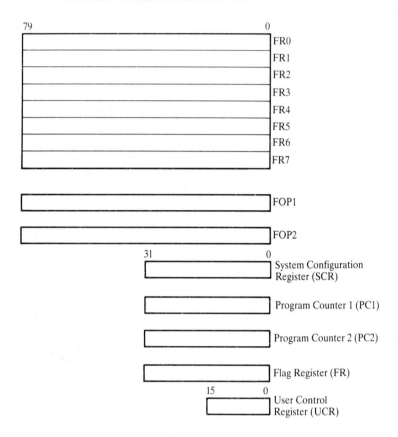

Figure 5.12   Z8070 floating-point unit register set.

C. PROGRAM COUNTERS

The two 32-bit program counter registers (PC1 and PC2) are used by the Z8070 to store the addresses of the instruction being executed (PC1) and of any instruction queued by the co-processor (PC2). PC1 and PC2 can be read by the Z80000, so that the CPU is able to correctly restart a program interrupted by some co-processor exception.

D. SYSTEM CONFIGURATION REGISTER

The system configuration register (SCR) is shown in Figure 5.13. This register can be accessed only in system mode, since it is used to program the Z8070 basic working mode and cannot be freely manipulated without affecting the system reliability.

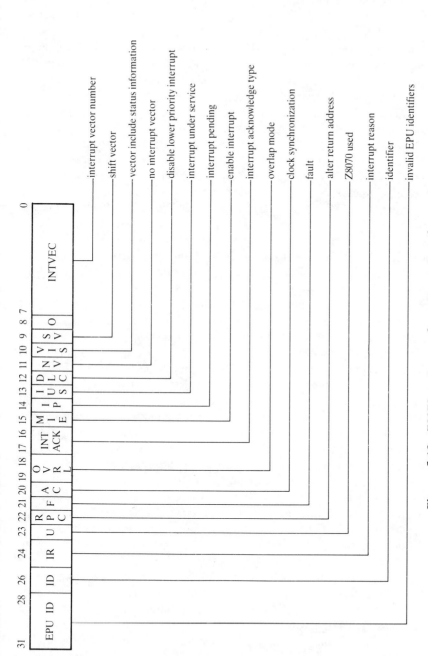

Figure 5.13 Z8070 system configuration register format.

The least significant byte in the SCR contains the interrupt vector that the Z8070 sends to the CPU when it performs a vectored interrupt acknowledgement cycle, and is used by the Z80000 to fetch the address of the interrupt service routine. The SV bit signals to the co-processor to indicate whether the interrupt vector should be shifted left one position before being transmitted to the CPU. Several other bits in the SCR are devoted to controlling interrupts generated by the Z8070.

The VIS bit in Figure 5.13 specifies whether the interrupt vector must include status information, while NV inhibits the vector mechanism, so that interrupts issued by the co-processor must be processed by the CPU as non-maskable or non-vectored exceptions. To this end, the INTACK field is tested by the co-processor to decide which type (maskable, vectored, non-vectored) of interrupt must be answered among the interrupt acknowledge cycles initiated by the CPU. In this way, the Z8070 can be connected to the non-maskable, vectored or non-vectored interrupt lines of the Z80000, depending on the system requirements.

Interrupts can be disabled by clearing the MIE bit, while IUS informs the co-processor that an interrupt is under service by the CPU. IP is set when an interrupt is pending and waits for service by the Z80000. The F bit is used to signal to the CPU that the interrupt handler will not be able to return to the interrupted co-processor program properly. This happens when two or more floating-point instructions are fetched by the Z8070 in the time interval between the interrupt request issued to the Z80000 and the interrupt acknowledgement cycle performed by the CPU. In this case, the two program counter registers PC1 and PC2 are both changed so that the address of the interrupted instruction is lost and cannot be recovered. Similarly, the RPC bit reminds the Z80000 that the return address must be modified to restart the interrupted program correctly. This is necessary when a single instruction is obtained by the floating-point unit while waiting for the interrupt acknowledge.

Other fields in the system configuration register have been introduced to support the external processor identifier mechanisms. To this end, the ID bits are loaded with the system-wide identification code that is hardware-assigned to the co-processor. By comparing the ID with the identifier included in each co-processor instruction, the Z8070 can distinguish its own instructions from those of other co-processors. The EPUID field is a mask that can be set by the system programmer to activate the Z8070 interrupt mechanism when certain co-processor identifiers are found in a co-processor instruction. In fact, each bit in EPUID is associated with a different identifier (only four different co-processors can be included in a Z80000 system). When the Z8070 fetches an instruction concerning an external unit, whose associated bit in EPUID is set, it sends an 'invalid co-processor identifier' interrupt to the CPU. This mechanism can be usefully employed in systems including the Z8070 to automatically trap instructions concerning non-existent co-processors. By suitably programming the EPUID field, the system designer can cause an exception to be raised by the floating-point unit whenever an illegal co-processor instruction is processed by the CPU.

Since several events can lead the Z8070 to interrupt the CPU, two bits in the configuration register (IR) are used to encode the interrupt reason (arithmetic, invalid operation code, invalid co-processor identifier and privileged mode violation), so that the Z80000 can properly process different exception requests issued on the same interrupt line.

Finally, another field (OVRL) provided allows the system designer to specify whether the CPU and co-processor operations must be overlapped or not. When overlapping is used, the CPU and the floating-point unit can work in parallel. This situation is illustrated in Figure 5.14(a). The Z80000 starts a Z8070 instruction and then continues

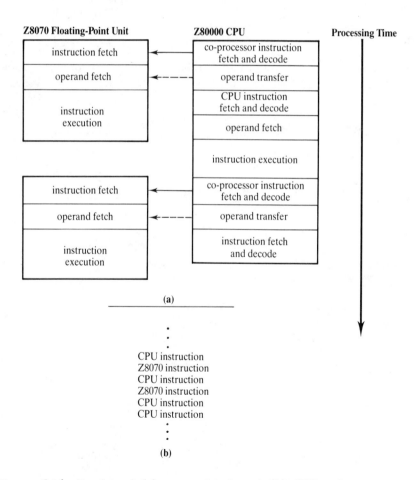

(a)

CPU instruction
Z8070 instruction
CPU instruction
Z8070 instruction
CPU instruction
CPU instruction

(b)

Figure 5.14 Overlapped (a) versus interleaved (b) CPU and co-processor instruction executions in a Z80000 system.

its program execution. When another floating-point operation must be performed, the $\overline{\text{EPUBSY}}$ line is checked and, possibly, the Z80000 waits until the previous co-processor instruction execution is terminated. On the other hand, if the Z8070 is ready, the new floating-point operation is immediately started and no CPU time is wasted. From this point of view, a good programming technique is to interleave CPU and co-processor instructions as shown in Figure 5.14(b). In this way, the Z80000 waiting time can be greatly reduced and in some cases eliminated.

When no overlapping is selected by means of the OVRLP field, the situation looks like that shown in Figure 5.15. In this case, the CPU waits for each co-processor instruction completion independently of the $\overline{\text{EPUBSY}}$ line status, and there is no parallel processing, since the CPU and co-processor operations are serialized.

E. FLAG REGISTER

As shown in Figure 5.16, the flag register (FR) is a 32-bit word containing all the status information related to the instruction execution. The least significant byte in the FR contains the so-called 'sticky flags',

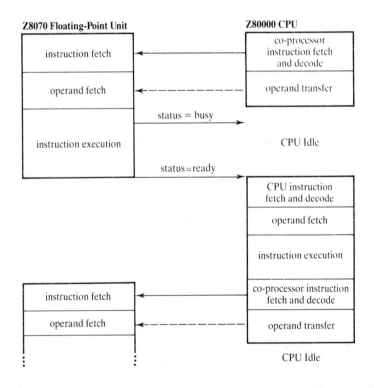

Figure 5.15 Sequential CPU and co-processor instruction execution.

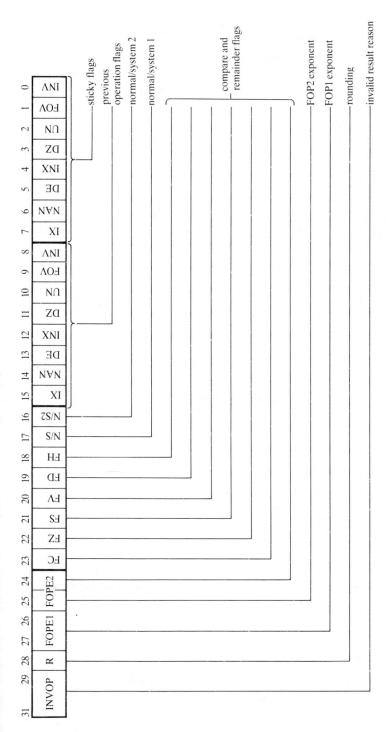

Figure 5.16 Z8070 flag register format.

which are set when an arithmetic exception occurs during the current instruction execution. Flags were introduced for errors such as underflow, overflow, divide by zero, inexact result, denormalized number, not a number, integer exception and invalid operation. An exception flag remains set until it is explicitly cleared by the programmer. Most of the arithmetic exceptions are those included in the IEEE P754 Standard (Section 2.2.2), while the others are related to the Z80000 system characteristics. The integer exception, for example, is raised whenever a floating-point number is too large to be converted to the integer format, or when the user attempts to convert a not-a-number or NaN value to an integer.

Bits 8–15 in the FR contain the same flags as the least significant byte, referred, in this case, to the previous arithmetic operation performed by the Z8070. The N/S1 and N/S2 bits in FR refer to the program counter registers PC1 and PC2, respectively, and are used to signal whether the associated PC contains a system or normal mode address. Bits 18–23 are called 'compare and remainder' flags and are used as condition bits to hold the result of comparison operations. The FOPE1 and FOPE2 fields are used to store the two most significant bits of the exponent of operand registers FOP1 and FOP2, respectively, when an overflow exception occurs. In this way, the exception-handling routine can use the FOPE1 (FOPE2) and FOP1 (FOP2) contents to take the appropriate actions in processing the overflow condition.

The rounding bit is a flag signalling whether the result of the most recent computation was rounded or not. The FR also contains an 'invalid operation' field that is set when an invalid operation occurs.

F.   USER CONTROL REGISTER

The user control register (UCR) is a 16-bit word whose format is shown in Figure 5.17. It contains fields used by the programmer to specify the requested rounding mode (RM) and to enable/disable arithmetic traps selectively. Hence, the same exception types specified by the least significant byte in the flag register can be individually enabled or disabled. Moreover, four rounding modes can be specified by means of the RM field; that is, rounding to the nearest integer, towards zero, and to positive or negative infinity.

5.11.2   Z8070 co-processor instructions

The Z8070 instruction set includes floating-point operations in addition to compare, data transfer and control instructions. Floating-point instructions consist of the basic IEEE P754 operations plus some additional functions particularly useful in mathematical computations. Hence,

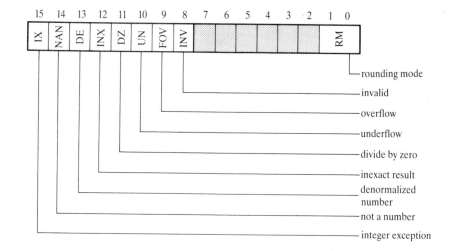

Figure 5.17   User control register structure.

operators for floating-point addition, subtraction, multiplication, division and square root evaluation are provided. Each one of these operations accepts input operands that can be stored in the CPU registers, in main memory or in the co-processor data registers. However, results are always stored in the Z8070 floating-point registers. Suitable operators are also included to compute the remainder of the division of two input operands. In addition to the IEEE P754 typical operations, the Z8070 supports instructions to compute the absolute value of a floating-point operand, to clear and negate a floating variable and to round a floating-point number to the nearest floating-point integer.

The Z8070 compare instruction group includes operators to compare two floating-point operands and to compare an input operand with zero. Other operators are able to transfer comparison flags to the CPU at the end of the operation. In addition, the programmer can also request an 'unordered' exception to be raised (Section 2.2.2), depending on the comparison result, by using other special comparison instructions.

A complete set of data transfer instructions is supported by the co-processor. Transfer instructions are used to store an operand in a floating-point register. The source operand (when a floating-point register must be loaded) or the destination operand (when a floating-point register content must be stored) can be located in a CPU or co-processor register or in main memory. The transfer instructions can convert the source operand in the Z8070 extended format before writing its value in the co-processor registers. Similarly, data are converted to the destination operand format when they are moved from floating-point registers to the CPU or to the main memory (under the CPU control). All conversions between floating point and binary and decimal integer formats are supported.

Finally, some instructions have been introduced to allow the programmer to control the Z8070's operation directly. This group includes operators to read and write the co-processor control registers, to set and reset the Z8070 internal flags and to enable/disable the arithmetic traps by means of the user control register.

5.12   Conclusion

The evolution of the Zilog Z8000 microprocessor family has led to the design of the new 32-bit Z80000 CPU. This microprocessor incorporates powerful supports for high-level language programming and modern operating system development. Basic data types, addressing modes and instruction set have been selected to cope with advanced system design and implementation requirements. An instruction and data on-chip cache memory allows the overall performance to be significantly enhanced by reducing the time needed by the CPU to read code and operands in the main memory.

The Z80000 also includes a powerful on-chip memory management unit that allows sophisticated virtual memory system to be implemented and separate access domains for task and procedures to be easily obtained.

Finally, a general-purpose co-processor interface allows external co-processors to be used in conjunction with the CPU to carry out specialized tasks in the most efficient way. The Z8070 floating-point co-processor, for example, has been designed to extend the processing facilities offered by the Z80000 with floating-point operations according to the IEEE P754 Standard.

EXERCISES

5.1   The INDEX instruction is intended to simplify address computations for elements in multidimensional arrays. INDEX multiplies the length of the array dimension (DIM), specified by the user, by the value of an accumulating operand (ACC) and adds to the product the current array subscript (SUB) before storing the result in ACC, so that ACC = ACC * DIM + SUB. Thus, it is possible to evaluate an element address in an n-dimensional array by executing the index instruction $(n - 1)$ times. Show the values of ACC, DIM and SUB before and after each INDEX execution when the address of $A(3, 5, 9)$ must be computed. The array A is declared in Pascal with dimensions [1..5, 1..10, 1..30].

5.2 Describe the operations that an operating system routine must carry out in a Z80000 system to perform task context switching in the following cases:

(a)   when the cache is disabled;

(b)   when the cache is enabled for system instructions and data;

(d)   when the cache is enabled for system and user instructions and data.

What about the translation lookaside buffer contents?

5.3 Which special Z80000 instructions are needed to perform the operations in Exercise 5.2? Which control structures are affected?

5.4 Draw the flowchart of a routine implementing the Z80000 address translation algorithm in software.

5.5 How can semaphores be implemented using the increment and decrement interlocked instructions? Can your solution be used both in mono- and multiprocessor systems? Why?

5.6 Draw the flowchart of a routine for processing access rights violation traps in a Z80000 system.

5.7 Explain the meaning of the two program counter registers in the Z8070 floating-point unit. How should these registers be used by a trap-handling routine in processing a floating-point exception? Which information bits have to be accessed in the Z8070 registers to distinguish between different exception conditions? Why?

5.8 How many significant (decimal) digits can be represented using the three different floating-point formats supported by the Z8070?

5.9 Discuss the main advantages/disadvantages of the Z80000 three-level address translation mechanisms. When is it possible to skip one or more translation levels without affecting the system's behaviour?

5.10 Assume that in a Z80000 system a read cycle from the main memory requires two clock periods (no wait states). Estimate the address translation time in the following cases:

(a)   when the cache is disabled, three translation levels are used and the TLB buffer has been purged;

(b)   with the same conditions as for (a), but only using two levels;

(c)   with the same conditions as for (a), but only with a single level.

How much does the number of translation levels affect the total translation time?

5.11 Try to explain, with an example, why it is dangerous to allow shared variables to be cached inside each CPU in multiprocessor systems. Does the Z80000 architecture circumvent this problem? What about shared program areas?

5.12 Draw the flowchart of a routine intended to manage trace traps in the Z80000 system. Why are the two bits T and TP in the flag and control register provided?

5.13 Draw the flowchart of a routine for computing the value of $x = (a + b)/(c - d)$ using the Z8070; a, b, c and d are single precision floating-point numbers. How can the CPU and co-processor operations be overlapped to speed up the computation of x?

CHAPTER 6

THE MOTOROLA MC68020 FAMILY

OBJECTIVES

The aims of this chapter are as follows:

- to illustrate the architecture of the Motorola MC68020 CPU and its basic interface mechanisms to the external world;

- to introduce the main MC68020 features for basic data types processing, operand addressing and the CPU instruction set;

- to show how the MC68020 architecture supports exception management by means of powerful mechanisms for interrupt and trap handling;

- to show how the CPU can be used in conjunction with external special-purpose co-processors, and to present the MC68020 uniform co-processor interface;

- to discuss memory management in the MC68020 system by illustrating the characteristics provided by the MC68851 memory management unit for virtual-to-physical address translation, memory protection and virtual memory organization;

- to analyze the main features of the MC68881 floating-point co-processor.

6.1 Introduction
6.2 CPU architecture
6.3 Cache memory
6.4 Basic data types
6.5 Registers
6.6 Addressing modes
6.7 Instruction set

6.8 Exceptions
6.9 Co-processors
6.10 Memory management
6.11 The MC68881 floating-point co-processor
6.12 Conclusion

6.1   Introduction

The MC68020 is the most advanced microprocessor belonging to the Motorola MC68000 family. From a general overview of this component, and of related chips, such as the MC68881 floating-point co-processor and the MC68851 MMU, it can be seen that the whole MC68020 project has three primary goals.

The first goal is to offer a number of basic supports for the development of complex systems based on advanced tools such as virtual memory management, multiprocessing facilities and efficient mechanisms for the use of high-level languages, not only in business and management applications, but particularly in real-time environments such as robotics, process control and industrial automation.

For these applications, a very high performance had to be implemented in the microprocessor and this was achieved in several ways. For example, the MC68020 is able to work with a very high clock frequency (16 MHz), and higher clock rates are expected to be used in the next few years. Moreover, the microprocessor architecture is totally based on 32-bit data paths, which greatly increase its processing power. Both the MC68020 address bus and data bus are 32-bits wide and are not multiplexed; consequently, the CPU is able to read or write a 32-bit word of information in a single bus cycle, and to address directly a physical memory space larger than 4 Gbytes.

The second goal is to maintain a high degree of compatibility with other components in the family, and so save user investments both in software and hardware. Since the MC68020 is object-code compatible with its predecessors, several applications can be run directly on the 32-bit CPU without any additional requirement (that is, without recompilation) even though obtaining only some benefits from the 32-bit architecture.

Finally, the third goal of the MC68020 project is to offer a microprocessor with a computing power typical of the last generation of VLSI chips, but which is also easy to use and with a simple, linear structure, at least from the programmer's point of view. For this reason, the MC68020 can be thought of, to a certain degree, as the logical evolution of other Motorola CPUs (MC68000, MC68008 and MC68010), being able to extend their main characteristics to the 32-bit environment and to add powerful new features.

6.2   CPU architecture

6.2.1   Internal organization

Figure 6.1 shows the block architecture of the CPU. It is easy to see that the whole microprocessor is organized into basic units able to carry out special functions in parallel with a high degree of independence. In other words, the typical operations performed by the CPU have been de-coupled whenever possible, for efficiency and to increase performance.

The instruction prefetch unit, for example, is used to load instruction words from external memory into the decode unit via the data bus. However, the instruction stream is also stored in the on-chip cache memory to grant very short access times to the execution unit. In fact, when the fetched instruction is in the cache, only two clock cycles are needed to access each word, while three or more cycles are necessary when the external memory is addressed. Furthermore, the CPU is able to read or write operands to or from the external storage while fetching instructions from the on-chip cache. The sequencer and control units are used both to select the next instruction to be executed and to manage the internal bus communications and synchronization of blocks in Figure 6.1. The execution unit carries out all the logical and arithmetic operations involved in the instruction execution. This is also accomplished by means of special hardware, such as a barrel-shifter circuit that allows logical or arithmetic shifts and rotations to be executed in a fixed time, independently from the number of bits to be shifted.

The parallel operations of the different units in Figure 6.2 greatly reduce the code execution time. In fact, the sequencer control unit and the bus controller can operate on the same instruction at the same time. More generally, however, the main phases of the instruction processing, such as fetch, decode and execute, are pipelined inside the MC68020. This reduces the apparent execution time of certain instructions to zero; in other words, they are hidden from the user because of the execution of

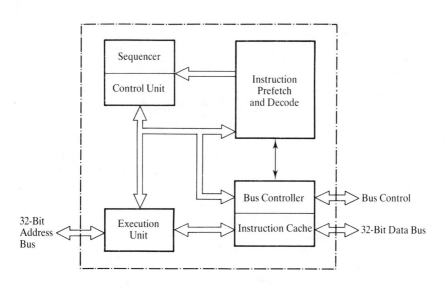

Figure 6.1   MC68020 block architecture.

code that comes shortly before or after the 'shadow' instruction in the program. For example, while the sequencer is engaged in decoding the current instruction, or in calculating the effective address of an operand, the bus controller can execute some bus cycles related to a previous or following instruction. The executions of two subsequent instructions can in this way be partially or totally overlapped. This is particularly true for the MC68020 architecture as it does not make use of simple instruction queues. In fact, queues do not offer the advantages of pipelines, even though the former allow a greater degree of concurrence than the latter. Instruction pipes are preferable when changes in the program flow occur – for example, branches or calls. In this case, the whole instruction queue content must be discarded, thus causing inefficiency (that is, prefetch of unneeded code leads to bus saturation). This is in contrast to pipes where only a small amount of prefetched code is rejected with pipes. On the other hand, pipes, unlike instruction queues, must be filled before the execution of a new instruction can begin and this happens at each change in the flow. However, a careful choice of the pipe depth leads to a satisfactory tradeoff where 'idle' filling times are suitably reduced without lessening the other advantages.

Another important characteristic of the MC68020 is the co-processor interface support. The CPU architecture includes special mechanisms to control the interactions with external co-processors. Furthermore, the programmer can use particular instructions to access co-processor processing facilities, and this is true both for the MC68000 family devices and user-defined co-processors.

6.2.2   CPU signals

Figure 6.2 shows the I/O signals used by the MC68020. Besides the address and data buses, the three function code lines FC0–FC2 are particularly important. The microprocessor address space is structured in five subspaces that are logically and physically disjointed. In each processing phase, the MC68020 refers one and only one address subspace at a time. These hardware recognized areas are user program, user data, supervisor program, supervisor data and CPU space, respectively. User program and data areas contain code and related operands for user tasks, while supervisor spaces are dedicated to privileged programs and databases that usually build up the active operating system. Finally, the CPU address space is accessed during particular processing cycles, such as interrupt acknowledges, module calls/returns (see Section 6.7.6) and co-processor communications (see Section 6.9), for example. These differ from the classical instruction fetch and data read/write operations. When addressing the external memory, the MC68020 outputs the code of the involved address subspace on the FC0–FC2 lines. Hence, the external

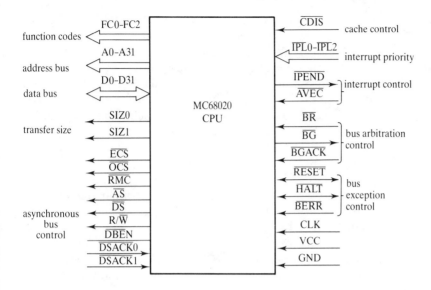

Figure 6.2   MC68020 I/O signals.

hardware can decode these bits to implement physically disjointed storage areas.

The asynchronous bus control signals contain all the I/O lines used by the CPU to manage different external bus cycles. They include, for example, strobe signals for the address ($\overline{AS}$) and data ($\overline{DS}$) lines, a read/write ($R/\overline{W}$) line to indicate the direction of the bus transfer cycle, and so on. The two transfer size signals, SIZ0 and SIZ1 in Figure 6.2, are used by the microprocessor in conjunction with the $\overline{DSACK0}$ and $\overline{DSACK1}$ lines during I/O operations. The MC68020 supports data transfer to and from 8-, 16- and 32-bit data ports with automatic bus sizing. When an I/O port is selected for a data transfer it must reply to the CPU by properly driving the 'data transfer and size acknowledge' lines, to notify the CPU of the port width. The microprocessor then proceeds to move the requested amount of data to or from the peripheral by automatically providing a suitable number of transfer cycles. For example, if a 32-bit datum must be read from an 8-bit port, the MC68020 executes four subsequent byte-read operations according to the information placed on $\overline{DSACK0}$–$\overline{DSACK1}$ by the selected input port when the move operation is started. Furthermore, during any elementary read cycle, the CPU encodes on the SIZ0 and SIZ1 lines the number of bytes that must be transferred during the next bus cycle.

The interrupt control signals in Figure 6.2 are used to manage the occurrence of external asynchronous events. An interrupting device presents its request on the $\overline{IPL0}$–$\overline{IPL2}$ lines. Seven priority levels are provided for interrupts, seven being the most privileged (non-maskable) level. When an interrupt request is presented on $\overline{IPL0}$-$\overline{IPL2}$, the MC68020 compares the priority level with the internal interrupt mask, which can be altered by the programmer. If the current level is higher than the masked level the request is honoured and the interrupt pending ($\overline{IPEND}$) line is forced to zero. Otherwise, the interrupt request is ignored and the CPU operations continue without any status change. Note, however, that the seventh priority level can never be masked. The $\overline{AVEC}$ signal is used to inform the CPU that the interrupt vector – the address of the interrupt handler (see Section 6.8) – is generated internally and is not provided by the interrupting device.

The bus arbitration control signals are used by external devices or other processors to request, and possibly obtain, bus mastership of the MC68020.

Three processing states are possible for the MC68020: normal, exception and halted. In the normal condition, the microprocessor executes program instructions; hence, normal bus cycles occur, including instruction fetch and operand read/write. Exception processing concerns interrupts and other special events generated either by the software or by the hardware that require a prompt service by the microprocessor. Finally, in the halt state, the CPU is stopped and can be restarted only by means of a reset signal. The halt condition is usually generated by some unrecoverable failure.

When executing an instruction, the microprocessor can be in two different privileged states: user and supervisor. At the supervisor level, each machine operation can be performed, even those that heavily affect the system's behaviour, such as peripheral reset or control register manipulations. For this reason, user programs are generally run at the user level, where critical, protected instructions cannot be executed.

Three additional signals allow the management of exceptional conditions by the CPU. The $\overline{RESET}$ line is forced to zero by a reset instruction and allows the external devices to be re-initialized. However, $\overline{RESET}$ is also used as an input to cause the MC68020 reset operations. Similarly, the $\overline{HALT}$ line is used either to put the CPU in the halt condition or is asserted by the microprocessor when the program execution is stopped because a stop instruction was decoded, or a double bus error has occurred. The bus error line ($\overline{BERR}$) is driven by the external logic to inform the MC68020 that the current bus cycle cannot be completed successfully for some reason, such as non-responding devices or illegal accesses detected by an external MMU.

6.3   Cache memory

The MC68020 on-chip instruction cache is organized as shown in Figure 6.3. When a new instruction is fetched, the address bits A7–A2 are used to select one of the 64 entries in the cache. In addition, the value of the FC2 line, indicating the supervisor or user address space, and the bits A31–A8 are compared to the 25-bit TAG field of the selected entry. The fetched instruction is present in the cache when a match occurs and the valid bit (V) in Figure 6.3 is set. In the case of a cache hit, an instruction word specified by A1 is read directly from the on-chip cache memory. When the instruction is not in the cache, either because the compared tags are different or the valid bit is cleared, the new tag is loaded in the cache, the instruction is fetched from the external memory and is written in the cache – both the upper and lower words – and the valid bit is automatically set. The privileged programmer can affect the cache behaviour by modifying bits in the cache registers (as shown in Figure 6.6). The cache control register (CACR), for example, contains only four meaningful bits: enable cache (EC), freeze cache (FC), clear entry (CE) and clear cache (CC). EC is used to enable, when set, or disable the cache working mode; cache disabling is particularly useful in system debugging and emulation, when the CPU must be forced to access the external memory to check the behaviour of the software and hardware under test.

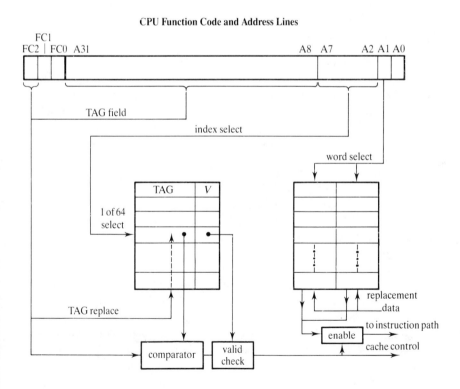

Figure 6.3 MC68020 instruction cache organization.

Similarly, FC does not disable the cache, neither does it allow entries to be replaced by new data when misses occur. In other words, the cache is enabled, but its contents cannot be altered so that it is possible to stop a program execution temporarily, perform some management functions, and then resume the interrupted task without modifying the processor internal status. Such a facility can be conveniently used by emulator designers to make emulation transparent to the user.

The CE bit allows the programmer to reset the valid bit associated with the cache entry selected by the cache address register (CAAR), and hence can be used to cause a miss when the referred entry is addressed. Finally, CC is used to clear all the entry valid bits so that the content of the whole cache can be discarded – for example, for debugging purposes.

6.4   Basic data types

MC68020 can manipulate four different types of basic operand, which can be addressed in 11 modes. In particular, the CPU architecture includes support for accessing integers, BCD numbers, bits and bit fields.

6.4.1   Integers

Integer operands can be 1, 2 (word), 4 (longword) or 8 (quadword) bytes long. Both signed and unsigned integers are allowed. Since the microprocessor memory space is organized as a sequence of bytes where lower addresses are associated with higher order bytes, the location of a word or longword operand in memory is fully specified by its base address – that is, the address of its highest order byte. Moreover, each longword operand exactly fills each CPU register that can be loaded during some computation.

When loaded into registers, words occupy the 16 least significant bits, while byte operands are always located in the less significant octet of each CPU register. Each instruction acting on a subfield of a 32-bit register, such as a word or a byte, does not affect the remaining part of the 32-bit field. In other words, the bits not involved in the operation are not modified.

Quadwords seldom appear as source or destination operands in a machine instruction. They are used essentially during the multiply and divide instructions, to store the product of the multiplication of two 32-bit integers, or to hold the 64-bit dividend in a long signed or unsigned division. As for word and longword data, quadword addresses are specified by means of the memory location of their most significant byte. Furthermore, quadword operands occupy a pair of 32-bit registers when they are loaded in the CPU.

6.4.2   BCD digits

BCD operands are used in decimal arithmetic instructions. Two kinds of BCD data are supported by the MC68020 architecture: packed and unpacked. In the packed form, two digits are stored in a single byte of memory, while each unpacked byte contains only one BCD digit. Packed digits are used to save memory resources, but data should be unpacked when I/O operations are executed. For this purpose, the programmer can use a couple of suitable pack/unpack instructions that allow format conversions and the simultaneous addition of a user-selected constant to the BCD digit. This is particularly useful when decimal digits must be transformed into ASCII characters and vice versa.

6.4.3   Bits

As in other modern microprocessors, the MC68020 is capable of accessing single-bit operands. Bits can be tested, set and cleared by a number of machine instructions. The memory address of a bit operand consists of two elements: the base address and the bit number. The base address is the physical location of the byte containing the bit; the bit number can range from zero (least significant) to seven (most significant) and is used to locate the bit operand inside the byte. Obviously, the number of register bits is greater than or equal to zero, but less than 32.

6.4.4   Bit fields

In several instructions the programmer is able to specify operands consisting of a bit string with variable length (from 1 to 32 bits). Bit fields can be cleared, inserted, extracted and scanned by means of suitable machine operations that allow these data manipulations to be performed in a very efficient way. The memory reference for a bit field consists of three main parts: base address, offset and width. The base address is used to point to a byte in main memory that represents the displacement for locating the bit field. The offset parameter is the signed distance – in bits – between the most significant bit of the reference or base byte and the 'leftmost' bit in the operand string. Thus, as shown in Figure 6.4, positive offsets ($\leq 2^{31} - 1$) are used to identify bit fields beginning in the base byte or in a byte with a higher address, while negative offsets ($\geq -2^{31}$) are used to select bit operands whose origins are in a byte with an address lower than the base byte. The third component, the field width, is then necessary to indicate the number of bits (≤ 32) in the field. Bit-field operands belonging to the CPU registers can also be selected.

No MC68020 data operand has to be aligned on some boundary in memory. The CPU, in fact, is able to access data placed at different byte

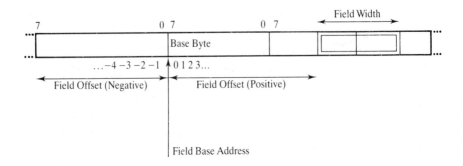

Figure 6.4 MC68020 bit-field specification.

boundaries, even though they differ in performance. On the other hand, instruction words must be aligned on even-byte addresses or an address error exception occurs when the CPU tries to fetch the misaligned code.

6.5   Registers

6.5.1   General-purpose registers

A typical MC68020 user can only access a subset of the processor registers as shown in Figure 6.5. The data register group consists of eight 32-bit registers (D0–D7) intended for storing any kind of operand. The address group is also composed of eight registers (A0–A7); even though address registers can be specified in some data computations, these are registers used primarily to hold operand addresses and, somehow, to point to operands in memory. Moreover, the eighth register, A7, is recognized by the CPU as the stack pointer, and is implicitly used in each instruction involving stack operations.

Generic users can also access the program counter (PC) and the condition code register (CCR). Program counter indirect manipulations are allowed, for example, by branch, call or return instructions. The condition code register physically consists of the low-order byte of a 16-bit status register; nevertheless, only the condition code bits are visible to the programmer. Condition codes are handled automatically by the CPU during logical/arithmetic computations to reflect the result of the operation being executed. The user is able to test five different condition bits: overflow (V), zero (Z), negative (N), carry (C) and extend (X), the last being used in extended precision arithmetic.

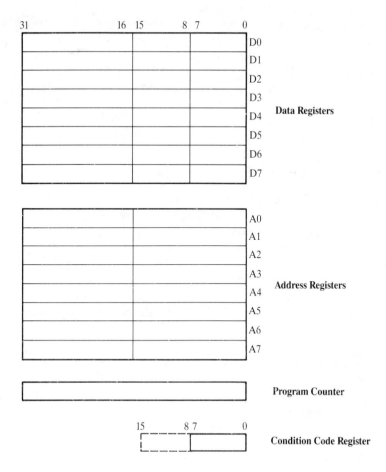

Figure 6.5 Normal user programming model.

6.5.2 Control registers

The generic programmer's view of the MC68020 architecture is not very different from classical 8- or 16-bit microprocessor models. The system designer, however, must have more complete control of the CPU; hence, privileged users, such as operating systems running in the supervisor mode, are allowed to access and manipulate the status and control registers shown in Figure 6.6, in addition to the common registers of Figure 6.5. For example, supervisor programs can read and write the high-order byte of the status register (SR) in addition to the condition code bits. The status register also contains seven additional bits, used to affect the CPU operations. A 3-bit interrupt priority mask is used to enable or disable interrupt priority levels when needed, so that complex interrupt service schemes based on priorities can be implemented by suitably nesting the different requests. A supervisor or user bit (S/$\overline{U}$) signals that the CPU is running either in the supervisor or user mode, and so privileged instructions are or are not allowed. For protection reasons, the normal user is not able to toggle the S/$\overline{U}$ bit directly and put the CPU in the supervisor state. In fact, S/$\overline{U}$ is automatically forced to one by the MC68020 when an exception occurs requiring supervisor rights to be handled. Such exceptions include interrupts as well as certain errors. Since normal users can cause software-generated exceptions by suitable instructions, system services by a privileged task, such as an operating system test, can be invoked in a controlled and safe way. In other words, the MC68020 offers the programmer a way of requesting protected services, which must be executed at the supervisor level by means of a set of reliable instructions like system calls. These are based on exception mechanisms that force the CPU into the privileged mode (see Section 6.8).

The privileged programmer can access and modify the S/$\overline{U}$ bit and the other fields in the status register. A bit in the status register –

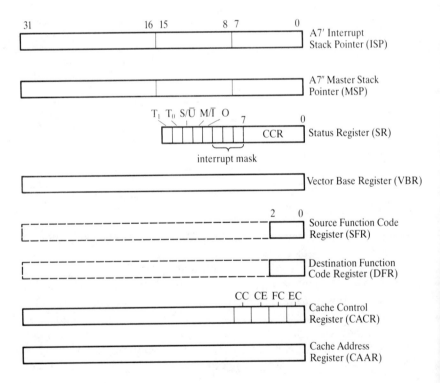

Figure 6.6 Supervisor additional registers.

master/interrupt, M/$\overline{\text{I}}$ – remembers that the CPU is currently processing an exception generated either by an external interrupt request, or by some other exceptional hardware or software event. This is particularly useful to operating system writers and when different users' tasks share the CPU resources with other I/O processes such as interrupt drivers. As is well known, multitasking is efficiently implemented by associating each user task with a system stack used to save the task status and related information when the context is switched. Since the MC68020 supports two different system stacks, accessed by the master stack pointer (MSP) and interrupt stack pointer (ISP), respectively, it is convenient to associate the master stack with the currently running task and to switch it between the different user processes. In the meantime, all the interrupt-related stack operations make use of the dedicated interrupt stack. The CPU is able to distinguish the stack in use from the M/$\overline{\text{I}}$ bit in the status register; this can be set or reset by each privileged user. Moreover, when an interrupt or some other exception occurs, the CPU saves a copy of the status register, including the M/$\overline{\text{I}}$ bit, so that the master or interrupt state can be correctly restored when the exception processing is completed. The S/$\overline{\text{U}}$ bit is not affected by the M/$\overline{\text{I}}$ condition. Alternatively, when an interrupt request is acknowledged by the CPU, the M/$\overline{\text{I}}$ bit is automatically cleared – if set – to reflect the interrupt processing state.

The two most significant bits in the status register are used to enable and disable tracing by the CPU with different variants. Tracing mechanisms give the user a tool for analyzing the program flow during its execution. The MC68020 is able to generate 'trace exceptions in the hardware on conditions selected by the programmer so that a trace-handler task can be automatically run when needed to supply the user with the required information.

The other registers in Figure 6.6 are used to control some basic microprocessor functions and are generally used only by routines belonging to the operating system kernel to gain complete access to the processor resources. The cache control register (CACR) and cache address register (CAAR), for example, affect the on-chip instruction cache operations, either for debugging or management purposes as explained in Section 6.3. The vector base register (VBR) is used to hold the displacement of the memory area containing pointers or vectors to routines dedicated to interrupt and other exceptions handling (see Section 6.8). The VBR allows exception vectors to be dynamically relocated in memory with the following effects. First, an operating system can use different tables of pointers to exception handlers at the same time, which can be switched by simply changing the vector base register content. Secondly, a memory management system can, when needed, move the vector table from one area to another by copying it into the new destination and then modifying the VBR.

Finally, two additional registers are provided to enable programs running in the supervisor state to access each address space visible to the CPU. This is needed, for example, in systems implementing physically separate user or system memory spaces, when supervisor modules must alter user program and data areas. This is used for page swapping and program loading to or from backing stores. Hence, the source function code (SFR) and destination function code (DFR) registers are used by the privileged programmer to read and write memory words in different address spaces by means of suitable move operations. SFR and DFR can be loaded with the source or destination space code via a privileged instruction.

6.6   Addressing modes

6.6.1   Operand addressing

Modern microprocessor performance depends on a variety of modes, supported by the hardware, to address instruction operands. Powerful addressing facilities, for example, are requested by compiler implementors for high-level languages to grant efficient and fast access to data structures such as arrays, lists and records. The MC68020 architecture includes, amongst other things, addressing mechanisms that could only be found in minicomputers or mainframes until recently.

Obviously, the CPU supports the common direct modes, such as register operands, contained either in data (D0–D7) or in address (A0–A7) registers. Similarly, immediate data are also implemented in the byte, word and longword formats.

The MC68020 allows two different encoding forms – that is, short and long – for absolute addresses of memory direct operands. Short addresses are 16 bits long and are sign extended to the long form (32 bits) when they are used by the hardware. Long absolute addresses, on the other hand, are contained in two consecutive words of memory, concatenated to form the operand physical address.

Besides the direct modes, address registers can be used to access operands indirectly. In other words, they can point to data in main memory. The address register indirect mode corresponds to register indirect addressing of Section 1.5.3, while the register indirect with postincrement/predecrement modes correspond to the autoincrement/autodecrement mechanisms described in Section 1.5.4.

Another mode available is the address register indirect with displacement, which is the base displacement indirect mode of Section 1.5.6 with a 16-bit displacement. In this case, when the program counter is used as an address register, the relative mode described in that section is obtained.

More powerful mechanisms use an additional register, called the index register (Xn). This can be either a data register or another address register. The MC68020 also allows the programmer to specify the index register length (word or longword) and a scale factor, which can be equal to one (no scaling), two, four or eight. This yields the base displacement indexed indirect mode of Section 1.5.7, which corresponds to the MC68020 address register indirect with index mode. Note that either an address register or the program counter can be used as the base register and, moreover, byte, word and longword displacements are allowed.

The most complex and flexible addressing modes supported by the MC68020 architecture are the memory indirect modes. In this case, the content of the memory location, selected via a more or less sophisticated combination of register arguments and constants, is used as a pointer to the final operand. The reference to the operand in memory is obtained by combining four elements specified by the user. Each element, however, can be suppressed, so that a variety of alternate addressing modes can be obtained.

As in the register indirect modes, the programmer is able to select an address register, An, a 16- or 32-bit displacement ($d1$) and an index register, Xn. Furthermore, a second displacement ($d2$) is also allowed. The effective address (EA) computation is performed in two possible ways, depending on the use of the index register, Xn. Hence, the memory indirect or postindexed mode corresponds to the base displacement indirect displacement indexed indirect mode of Section 1.5.13, while the memory indirect preindexed mode is equivalent to the base displacement indexed indirect displacement indirect mode of Section 1.5.16. The program counter can also be used as a base register with the memory indirect modes.

Table 6.1 summarizes the addressing modes supported by the MC68020 architecture. The effective address calculation greatly affects the total instruction execution time. In general, the time required to evaluate an operand address depends on the addressing mode itself and on other factors such as the presence or absence of parts of the instruction code in the internal cache memory. The last column in the table shows the number of clock periods required to form the effective operand address, assuming that the on-chip cache is disabled, the data bus is 32 bits wide and the external memory is so fast that no wait states must be inserted by the CPU in the instruction execution cycle.

6.6.2   Instruction format

The operand addressing modes not only affect execution times, but also the instruction formats and lengths. The MC68020 instruction size can range from one to 11 words when a complex addressing mode is selected

Table 6.1 MC68020 addressing modes.

Type	Addressing Mode Motorola Notation	EA Computation	Computation Time best case (clock cycles)
Register direct	Data/address register direct	EA = Dn, An	0
Immediate	Immediate	EA = next word(s)	0
Memory direct	Absolute short/long	EA = (next word(s))	3
Register indirect	Address register indirect	EA = (An)	3
Autoincrement indirect	Address register indirect with postincrement	EA = (An) +	4
Autodecrement indirect	Address register indirect with predecrement	EA = −(An)	3
Base displacement indirect	Address register indirect with displacement	EA = (An) + $d16$	3
Relative	PC indirect with displacement	EA = (PC) + $d16$	3
Base displacement indexed indirect	Address register indirect with index	EA = (An) + (Xn) + $d8/d16$ EA = (PC) + (Xn) + $d8/d16$	4 4
Base displacement indirect displacement index indirect	Memory indirect postindexed	EA = ((An) + $d1$) + (Xn) + $d2$ EA = ((PC) + $d1$) + (Xn) + $d2$	17 17
Base displacement index indirect displacement indirect	Memory indirect preindexed	EA = ((An) + (Xn) + $d1$) + $d2$ EA = ((PC) + (Xn) + $d1$) + $d2$	10 10

Notes: Xn: index register; $d8$: 8-bit displacement; $d16$: 16-bit displacement; $d1$, $d2$: 16- or 32-bit displacement.

for each operand in the operation. Each instruction consists of at least one word, structured as shown in Figure 6.7. The ten most significant bits (15–6) are devoted to the opcode, while the remaining bits are used to specify the effective address computation mode. The EA field is logically divided into two subfields: mode and register. The mode bits are used to select the addressing mechanism; absolute operand references and immediate data do not need any further information and the physical address of the operand itself is contained in the following word(s), depending on the register subfield content. Generally speaking, very simple instructions such as register-to-register operations do not need extra words. Moreover, in several cases one of the operands involved in the computation is specified directly in the opcode. However, when sophisticated addressing modes are used by the programmer, additional information is encoded in the second and following words.

The MC68020 architecture supports two different extension formats: brief and full. Figure 6.8 shows the organization of data in both the encoding types. The short form contains subfields used to specify the index register type (data or address D/A), its number (Reg) and its length (W/L). Moreover, the scale subfield contains the value of the scale factor used in the indexed addressing modes. The low-order byte in the brief format can specify the 8-bit displacement used in a variant of the register indirect indexed mode.

The full format, in contrast, is used when long base displacements, of 16 or 32 bits are required, or when a second displacement is used for operand addressing, as in memory indirect modes. The first word in the full extension form contains the same indexing information as the brief format. However, bit number eight is used by the CPU to distinguish between the two different instruction encoding types. Furthermore, the first full word also holds subfields concerning the base displacement and its size.

The base suppress field (BS) is used to tell the CPU whether or not a base displacement must be added to the other components building up the operand address. The index suppress subfield (IS) is similar; when

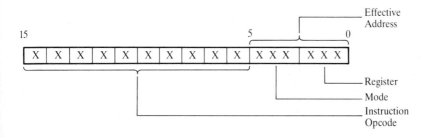

Figure 6.7   First instruction word format.

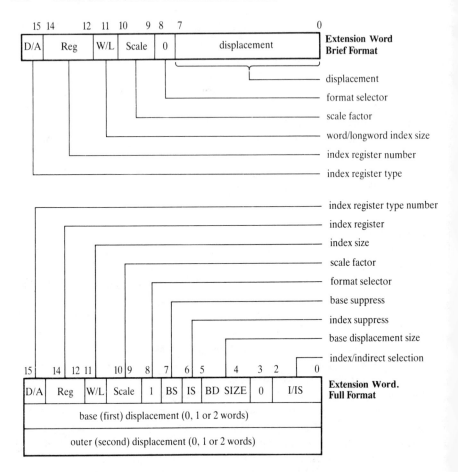

Figure 6.8   Extension word formats.

this bit is reset, no index register is involved in the EA evaluation. Moreover, the base size field (BD SIZE) specifies the actual length of the base displacement, while the index/indirect bits are interpreted in conjunction with the IS to distinguish between the different memory indirect modes – without indexing and with pre- or postindexing. It also selects the second displacement size: no displacement, word or longword displacement. Displacements, when used, occupy other extra memory words as shown in Figure 6.8. In this way, the longest MC68020 instruction consists of 11 words: one opcode word and a pair of full format extension frames, five words long, needed to specify the effective address of the source and destination operands.

6.7 Instruction set

The MC68020 instruction set contains several groups of operations designed to allow efficient data processing and system control by the CPU. The whole set can be logically divided into seven classes dedicated to data transfer, integer and BCD arithmetic operations, logical and shift operations, bit and bit-field manipulation, array processing, program flow control and CPU control. The MC68020 also supports special instructions used with external co-processors and these are discussed in Section 6.9.1.

6.7.1 Data transfer instructions

There are eight different instruction types used for data transfer; general data movements occur from register to register, memory to register and vice versa, or from memory to memory by means of the MOVE instruction. Furthermore, register contents can be exchanged via EXG. Address transfer can use the load effective address (LEA) and push effective address (PEA) functions. The former allows the address of an operand to be loaded in an address register, whereas the latter is used to push the operand EA on to the stack. When the destination of an operand transfer is one of the address registers a move address (MOVEA) instruction can also be used.

Multiple register transfers are also allowed in a single MOVEM operation. MOVEM loads a sequence of registers, specified by the programmer by a suitable mask, into a contiguous set of memory locations. Three MOVEM variants are possible – normal, predecrement and postincrement – depending on the addressing mode chosen to specify the memory area. When the normal mode is used, registers are stored or loaded starting with D0 and ending with A7, through progressively higher addresses. Predecrement mode, in contrast, only allows register-to-memory transfers. Register words are stored from A7 to D0 in progressively lower addresses, computed by decrementing the contents of the specified address register by two. Similarly, postincrement mode only supports memory-to-register transfers as the normal mode does, but also incrementing the content of the base register selected for the operation.

Data register loading with one byte of immediate data is performed by the MOVEQ instruction. A special move peripheral data (MOVEP) instruction allows the MC68020 to be incorporated into systems with a 16-bit data bus, and to use typical 8-bit peripherals. In fact, data are moved on a byte-per-byte basis between a data register and the memory using alternate addresses. Either an even or an odd starting address can be specified.

6.7.2   Integer and BCD arithmetic instructions

The MC68020 supports all the basic types of integer arithmetic operations with different operand sizes. Some instructions also allow arithmetic computations directly in the decimal form. For example, integer addition of two data operands can be performed by the ADD, add immediate (ADDI) and add quick (ADDQ) operations. Furthermore, data can be added to an address register by the ADDA instruction, whereas ADDX allows the system to sum two data registers, or two memory operands, with the extend bit (X), so that 64-bit operand additions are made possible.

A corresponding group of machine operations (SUB, SUBI, SUBQ, SUBA and SUBX) exists for the different types of integer subtraction. Other instructions allow the programmer to compare a selected operand with the content of a data or address register (CMP, CMPA), or with an immediate datum (CMPI). Memory-to-memory comparisons are also possible with a CMPM instruction.

Other instructions include CLR, which allows the user to clear all the bits in an operand, and NEG and NEGX, which replace a destination operand value with the difference between zero and the operand itself, or between zero, the operand and the extend bit (X), respectively. Two further instructions, EXT and EXTB, have been introduced for sign extending 8- and 16-bit operand lengths to 32 bits.

Multiplying signed or unsigned integers is performed by the MULS/MULU pair on 16- or 32-bit operands; results can be 32 or 64 bits long when 32-bit factors are used. Signed or unsigned divisions are accomplished via DIVS, DIVSL or DIVU, and DIVUL operations. Several operand sizes leading to different remainder and quotient lengths can be specified.

Decimal arithmetic is carried out by five specific instructions. As mentioned in Section 6.4, the PACK/UNPK pair allows fast switches between the packed and the unpacked formats, saving valuable memory resources. Decimal addition, subtraction and negation are managed by add, subtract and negate decimal with extend instructions (ABCD, SBCD and NBCD). Each instruction involves the extend bit (X) in the related computations together with the operands specified by the programmer, so that decimal multiprecision operations are also possible.

6.7.3   Logical and shift instructions

Logical instructions consist of the classical 'and' (AND, ANDI), 'or' (OR, ORI), 'exclusive-or' (EOR, EORI) and complement (NOT) operations, and can be used with each kind of integer operand (8, 16 or 32 bits long). Moreover, a test function (TST) allows a user-specified operand to be compared with zero and the condition codes to be set accordingly.

A number of shift and rotate operators also exist. Logical and arithmetic shifts, for example, are supported for byte, word and longword data by ASL and ASR (arithmetic shift left, right), together with the LSL and LSR (logical shift left, right) instructions. The user can always specify the number of positions to be shifted. Similarly, operand rotations to the left or right are possible, with or without the extend bit, using the ROXL and ROXR (rotate left, right with extend), and ROL and ROR (rotate left, right) instructions. The programmer can also specify the number of positions involved in the rotation. A SWAP operation allows two words in a data register to be exchanged.

6.7.4 Bit and bit-field instructions

Bit instructions are supported by each MC68000 family CPU, so it is possible to complement (BCHG), reset (BCLR), set (BSET) and test (BTST) a bit value, either in a memory or register operand, with a single operation. Note, however, that only byte operands are allowed to be specified in memory, while 32-bit data are considered when working with registers.

In contrast, bit-field manipulations are typical of the MC68020. Thus, operations such as negate (BFCHG), clear (BFCLR), set (BFSET) and test (BFTST) are also allowed. However, the user must always specify the leftmost bit and width parameters for the field (see Section 6.4). In addition, a bit field can be sign extended or zero extended by means of the BFEXTS/BFEXTU pair. These instructions extract the user-defined field from the source operand and load the extracted bits into a data register after a sign- or zero-extension operation. Another powerful operator is BFFFO – find first one in a bit field. This searches for the first bit in the field set to one, and loads its offset in a data register. The condition codes are then set accordingly with a single machine instruction. Finally, the programmer can store a register field in a memory operand by means of the insert bit field (BFINS) operation.

6.7.5 Array instructions

The MC68020 also supports special instructions for array processing. CMP2 allows a register content to be compared with a pair of user-selected limits to set the condition codes. CHK compares a data register content (Dn) with zero (the lower limit) and an operand (the upper limit) specified by the user. An exception is raised (see Section 6.8) when the argument does not fall in the selected interval. Similarly, CHK2 allows both the upper and lower limits used in the comparison to be selected by the programmer as for CMP2, but in this case an exception is also raised when the limits are exceeded.

CMP2, CHK and CHK2 can be used by program compilers to develop efficient run-time checks on the values assumed by the array indices as required in several high-level languages.

6.7.6 Program flow control instructions

The program flow control group contains instructions that affect the program counter content in different ways. Hence, unconditional and conditional jumps are included in this class of operations. For example, two kinds of conditional branch are available: branch conditionally, Bcc, and test condition, decrement and branch, DBcc. The former allows a program jump on a condition code bit, cc, whereas the latter is more complex and powerful. In this case, the condition is first tested and if the result is true the instruction execution ends, otherwise the data register specified by the programmer is decremented and then its content is checked. A branch only occurs when the register contains a value not equal to -1. This instruction is particularly useful for implementing loops that must be executed until a certain condition is or is not satisfied, or, alternatively, for a maximum number of times. These situations occur in the **repeat...until** and **while...do** high-level language constructs. Moreover, by choosing cc = false, the condition is never true and the loop ends only when the number of iterations selected by the data register is exhausted. In this way, **for...do** loops can also be efficiently implemented.

Unconditional branches are obviously supported by the MC68020 architecture. The branch instruction BRA causes a jump relative to the program counter. It can also be used to skip a number of bytes in the instruction flow. JMP allows the program execution to be continued starting with the address specified by the user. The instruction pair branch to subroutine (BSR) and jump-to-subroutine (JSR) are used for short and long subroutine calls, respectively, relative to the program counter. Returns from subroutines are achieved by the return (RTS) and return and de-allocate parameters (RTD) together with the return and restore condition code (RTR) instructions. The first simply loads the program counter with the return address, obtained from the top of the stack, while the second also allows a user-specified displacement to be added to the stack pointer, so that a variable length stack area is automatically de-allocated when returning to the calling program. RTR pops from the stack and restores the condition code register besides the program counter.

Two special instructions are provided to simplify memory allocation from the stack storage area. They are useful when nested procedure calls must be implemented, supported in high-level languages such as Pascal and Ada. The LINK instruction allows the programmer to reserve a variable number of bytes in the current stack, whereas the unlink

(UNLK) function returns stack areas that were previously allocated by means of a LINK invocation. Figure 6.9 shows the behaviour of the LINK/UNLK pair. During the LINK execution, the address register, A*n*, specified by the user, is saved into the stack and the updated stack pointer (SP) is copied into A*n*. Finally, the number of words to be reserved, specified by the programmer by means of a negative displacement, is added to the stack pointer content. The UNLK instruction simply loads the accessed address register, A*n*, into the current stack pointer and then pops the old A*n* content from the stack, thus restoring the original situation.

It is worth noting that no push or pop instruction is included in the MC68020 instruction set, so that explicit register saving or restoring to and from stacks is possible only via the link/unlink instructions, or by using the register indirect addressing modes with predecrement and postincrement. Users can implement additional stacks with the register indirect modes in conjunction with the move instructions by specifying an address register other than A7.

By using special hardware, the MC68020 supports instructions to implement sophisticated procedure calls, with additional features such as automatic parameter passing and access rights checks. User and supervisor programs, in fact, can be organized as a set of, possibly autonomous, modules. Modules can be seen as a collection of routines

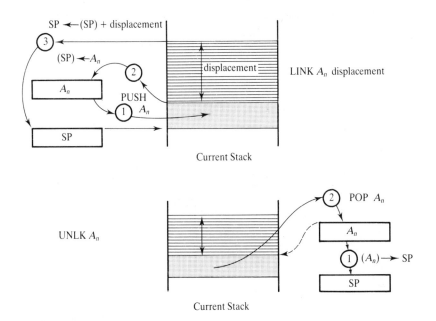

Figure 6.9 Link/unlink instructions behaviour.

that can be invoked by another module – they are able to perform some task and to return to the caller. Access rights can be associated with each module, so that it is possible to verify whether the user invoking the module is authorized to request its services. Modules are accessed by the call module (CALLM) and return from module (RTM) instructions.

Each module in the system is described by a **module descriptor**, specified in the CALLM instruction, whose format is shown in Figure 6.10. The first longword in the descriptor is used to encode information about type and parameter-passing characteristics. For example, the option bits can equal only 000 or 100, otherwise a format exception occurs (see Section 6.8) when the descriptor is accessed by the MC68020. A zero field means that arguments are passed directly to the called module in the stack, while in the other case a pointer to the parameters is pushed on to the stack by the calling module. The type field is used by the CPU to distinguish between different types of module. In practice, only two type values are recognized by the MC68020 and neither causes a format exception. Type zero modules do not require any access rights change when they are called, while type one descriptors imply access rights changes and possibly stack-swapping operations. Hence, the access level field in Figure 6.10 is meaningful only for type one descriptors and contains the privilege level code associated with that module.

Note that 256 access levels are possible inside each user or supervisor privilege state. The module entry word pointer is used to

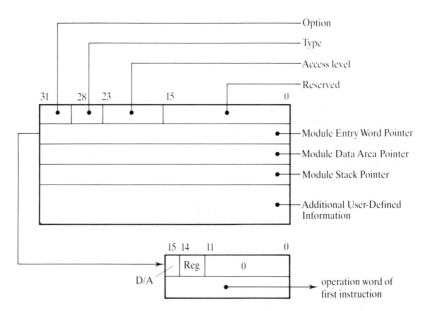

Figure 6.10   MC68020 module descriptor format.

address the module entry word shown in Figure 6.10. As can be seen, the most significant entry bytes contain the type – data or address – and the number of the register that must be loaded with the module data area pointer during the execution of the CALLM instruction. The contents of this register are automatically saved into the stack by the CPU during CALLM processing. Finally, the least significant entry bytes contain the first word of the module starting instruction. The module stack pointer in Figure 6.10 is used only with type one descriptors requiring stack changes. In this case, the old stack pointer is saved into the new stack, while the new stack pointer is loaded from the fourth longword in the module descriptor. Any other information field depicted in Figure 6.10 is user defined. When executed, the CALLM instruction saves the information related to the current module into the stack by means of a frame whose format is shown in Figure 6.11. Moreover, the new module status is loaded from the descriptor specified by the programmer. The option and type fields in Figure 6.11 are copied directly from the corresponding bits in the caller module descriptor (see Figure 6.10) and are used to restore the correct status when the module returns. In addition, the number of argument bytes specified by the user in the CALLM instruction is saved, together with the condition code bits and the program counter.

The module descriptor and the data area pointers in Figure 6.11 are used to address the called module descriptor and the caller data area,

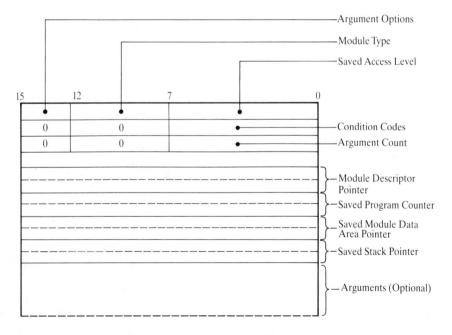

Figure 6.11 Module frame format.

respectively, so that no information reference is lost in the module swapping and it can be retrieved whenever needed.

The MC68020 relies heavily on the availability of suitable hardware for the execution of CALLM and RTM instructions requiring access level changes. The access level mechanism is not implemented within the CPU, which cooperates and exchanges information with special external circuits to allow correct privilege-level manipulations. Whenever a CALLM or RTM is executed the MC68020 reads and/or writes some particular locations in the CPU address space used to implement the interface between the microprocessor and the special-purpose hardware. During these accesses, bits 19–16 of the address bus are always set to 0001. The least significant bits are used to select interface locations with different meanings. For example, the lowest addresses are assigned to four external registers called current access level (CAL), STATUS, increase access level (IAL) and decrese access level (DAL). The CPU assumes that CAL, IAL and DAL can be correctly written to during a CALLM/RTM execution, and that responses from the external circuits can be read via the status register. If a CALLM is executed with a type zero module, the MC68020 simply builds the stack frame and fills it with the required information. However, when access rights changes are involved, the CPU first reads the CAL register to obtain the current access level code. Hence, the module descriptor address and the new access level are passed to the external hardware for validation by means of suitable write operations in the CPU address space – that is, in the IAR register if an increase in access rights is required, or in the DAR register for privilege restrictions.

The special-purpose circuits return responses to the microprocessor via the status register. Errors can occur, for example, if the user is not allowed to obtain higher privileges, or when the specified descriptor address is incorrect. This check prevents the user from forging module descriptors so obtaining, nevertheless, access to forbidden modules (erroneously or maliciously).

If an attempt to exceed access rights is detected by the external circuits, the CPU generates a format exception. Valid external responses are of two different types. For example, no access rights change can be made, and the CALLM processing ends (as in the type zero descriptor case), by creating a module descriptor frame in the stack and then starting the module execution at the first word specified by the first word pointer in Figure 6.10. When access rights must be increased or decreased, the special hardware requires a stack change by way of the status register. Here, the CPU saves the current stack ponter internally. Then the value of the new stack pointer is loaded from the module descriptor and a frame is created on top of the new stack and filled with the requisite information, including the old stack pointer, before the new module is executed.

The RTM instruction works in a similar way. Returns from type zero modules simply cause the program counter and module data area pointer to be reloaded with the information in the stack frame. The frame is removed from the stack and the stack pointer is incremented by the number of bytes specified in the argument count field in Figure 6.11, so popping from the stack the parameters used in the module call. Returns from type one modules, however, imply right level checks, as for the CALLM instruction, and possibly a stack swap operation.

6.7.7   CPU control instructions

The CPU control group includes four classes of instruction. The first class contains the privileged operations that can be executed only in the supervisor state and is needed to modify critical machine registers and/or working modes. The second class allows condition code register manipulations, whereas the third is composed of instructions capable of causing processing exceptions directly in software. The fourth class consists of special instructions required to implement correct concurrent access on shared variables in multiprocessor and multitasking environments.

Privileged instructions allow the system programmer to access control registers (see Section 6.5.2) such as the status register (SR), the vector base register (VBR), the destination and source function code registers (DFC and SFC), the master, interrupt and user stack pointers (MSP, ISP and USP), and the cache control and address registers (CACR and CAAR). The status register bits can be easily set or cleared, individually or in groups, by three instructions that perform the logical 'and' (ANDI), 'or' (ORI) and 'exclusive-or' (EORI) operations between the status register and a 16-bit immediate operand, and store the result in the status register. The status register can also be read or written into using the MOVE to/from status register instruction. In the same way, the supervisor can access the contents of the user stack pointer by the MOVE to/from user stack pointer operator. This allows USP to be copied in an address register specified by the programmer. Programs running in the supervisor state can also read or write to memory locations in different address spaces – for example, user data and program, supervisor data and program and CPU space – by the move to/from address space (MOVES) instruction.

When reading from memory into a register, the address space involved is specified by the content of the source function code register. Data transfer operations from registers are carried out using the destination space selected by the destination function code register. The programmer can read and change the contents of both these registers by using the move to/from control register (MOVEC) instruction. The same operation reads and writes to the other control registers (VBR, MSP, ISP and USP) as well as the cache registers (see Section 6.3).

Two other privileged instructions are included in the MC68020 architecture. The RESET operation allows the system programmer to assert the reset signal output by the CPU to initialize the external peripherals. The STOP statement causes the microprocessor to stop the instruction fetch and execute cycles. The MC68020 can exit the stop state only when an exception such as an interrupt, a reset or a trap is raised. RESET and STOP can therefore be dangerous for the system behaviour, so their use must be carefully controlled, even in the supervisor state.

The instruction group for condition code manipulation contains the four operators ANDI, EORI, ORI and MOVE. However, as one of the two operands specified by the user is always the condition code register, CCR, the condition bits X, Z, C, V and N can be cleared or set both individually and in groups. The MC68020 programmer generates processing exceptions directly in the software by means of suitable instructions. Exception handling by the CPU is described in detail in Section 6.8. The user can raise 16 different trap exceptions via the TRAP instruction. Conditional traps can also be created using the trap-on-condition code and trap-on-overflow (TRAPcc and TRAPV) instructions. TRAPcc also allows the programmer to specify an immediate operand to be inserted in the trap instruction code. The exception processing routine can then retrieve this information to obtain additional data related to the exception state.

Other interrupts to the normal program flow can be caused via the software by the check registers against bounds (CHK and CHK2) instructions mentioned in Section 6.7.5.

When multiprocessor systems must be implemented, some instructions have to be supported by the CPU to obtain mutual exclusion on shared variables at the lower level – that is, in the hardware. In particular, indivisible operations are required to modify memory locations accessible by different processors correctly. During the execution of these instructions, the CPU must not release the common bus mastership until the whole operation has been completed. MC68020 indivisible instructions cause the CPU to assert the $\overline{\text{RMC}}$ output signal to indicate that an indivisible bus cycle is being performed. Moreover, the processor does not honour the bus grant requests coming from other master devices until the read–modify–write cycle is ended. Indivisible instructions are test and set (TAS) and compare and swap operand (CAS and CAS2). TAS allows the destination byte to be tested and the condition code bits to be set accordingly; furthermore, the most significant bit in the operand is forced to one by the same instruction. CAS and CAS2, on the other hand, compare a memory operand with the content of a data register specified by the user. If the data are equal, the contents of another register, called update data register, are copied into the memory operand; otherwise the memory location is not modified but its content is loaded in the first compare register.

6.8 Exceptions

The MC68020 normal operating mode can be interrupted by several kinds of special events, which must be served before the suspended instruction processing is resumed. These events are generated both internally, by the CPU itself, and externally by special-purpose hardware, to tell the microprocessor that special actions have to be taken at once, having a priority higher than the current operation.

The exception recognition and processing sequence always requires the CPU to perform four initial steps to save the current internal status and to set the new context for the exception handler routine execution.

(1)   First, the MC68020 makes an internal copy of the status register, since the content of this register is altered during the following steps. Its value must be saved so that it can be restored correctly at the end of the exception processing.

(2)   The second step is required to select the exception handler associated to the event, interrupting the normal instruction flow. Pointers to the exception-handling routines are contained in a table in main memory organized as shown in Table 6.2. In fact, each kind of exception has its own software handler and the correspondence between the starting address of each routine, called **exception vector**, and the related exception type is given by the hardware-defined position of the exception vector in Table 6.2. During the second step the MC68020 obtains the exception type code – that is, the index in the vector table to be used for computing the interrupt vector address – from internal logic or external hardware.

(3)   The third step saves the current execution context into the stack. For this purpose, the CPU builds a special memory area on the stack, called an **exception frame**, and fills it with all the information required to handle the exception condition and to restore, eventually, the normal processing mode.

(4)   Finally, the exception vector address is computed by multiplying the index obtained in step 2 by four and adding the result to the contents of the vector base register, which contains the memory displacement of the exception table as outlined in the previous section. The exception handler starting address is then fetched from external memory and loaded into the program counter to begin the exception processing.

Table 6.2   MC86020 exception vectors.

Vector Number(s)	Vector Offset Hex	Space	Assignment
0	000	SP	Reset: initial interrupt stack pointer
1	004	SP	Reset: initial program counter
2	008	SD	Bus error
3	00C	SD	Address error
4	010	SD	Illegal instruction
5	014	SD	Zero divide
6	018	SD	CHK, CHK2 instruction
7	01C	SD	cpTRAPcc, TRAPcc, TRAPV instructions
8	020	SD	Privilege violation
9	024	SD	Trace
10	028	SD	Line 1010 emulator
11	02C	SD	Line 1111 emulator
12	030	SD	(Unassigned, Reserved)
13	034	SD	Co-processor protocol violation
14	038	SD	Format error
15	03C	SD	Uninitialized interrupt
16	040	SD	⎫
.	.	.	⎬ (Unassigned, Reserved)
23	05C	SD	⎭
24	060	SD	Spurious interrupt
25	064	SD	Level 1 interrupt auto vector
26	068	SD	Level 2 interrupt auto vector
27	06C	SD	Level 3 interrupt auto vector
28	070	SD	Level 4 interrupt auto vector
29	074	SD	Level 5 interrupt auto vector
30	078	SD	Level 6 interrupt auto vector
31	07C	SD	Level 7 interrupt auto vector
32	080	SD	⎫
.	.	.	⎬ TRAP #0–15 instruction vectors
47	0BC	SD	⎭
48	0C0	SD	⎫
.	.	.	⎬ (Unassigned, Reserved)
63	0FC	SD	⎭
64	100	SD	⎫
.	.	.	⎬ User-defined vectors (192)
255	3FC	SD	⎭

Notes: SP: supervisor program space; SD: supervisor data space.

Additionally, the status register bits are modified during the first step. In particular, the supervisor bit is set, so that the exception handler can be executed at the maximum privilege level. Furthermore, tracing is disabled by resetting the trace control bits, and the interrupt mask is updated if a reset or an interrupt has occurred.

The stack frame built by the MC68020 during the exception recognition phase can have six different formats and lengths, depending on the particular type of event, since different information must be saved in the stack concerning the internal machine state when the exception occurs. However, all these frames have a common part represented by the first four words as shown in Figure 6.12. When the normal working mode is abandoned, the status register and the program counter are stored in the stack frame. Moreover, the vector offset, obtained in the second processing step, and the frame type code are inserted in the fourth word of the frame to allow frame decoding during the exception processing.

The MC68020 exceptions can be roughly grouped into two classes – interrupts and traps – depending on whether they are generated externally or internally.

6.8.1. Interrupts

Typical external exceptions are bus errors, interrupts and resets. Bus errors can occur during an external memory cycle when the external circuits abort the operation and drive the CPU bus error pin ($\overline{\text{BERR}}$) to tell the microprocessor that an illegal memory access is being performed.

The bus error mechanism can be used, for example, by a MMU to implement a virtual memory system based on the paging philosophy. When the CPU outputs a logical address not associated with a physical storage page, the MMU must issue the bus error signal to activate the

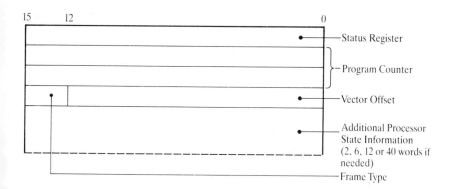

Figure 6.12 Exception stack frame format.

page fault or exception handler. This can then load the missing page into main memory and swap the memory pages not currently needed to the backing store. To make this possible, the CPU must be able to interrupt the execution of the instruction causing the bus error, and to resume execution when the required page has been loaded into main memory. Hence, when a bus error occurs, the MC68020 saves 12 additional words, containing the value of the internal registers (not accessible to the programmer) and the state of the pipeline stages in the fetch-and-decode unit, into the stack frame.

Because of the prefetch mechanism, faulty memory accesses can be performed by the MC68020 before the fetched instruction is actually needed by the execution unit, so causing the $\overline{\text{BERR}}$ signal to be driven by the external hardware. For this reason, while bus errors generated by data space accesses are processed immediately by the CPU, bus error exceptions due to program space accesses are not honoured by the MC68020 until the fetched code that caused the error is executed.

The interrupt mechanisms are the same as for other exceptions. Interrupts, however, are not honoured as soon as they occur; the CPU completes its current instruction before considering the pending requests, unless other conditions, such as the processing of another exception, further delay the interrupt service.

The interrupt vector index can be supplied by the interrupting device or generated internally by the CPU. During the interrupt acknowledge cycle, the MC68020 performs a read operation from an address in the CPU space. The device can then output its own vector index, so causing the execution of the related interrupt handler. Alternatively, the external circuits can drive the CPU autovector ($\overline{\text{AVEC}}$) input signal to make the CPU generate a vector index automatically.

Resets are an external exception that cause the MC68020 to initialize at power-on or re-initialize from unrecoverable failure or crash. When the reset signal is issued, the current state of the CPU is lost and the contents of the stack pointer and program counter registers are fetched from the first two exception vectors in Table 6.2. Unlike other exceptions, a stack frame is not built during reset, nor are the status register and program counter values saved.

6.8.2   Traps

The MC68020 architecture includes several other exceptions. For example, an exception is generated when the CPU attempts to fetch a new instruction from an odd address – an address error – or when the format of the first word in the fetched instruction is not correct – an illegal instruction. Some machine instructions can also cause an exception during their execution: TRAP, TRAPcc, TRAPV CHK, CHK2 and the division instructions all belong to this class. The module instructions CALLM and RETM can generate either a privilege violation or a format exception. The first is caused by an attempt to access a module without having the correct access rights, whereas the second is raised when the formats of the stack frames used by CALLM and RETM are not recognized by the CPU.

To simplify program debugging, the MC68020 architecture allows the programmer to generate a trace exception when an instruction has been executed. In this way, a trace handler is activated and information on the program behaviour can be collected and/or displayed. The user can control the tracing mechanism by modifying the T0 and T1 bits in the status register.

Breakpoint exceptions, however, are caused by the execution of a breakpoint (BKPT) instruction. When BKPT is processed, the CPU performs a read cycle from the CPU space address specified by the instruction itself. When the read operation is correctly performed, the microprocessor interprets the data obtained as the code of the next instruction to be executed. Otherwise, if a bus error occurs, the illegal instruction exception handler is activated. This facility allows debugging monitors to be implemented that can insert breakpoints in the program to be debugged. A monitor can, for example, replace the user code at the breakpoint with a BKPT instruction. Then, when the MC68020 executes BKPT, a monitor procedure is activated by means of the exception mechanism.

Finally, the exception state can be entered because of some co-processor action.

6.9 Co-processors

The MC68020 architecture includes special facilities for efficiently interfacing external co-processors to the CPU. These consist of general-purpose support for co-processor operations as extensions of the CPU basic instruction set. In this way, the programmer's model of the MC68020 system is kept uniform, and co-processor registers and instructions are considered as additional features offered by the main processor. The co-processor interface mechanisms are based on conventional bus cycles and signals, so no additional line is required to connect a Motorola or a user-defined co-processor to the system.

Communications between the CPU and the co-processor use address bus (A0–A31), data bus (D0–D31) and function code (FC0–FC2) lines. Information exchange is controlled by the CPU, which executes special-purpose co-processor instructions. During each co-processor operation, the MC68020 accesses predefined locations in the CPU address space; in particular, address lines A19–A16 are forced to 0010 during these read/write cycles to notify the external circuits that co-processors are involved in the data transfers.

The communication protocol followed by the CPU and the co-processor consists of requests from the MC68020 and answers from the special-purpose devices by means of a predefined set of interface registers. These allow concurrent processor operations to be synchronized on an instruction-by-instruction basis. Usually the MC68020 sends some operation request to a co-processor by writing information in a suitable register. Then the CPU looks for the co-processor's reply by repeatedly reading another interface register. The answer is used to select the next CPU operation: when the co-processor is busy, the MC68020 looks for another reply, otherwise the co-processor signals to the CPU that an exception must be raised because of a particular condition, or that additional services are required from the main processor to complete the invoked operation. Furthermore, the answer can tell the CPU that no additional service is necessary from the co-processor, and normal instruction processing can be continued.

The co-processor interface registers are predefined locations in the CPU address space, as shown in Figure 6.13. The MC68020 co-processor mechanisms assume that each co-processor using the standard interface is able to implement these basic registers. The command and operation registers, for example, are used by the CPU to pass the code of the requested functions to the co-processor by means of write bus cycles. The response register contains the co-processor's answers to the MC68020, while the control register is used by the CPU to acknowledge an exception request previously received from the co-processor and (possibly) to abort its current instruction.

In multitasking systems using a co-processor it is necessary to save the co-processor's internal state when the main processor is switched between different processes. The save register allows the CPU to stop co-processor operations and to save its internal state in a device-dependent frame that can be read by means of the save and operand registers. The restore register allows the MC68020 to restore a co-processor frame previously saved in main memory by writing to the restore and operand locations.

The condition register implements conditional instructions related to co-processor operations. When a conditional co-processor instruction is executed, the CPU writes the code of the condition to be tested in this register. The co-processor returns the CPU information about possible additional services needed and the check results – true or false – so that the conditional operation can be completed by the main processor.

The select register is used to implement single and multiple register transfers from the main processor to the co-processor, and vice versa. The other registers in Figure 6.13 save the co-processor's instruction

Address

31	15	0	
response register	control register		0
save register	restore register		4
operation register	command register		8
(reserved)	condition register		0C
operand register			10
register select	(reserved)		14
instruction address register			18
operand address register			1C

Figure 6.13   Co-processor interface registers.

addresses, basically for debugging purposes, and hold the effective address of operands in main memory. When the main processor executes a co-processor instruction, a command is written in the command or condition registers. The co-processor answers this request by loading a service request to the main processor in the response register.

Co-processor requests are grouped into five classes: processor synchronization, instruction manipulation, exception handling, operand transfer and register transfer. Processor synchronization commands tell the CPU that the co-processor is busy processing the current or previous instruction, or that the main processor can continue the instruction execution – for example, according to some condition. The instruction manipulation request commands obtain additional instruction words from the main processor. Exception-handling primitives cause the main processor to take and process an exception caused by the co-processor.

There are three kinds of exception that can be raised: immediately before, during or after the execution of a co-processor instruction. When an exception request is returned to the CPU, the co-processor also supplies the vector number to be used in the exception processing phase.

Finally, the operand and register transfer commands enable the co-processor to move general data and register contents under CPU control.

6.9.1   Co-processor instructions

The format of the first word of each MC68020 co-processor instruction is shown in Figure 6.14. This word always has the four most significant bits set to one, so indicating a co-processor operation, while the co-processor identifier field is used to distinguish between different co-processors in a system. Eight co-processors can be accessed by using this identifier: for

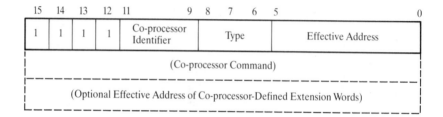

Figure 6.14   MC68020 co-processor instruction format.

example, the MC68881 floating-point co-processor identifier is zero, while the MC68851 paged MMU identifier is one. Users can also define other co-processors and assign them the identifiers six and seven. The type field in Figure 6.14 is used to select the different classes of operation. The MC68020 architecture supports general, branch, conditional, and save and restore co-processor instructions.

General co-processor instructions (cpGEN) are device dependent and are used for data movement and processing. Branch instructions (cpBcc) are used to insert branches in the CPU instruction flow, based on some co-processor condition. The conditional group includes operations to activate the trap mechanism (cpTRAPcc), to execute conditional loops (DBcc) or to set an operand (cpScc) depending on a co-processor condition. Finally, the save and restore operations (cpSAVE and cpRESTORE) allow the CPU to upload and download the co-processor's internal state.

6.10   Memory management

The MC68020 family has efficient and sophisticated supports for virtual memory management and memory protection. Most of this support has been included in an external MMU that cooperates with the CPU through the standard co-processor interface.

6.10.1   MC68851 MMU

The MC68851 is a special-purpose co-processor used in systems based on the MC68020 CPU that provides support both for virtual memory management, based on the demand paging philosophy, and for access rights checks and manipulations.

The MMU is interfaced to the MC68020 by the standard co-processor mechanisms described in Section 6.9. Figure 6.15 shows the block architecture of a simple system including the MC68851. The logical

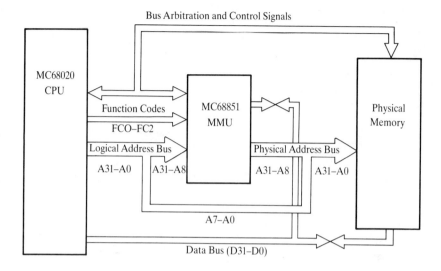

Figure 6.15   Block architecture of a simple system including the MC68851.

address bus outputs by the CPU are connected directly to the MMU, which is interfaced to the main memory by a physical address bus, where the eight least significant bits are obtained directly from the CPU logical address. The data bus is connected both to the MC68020 and to the MC68851, since the MMU needs to read and write data such as translation table entries from and to the main memory to carry out its operations.

Normally, users are not concerned with MMU behaviour, since it implements functions that are usually transparent to application programs. However, system designers and writers of operating systems can program and control the MMU working mode through the set of registers shown in Figure 6.16. These registers can be accessed in supervisor mode only. The MMU registers can be grouped according to their functions: the root pointer registers (CRP, SRP and DRP) and the translation control (TC) register are used to perform logical-to-physical address translation; the current access level (CAL), valid access level (VAL), stack change control (SCC) and access control (AC) registers are needed to implement the access rights check and protection mechanisms; the breakpoint registers allow the system to implement MC68020 breakpoint instruction support. The status and cache status (S and CS) registers allow the supervisor to obtain information about the MMU's internal state.

Privileged procedures can gain access to the MMU registers through a number of special co-processor instructions, such as PMOVE (move data to/from the MMU registers), PVALID (check the access level of a logical address), PLOAD (load the MMU translation cache with a

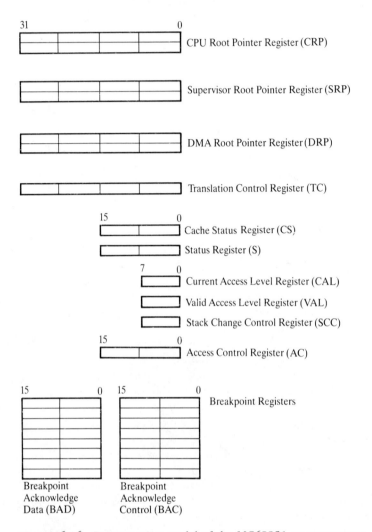

Figure 6.16   Programming model of the MC68851 co-processor.

translation entry), PFLUSH and PFLUSHR (used to flush the MMU translation cache in several ways). In addition, the conditional co-processor operation and the SAVE and RESTORE instructions are also implemented in the MC68851.

6.10.2   Address translation

The MC68851 translates logical-to-physical addresses by using translation tables stored in main memory. Since the translation process introduces a considerable overhead, because of repeated memory accesses during the

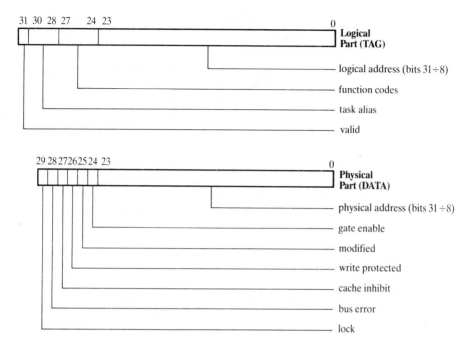

Figure 6.17 Entry format in the address translation cache.

table lookup, the MMU has an internal associative memory with 64 entries to store the most recently used translations and to avoid executing the time-consuming search algorithm on each CPU bus cycle. Figure 6.17 shows the organization of the cache entries: the 32-bit logical part builds up the TAG field while the physical part corresponds to the data entry field. A valid bit is used by the MMU to distinguish between valid and invalid entries. The TAG pattern is organized in three subfields: the logical address, for example, consists of the 24 most significant bits of the CPU logical address, while the function code bits are used in systems implementing separate address spaces and include the MC68020 FC2–FC0 address bits. In contrast, the task alias (TA) subfield is created and managed directly by the MMU itself. This is particularly useful in multitasking systems. In fact, the alias subfield allows entries related to different tasks in the system to be stored in the cache at the same time, even though they may have the same logical address and function code fields. In other words, the alias field marks each entry in the cache with a task identifier selected by the MMU. The MMU can then distinguish between the identical logical addresses belonging to different processes.

The 30-bit physical part of the cache entries contains the most significant bits of the physical address and additional information for use in the translation process. For example, a lock bit means that the cache entry contents cannot be replaced when a miss occurs in accessing the cache. This mechanism can be used by the operating system to prevent frequently used translations from being replaced by other, less important entries. The MC68851 architecture avoids filling the cache with locked descriptors by refusing to execute the lock operation when there is only one unlocked entry in the cache. Furthermore, this condition is signalled by setting a suitable bit in the cache status register. The cache inhibit field must be used when an external data cache has to be implemented. In this case, the MMU issues a signal to the cache controller that can disable the external cache filling operations (if a miss occurs) when accessing some particular memory locations, such as temporary buffers.

Finally, a gate bit is needed to inform the MMU whether or not a page is allowed to contain module descriptors; the MC68851 can therefore detect attempts by users to access or forge illegal module gates.

When the MC68020 outputs a logical address, the MMU compares it with the cache contents; if a 'hit' occurs, the physical address is at once presented on the physical address bus. In contrast, a 'miss' causes the MC68851 to abort the CPU bus cycle, with an indication that the cycle must be retried, and then to invoke the bus mastership. Then the MMU

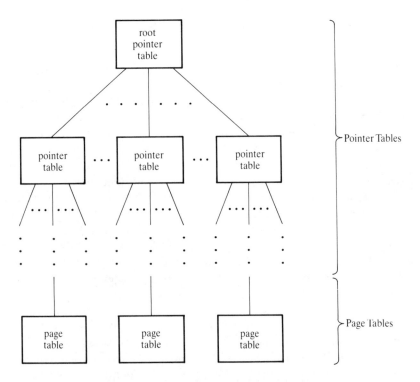

Figure 6.18 Translation table organization in main memory.

starts the lookup process, to find a translation for the logical address in the tables in main memory, and inserts it in the appropriate cache entry. The MC68020 is eventually allowed to retry the suspended bus cycle, which will now give a cache hit.

Translation tables are organized in tree structures and belong to two different classes: tables at the leaves are called **page tables** and contain physical addresses; root and intermediate node tables are called **pointer tables** as they contain pointers to other translation tables, as shown in Figure 6.18. The search algorithm implemented in the MMU scans the tables from the root to one of the leaves in the tree. For this purpose, the CPU logical address is interpreted by the MC68851 as a number of subfields, each one representing an offset in a table, as shown in Figure 6.19. Pointer table entries include the base address of a table at the next level in the tree.

Tables can contain two kinds of descriptors: short and long. The short format uses 32 bits to store physical addresses or table pointers, together with protection and state information, such as the format of entries in tables at the next level, write permission and so on. On the other hand, 64-bit (or long) descriptors also include a limit field to limit the table lengths at the next level in the tree. They also have an access level field that restricts accesses to certain addresses. The table size affects the number of levels in the tree, so that it should be carefully

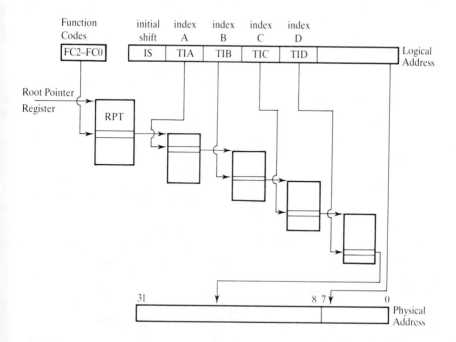

Figure 6.19 Address translation mechanism implemented in the MC68851.

selected by the system designer. In fact, short tables require several lookup levels and hence yield long translation times. In contrast, long tables are located in several physical pages that necessarily have to be contiguous. In addition, several page addresses must be saved for each table that it swapped to the backing store.

A system programmer can select the width of each index subfield of Figure 6.19 by suitably loading the translation control register. Moreover, the programmer can also choose the number of logical address bits that must be ignored by the MMU during the first search step and are specified by the initial shift subfield in Figure 6.19. This feature is particularly useful when the MC68851 is used in systems with logical addresses shorter than 32 bits. The translation control register also contains a page size field used to select the physical page length: the designer can choose page lengths equal to 256 or 512 bytes, and 1, 2, 4, 8, 16 or 32 Kbytes.

The MMU retains the base address of the current root table in one of three root pointer registers: the CPU root pointer (CRP) is used when the logical address accesses a location in the user address spaces, while the supervisor and DMA root pointer registers (SRP and DRP) are involved during the supervisor accesses or when a bus master other than the CPU requires an address translation. The SRP register can, however, be disabled by resetting a suitable bit in the translation control register. In this case, supervisor accesses also cause the CPU root pointer register to be used. The MMU selects the root pointer register for the address translation on the basis of the function code bits FC0–FC2, driven by the CPU.

The MC68851 architecture also includes an eight-entry root pointer table (RPT) to support efficient translation in multitasking environments. Here, a private translation tree is usually associated with each task in the system. Global segments can then be implemented by allowing entries to access the same physical pages either directly or by means of common subtrees in pointer tables belonging to different trees. In general, each translation tree is accessed by a root pointer owned by a task. When context switching occurs, the operating system must reload the CRP register. From the MMU's point of view, each process is associated with a different, system-wide root pointer.

The root pointer table can hold root pointers for the eight most recent tasks. Each pointer in the root table is marked by the MMU with a label called **task alias**, consisting of the index of the pointer in the table. The table is implemented as a small associative memory. When the root pointer register is reloaded, the root pointer table is addressed and the TAG field (or root pointer) is compared with the new pointer. If a match occurs, the pointer is already in the cache and has an associated task alias. Hence, all the entries in the translation cache (except the root pointer table) having the same alias field are still valid because they are related to the same task (see Figure 6.17). If a miss occurs in the table, the root pointer is loaded in both the CRP register and in the table so that the alias or index is re-used for the current task. In this condition, the translation cache entries marked by the re-used alias are invalidated, because they were associated with another task.

The table lookup process usually starts by using the function code bits for accessing an entry in the root table, as shown in Figure 6.19, and this is always true when the MMU uses the DMA root pointer register. However, when the supervisor and CPU root pointer registers are involved, the system programmer can inhibit the function code index mechanism by resetting a bit in the translation control register. When this happens the lookup sequence begins by using the TIA fields (Figure 6.19) so that only four levels of tables are allowed.

6.10.3 Memory protection

The MMU also implements protection mechanisms fully compatible with the MC68020 CALLM and RETM instructions introduced in Section 6.7.6. Besides the current access level (CAL), increase access level (IAL) and decrease access level (DAL) registers, the MC68851 also uses a valid access level (VAL) register. Moreover, the number of access levels managed by the MMU can be one, two, four, or eight as chosen by the system designer. Access levels are detected by examining the most significant bits (A31–A29) of the CPU logical address; obviously, the number of bits considered by the MMU depends on the number of access levels selected. If no level is selected, the MMU does not perform any check when a module instruction is executed by the MC68020.

During a CALLM instruction, the CPU first verifies that the caller is allowed to access the module descriptor by reading from the descriptor address, then the module descriptor is checked for validity. For this purpose, the MC68020 writes the module descriptor address in an internal MMU register selected by means of the function code lines. Then the MMU verifies that the page the descriptor is in can contain module gates by testing the gate bit in the page descriptor. This is done to detect users forging module descriptors to bypass the protection mechanisms. When the descriptor is correct, the CPU asks the MMU to update the access level in use. This is achieved by writing the new access level value in the IAL register. The MMU compares the content of the IAL register to that of the CAL register: if IAL $\leq$ CAL the access rights check passes, since the called module has more access rights than the caller. Hence, the CAL content is written in the valid access register and IAL is copied into CAL. Similarly, during a RETM instruction, the return access level is written in the DAL register and compared with CAL. The check does not fail when DAL $\geq$ CAL; in this case, the DAL is copied into CAL and VAL. When a right-check error occurs, either because the module descriptor is incorrect or the level changes are illegal, some bits in the access level status (ALS) register are set to reflect the error state. The MC68020 tests the ALS register during the CALLM/RETM instructions and takes a format exception when an error occurs.

The VAL register is used by the co-processor's PVALID instruction to validate parameters passed during a CALLM operation. When PVALID is executed, the MMU compares the access level bits of the incoming logical address with the VAL content; the check fails when the incoming access level is higher than the VAL level. In this case, the error is detected and a suitable bit in the access status register is set. PVALID can be used by privileged modules to verify that parameters obtained by caller modules, such as data area pointers, do not require access rights higher than the caller itself, otherwise users could violate the system by passing a pointer to a memory area to a privileged module they are not allowed to access.

6.10.4   Virtual memory management support

Some special mechanisms have been included in the MC68851 unit to implement efficient virtual memory management. In particular, protection and other information is contained in the physical part of each entry. This is loaded in the address translation cache, as shown in Figure 6.17. The bus error bit, for example, when set, causes the MMU to issue the bus error ($\overline{\text{BERR}}$) signal when the associated physical page must be accessed by the CPU, because no translation has been found in the lookup operations. A page fault results. It follows that this bit can be used to obtain a signal when no physical memory is associated with the logical page, so that suitable page swapping operations can be enabled and carried out.

The write-protected and modified bits are used to inform the MMU that the write operations are forbidden on a memory page and that the page accessed by the descriptor has been modified during a CPU write cycle. In this way, the operating system is able to recognize pages that must be copied back to mass storage during the page swapping process.

6.10.5   Program debugging support

The MC68851 is able to support CPU breakpoint facilities by using breakpoint registers as shown in Figure 6.16. When the MC68020 executes breakpoint instructions, a read operation is performed from a CPU address space location mapped into one of the breakpoint register addresses by the MMU. Each breakpoint address corresponds to a couple of registers; that is, the acknowledge data register (BAD) and the acknowledge control register (BAC), as shown in Figure 6.20. A breakpoint is enabled when the BPE bit in the BAC register is set. If the skip-count field is not zero, the MMU responds to the read request by providing the CPU with the opcode of the next instruction to be executed. This is contained in the BAD register. The skip-count field is decremented by one to reflect the fact that another breakpoint acknowledge cycle has been completed. When the skip count equals zero, the read request is not honoured and the bus error signal $\overline{\text{BERR}}$ is issued, raising an MC68020 exception. In this way the programmer can use eight breakpoints at the same time, which are acknowledged a number of times, depending on the contents of the skip-count field.

6.11 The MC68881 floating-point co-processor

The MC68881 floating-point co-processor provides floating-point arithmetic facilities to systems requiring powerful mathematical computation. Both end-users and system software designers can consider the CPU–co-processor pair as a single chip that supports an enhanced instruction set. The instructions are based on CPU instructions with additional floating-point operations in single, double and extended precision.

6.11.1 Registers

The programmer's model consists of the basic CPU register shown in Figure 6.5 in addition to the floating-point co-processor registers depicted in Figure 6.21. The MC68881 offers the user eight 80-bit floating-point data registers (FP0–FP7), and three 32-bit registers to control and check the co-processor status and operating mode. The control register (FPCR) in Figure 6.21 uses only the two lowest bytes. Bits 15–8 are used to enable or mask the different kinds of exception traps activated by the co-processor – this includes overflow, underflow and divide by zero (see

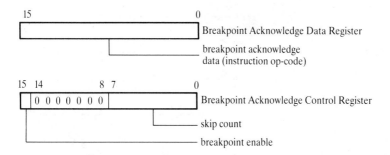

Figure 6.20 Breakpoint register formats.

Section 2.2.2). The others allow the user to select the precision required in the computations – double, single or extended – and the rounding mode to be used in the operations. Rounding modes can be to nearest, or towards zero, minus or plus infinity (see Section 2.2.2).

The status register (FPSR) contains four bytes that are important to the user: the condition code byte allows the CPU to perform conditional co-processor operations, and the quotient byte is used to save the least significant bits of the quotient in the divide operations. Exception status information is stored in the exception byte, whose bits correspond with those in the trap-enable field, and in the accrued exception byte. Finally, the instruction address register (FPIAR) is implemented for debugging and exception-handling purposes, since FPIAR is a pointer to the main memory location containing the last

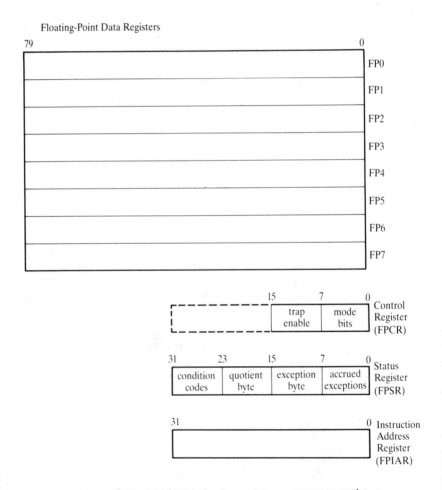

Figure 6.21   MC68881 floating-point co-processor register.

executed floating-point instruction. It is therefore possible to retrieve an instruction that raised an exception by examining the content of FPIAR.

The MC68881 is interfaced to the MC68020 by standard co-processor interface mechanisms, so that synchronization and all the data movements between the CPU and the floating-point unit rely on conventional bus cycles. In addition, the MC68881 is not able to fetch and store operands directly in main memory. In other words, the MC68881 is not a DMA co-processor. It follows that operand address calculations and data transfers to/from the main memory must be executed by the CPU according to requests issued by the co-processor.

6.11.2   MC68881 co-processor instructions

The floating-point unit supports all the integer data types included in the MC68020 architecture; hence, it is able to manipulate byte, word and longword data. The co-processor also recognizes the different types of floating-point format that conform to the IEEE P754 Standard (see Section 2.2.2) and depend on the precision selected as shown in Table 6.3.

Table 6.3   MC68881 floating-point data types.

Data Format (precision)	Exponent Bits	Mantissa Bits
single basic	8	23
double basic	11	52
extended double	15	64

All computations are carried out by the co-processor in double-extended precision and the results are stored in the floating-point registers using the same format; however, data are transferred to/from the main processor with the precision selected by the user.

The MC68881 can also input real operands in the packed decimal string format. This consists of a three digit, signed exponent and a seventeen digit, signed mantissa, both to base 10. Computation results, however, cannot be obtained from the co-processor as a packed decimal string.

The instruction set of the floating-point co-processor contains five operation classes. The first includes operators for moving data between a pair of floating-point registers or between a register and the main memory, by means of the main processor. The second class consists of

dyadic floating-point operations such as addition, subtraction, division, multiplication and so on; operands are contained either in a pair of registers or in a register and in main memory. The results of the computations, however, are always stored in floating-point registers. The third class is composed of **monadic operators**; it includes, amongst others, instructions for performing trigonometric and transcendental computations as depicted in Table 6.4. A fourth class allows the user to control the main processor program depending on certain co-processor conditions, as outlined in the previous section. Table 6.5 summarizes the conditions that can be specified for the MC68881. The programmer is also able to raise an exception when the computation result is unordered (see Section 2.2.2) by using the operators listed in the first column of Table 6.5.

The last instruction class includes the save, restore and conditional trap operations needed to invoke system services on particular conditions, and to implement context switching efficiently or to manipulate the co-processor's internal status in multitasking systems.

Table 6.4   MC68881 monadic operators.

Instruction	Function
FABS	Absolute value
FACOS	Arc cosine
FASIN	Arc sine
FATAN	Arc tangent
FATANH	Hyperbolic arc tangent
FCOS	Cosine
FCOSH	Hyperbolic cosine
FETOX	e^x
FETOXM1	$e^x - 1$
FGETEXP	Extract exponent
FGETMAN	Extract mantissa
FINT	Extract integer part
FINTRZ	Extract integer part, rounded-to-zero
FLOGN	$\ln(x)$
FLOGNP1	$\ln(x + 1)$
FLOG10	$\log_{10}(x)$
FLOG2	$\log_2(x)$
FNEG	Negate
FSIN	Sine
FSINH	Hyperbolic sine
FSQRT	Square root
FTAN	Tangent
FTANH	Hyperbolic tangent
FTENTOX	10^x
FTWOTOX	$2^x \cdot$

Table 6.5   Floating-point co-processor condition codes.

Trap on Unordered		No Trap Unordered	
GE	Greater than or equal	OGE	Ordered greater than or equal
GL	Greater than or less than	OGL	Ordered greater than or less than
GLE	Greater than or less than or equal	OR	Ordered
GT	Greater than	OGT	Ordered greater than
LE	Less than or equal	OLE	Ordered less than or equal
LT	Less than	OLT	Ordered less than
NGE	Not (greater than or equal)	UGE	Unordered or greater than or equal
NGL	Not (greater than or less than)	UEQ	Unordered or equal
NGLE	Not (greater than or less than or equal)	UN	Unordered
NGT	Not greater than	UGT	Unordered or greater than
NLE	Not (less than or equal)	ULE	Unordered or less than or equal
NLT	Not less than	ULT	Unordered or less than
SEQ	Signalling equal	EQ	Equal
SNE	Signalling not equal	NE	Not equal
SF	Signalling always false	F	Always false
ST	Signalling always true	T	Always true

6.12   Conclusion

The MC68020 is one of the most advanced microprocessors recently put on the market. In fact, this CPU provides system and application designers with powerful supports for high-level language programming and operating system mechanisms development. Basic data types, addressing modes and instruction set allow the design and implementation of microprocessor systems with very different requirements.

An instruction on-chip cache memory allows the overall performance to be significantly enhanced by reducing the time needed by the CPU to fetch code in main memory.

Exceptional events such as interrupts and traps are managed by the MC68020 by means of uniform mechanisms that allow quick and efficient exception recognition and processing according to the urgency of the event being considered.

A general-purpose co-processor interface has been introduced to allow external co-processors to cooperate with the CPU in carrying out specialized tasks in the most efficient way.

The MC68020 can be used in conjunction with the MC68851 memory management unit to develop virtual memory systems, to implement separate access domains for task and procedures and to simplify program development by means of the memory management unit program debugging supports.

Finally, the MC68881 floating-point co-processor is able to extend the processing facilities offered by the MC68020 with floating-point operations according to the IEEE P754 Standard.

EXERCISES

6.1 Draw the flowchart of a program managing circular buffers of N elements, 32-bits long. The program must support suitable functions to append or remove an element to or from the buffer using a first-in–first-out strategy. When the user tries to insert elements in a full buffer, or to read data from an empty buffer, an exception handler must be activated. (*Note*: Use the MC68020 postincrement and predecrement addressing modes. Also use the trap mechanism.)

6.2 Describe the structure of a routine that can convert a buffer of N ASCII digits into another buffer of $N/2$ packed BCD bytes, without using the PACK instruction. How can an efficient routine be implemented by means of the PACK and DBcc instructions?

6.3 Solve the following problem with and without the use of the MC68020 bit-field instructions. A memory buffer contains N integer operands, m bits long, where $16 \leqslant m \leqslant 256$, in 2's complement form. Transform the buffer by two's complementing each number. How must the routine be modified when m is not a multiple of 8?

6.4 Draw the flowchart of a simple trace handler for the MC68020. When a trace event occurs, the address, opcode and operands of the instruction just executed must be saved in a memory buffer for subsequent examination by the user.

6.5 Assume that an MC68020 system does not include special hardware such as the MC68851 for access rights checks, but instead implements separate address spaces. Design a system so that normal user tasks P_i, where $i = 1...N$, can execute protected code without being able to destroy or alter it. Note that the protected programs must be able to operate on different user data. Consider, for example, a compiler or editing program executed concurrently by several user tasks. How must user processes, protected programs and data be allocated in main memory? How can P_is access the protected software? How can protected programs read and write user data?

6.6 Draw a detailed flowchart for a routine to perform context switching, including the status save and restore operations. Is it necessary to save or restore the context of the numerical co-processor? When and how should this operation be carried out? What about the MMU root pointer registers?

6.7 Draw the flowchart of a routine to handle page faults. Which exceptions must activate this routine? Which control structures need to be tested and/or updated? Must the move to or from address space instruction be used? Why?

6.8 Design a program to solve the equation $ax^2 + bx + c = 0$, where a, b and c are floating-point numbers 64 bits long, using the MC68881 floating-point co-processor.

6.9 Discuss the main advantages and disadvantages introduced by the MC68851 multi-level address translation mechanism.

6.10 How can private and global data or program areas be implemented with the MC68851?

6.11 Draw the flowchart of a program simulating the MC68851 lookup algorithm for finding an entry to be placed in the translation cache. (*Hint*: Use the MC68020 bit-field instructions.)

6.12 A memory management system based on the MC68851 must have the following parameters:

- a physical page length of 512 bytes;
- a total physical memory of 128 Kbytes; and
- a logical address space of 8 Mbytes.

Select the value of the IS field and the width of the translation index fields to give the minimum possible number of translation levels. Each table cannot fill more than one memory page.

6.13 Assume that a MC68020 development system also contains the MC68851 chip. Design an exception handler to save the CPU and MMU registers in a suitable memory area when a breakpoint instruction is issued by the user program. The register information must be collected only on the Nth occurrence of the breakpoint and the system must be able to manage up to eight different breakpoints at the same time.

CHAPTER 7

THE NATIONAL SEMICONDUCTOR NS32032 FAMILY

OBJECTIVES

The aims of this chapter are as follows:

- to illustrate the architecture of the National Semiconductor NS32032 CPU and its basic interface mechanisms to the external world;

- to introduce the NS32032 programming model, the supports offered by the CPU for basic data types processing, operand addressing and the CPU instruction set;

- to discuss the exception-handling mechanisms in the NS32032 for both interrupts and traps;

- to show how the CPU can be used in conjunction with external special-purpose co-processors, and to present the NS32032 co-processor interface;

- to discuss memory management in the NS32032 system by illustrating the characteristics provided by the NS32082 memory management unit for virtual-to-physical address translation, memory protection and virtual memory organization;

- to analyze the main features of the NS32081 floating-point co-processor.

7.1 Introduction
7.2 CPU architecture
7.3 Basic data types
7.4 Registers
7.5 Addressing modes
7.6 Instruction set

7.7 Exceptions
7.8 Co-processors
7.9 Memory management
7.10 The NS32081 floating-point co-processor
7.11 Custom co-processors
7.12 Conclusion

7.1   Introduction

The National Semiconductor NS32032 project was designed to overcome several drawbacks of earlier microprocessor architectures. The NS32032 developers included a number of supports for high-level languages, memory management and integer arithmetic computations in this CPU. The results are a new processor and an associated set of chips, including the NS32082 MMU and the NS32081 floating-point co-processor, which form a modern and efficient computing system. The NS32032 is well structured internally and has powerful addressing modes and a strong instruction set. It has a high degree of symmetry, so that each operand can be accessed by almost all the addressing modes, for example, and the same operators exist for each basic data type.

7.2   CPU architecture

7.2.1   Internal organization

Figure 7.1 shows the block architecture of the CPU. As with other advanced microprocessors, the NS32032 has a microprogrammed control unit to coordinate and supervise the CPU's operations and the execution of instructions. The external interface is implemented by a unit responsible for generating I/O signals, prefetching the instructions to be executed, and reading or writing data to/from the external memory and peripherals. The instruction queue in Figure 7.1 can contain up to eight bytes of code and is used to store instructions needed by the instruction decoder. A 32-bit ALU performs logical and signed/unsigned integer arithmetic operations on operands in a set of internal registers, which cannot be accessed directly by the programmer. These working registers are loaded from both the external memory, via the bus interface block, and the programmers' registers in a way that is transparent to the user. The ALU outputs are routed either to the main memory or to the user-accessible registers. The width of most of the internal data paths is 32 bits, so fast and efficient data transfers can be performed between the units inside the CPU, and between the CPU and the outside devices.

7.2.2   CPU signals

Figure 7.2 shows the I/O signals provided by the NS32032 architecture. The CPU uses a 32-bit data bus and a 24-bit address bus; the latter allows 16 Mbytes of memory space to be addressed directly. The 24 address lines and 24 least significant data bits (AD0–AD23) are multiplexed in time to reduce the number of I/O pins. The asynchronous bus control lines manage external memory read and write cycles, so they include signals to validate addresses ($\overline{\text{ADS}}$), to strobe data ($\overline{\text{DS}}/\overline{\text{FLT}}$), to indicate which bytes of a 32-bit longword are involved in a data transfer ($\overline{\text{BE0}}$–$\overline{\text{BE3}}$) and to select the transfer direction ($\overline{\text{DDIN}}$). However, the NS32032 cannot work properly without a special external timing unit (NS32201), which generates the two clocking signals PHI1 and PHI2. The NS32201 also generates several other complementary outputs, such as read and write and drives the CPU ready input line (RDY). This is necessary so that the CPU and the memory speeds can be tuned when low-speed external storage devices are used, by inserting a number of wait states, selected by the system designer, in each bus cycle performed by the CPU.

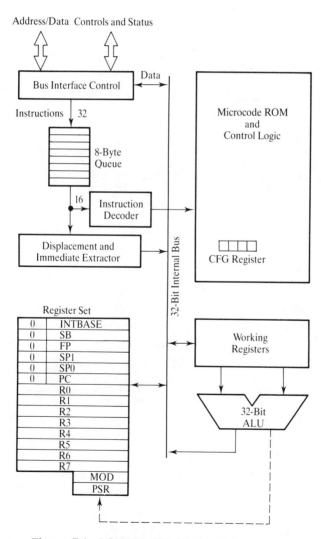

Figure 7.1   NS32032 CPU block architecture.

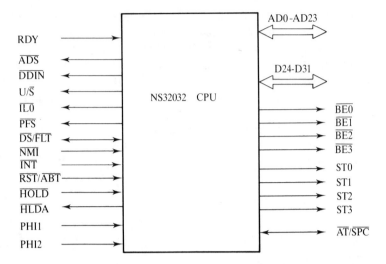

Figure 7.2   I/O lines in the NS32032 unit.

Table 7.1   Status information encoding by the NS32032 CPU.

Status Line Encoding (STO–ST3)	Meaning
0000	Idle: CPU inactive on bus
0001	Idle: WAIT instruction
0010	(Reserved)
0011	Idle: waiting for slave processor
0100	Interrupt acknowledge, master
0101	Interrupt acknowledge, cascaded
0110	End of interrupt, master
0111	End of interrupt, cascaded
1000	Sequential instruction fetch
1001	Non-sequential instruction fetch
1010	Data transfer
1011	Read–modify–write operand
1100	Read for effective address
1101	Transfer slave operand
1110	Read slave status word
1111	Broadcast slave identifier

The bus arbitration signal group includes I/O lines to support multiple bus masters ($\overline{\text{HOLD}}$ and $\overline{\text{HLDA}}$). The interrupt control group provides the signal for maskable ($\overline{\text{INT}}$) and non-maskable ($\overline{\text{NMI}}$) interrupt requests, or for memory cycle abort exceptions ($\overline{\text{RST}}/\overline{\text{ABT}}$).

Interface mechanisms to external co-processors are based on the standard address and data buses, and the status (STO–ST3) and slave processor control ($\overline{\text{AT}}/\overline{\text{SPC}}$) lines, as explained in Section 7.8. Finally, the NS32032 uses the four output signals ST0–ST3 to encode its internal status during the different types of bus cycle. This information can be decoded and used in several ways by the external logic, to obtain an interrupt acknowledge, for example, or to recognize an indivisible read–modify–write cycle. Table 7.1 summarizes the events and related codes that can be presented on the status lines by the NS32032 when an external bus cycle is performed.

7.3   Basic data types

The NS32032 hardware can manipulate five basic data types directly:

- integers (signed and unsigned),
- Booleans,
- BCD digits,
- bits, and
- bit fields.

Moreover, when the NS32081 floating-point unit is used, the CPU instruction set is extended with operations for floating-point operands in the IEEE P754 standard formats.

7.3.1   Integers

There are three possible lengths for integer operands: byte, word (16 bits) and doubleword (32 bits). Moreover, signed integers can be supported using the two's complement notation. When stored in CPU registers, 8- and 16-bit operands occupy the registers' least significant bytes. On the other hand, since the external memory is seen as a sequence of bytes by the NS32032, integers in main memory are accessed so that the least significant byte in the operand is placed at the lowest memory address.

7.3.2 Booleans

In practice, these operands are integers (8- 16- or 32-bits long), the least significant bit of which is used to represent the Boolean value – true when set, or false when reset. The CPU architecture, however, supports some special-purpose instructions for Boolean operations, in addition to the integer arithmetic and logical operators. During a Boolean operation, only the least significant bit of the specified operands is affected.

7.3.3 BCD digits

There are three possible lengths for unsigned decimal numbers, depending on whether a byte, word or doubleword is used to store the BCD number. A packed decimal instruction can manipulate two, four or eight BCD digits at the same time. The CPU architecture does not provide any special instruction for packed–unpacked format conversions, so these must be implemented using the conventional logical and shift operations.

7.3.4 Bits

The NS32032 can manipulate individual bits stored both in the CPU registers and in main memory. The position of a bit is specified using two address components. The base component is used to select the location in main memory or the general-purpose register containing the accessed bit. The offset component is a signed integer operand, indicating the position of the bit relative to the least significant bit (bit 0) of the base location; both positive and negative offsets are allowed. However, offsets must be in the range 0 to 31 for register bits.

7.3.5 Bit fields

The CPU can read and/or write unaligned bit fields in registers and main memory. A bit field is specified by three address elements: the base and offset, which are used to locate the least significant bit in the field, and the length component, which indicates the field width. The length of a field must always be in the range 1 to 32, inclusive.

7.4 Registers

7.4.1 General-purpose registers

The NS32032 programming model consists of both general-purpose and dedicated registers, as shown in Figure 7.3. There are eight 32-bit general registers (R0–R7). These can be used both to store data and address components. When data are shorter than 32 bits, only the least significant bytes of the registers are used. The remaining part is never affected by the instruction being executed. When used for addressing operands, the general-purpose registers can hold either a base pointer or an index value (see Section 7.5) to specify a data location in different addressing modes. Usually, each Ri, $i = 0...7$ can contain an instruction operand; however, in some circumstances (that is, extended arithmetic operations), general-purpose registers can be paired (R0–R1, R2–R3, ...) to hold 64-bit data.

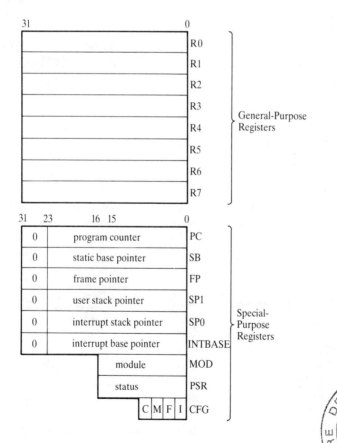

Figure 7.3 Programming model for the NS32032 microprocessor

7.4.2   Control registers

Dedicated registers form a heterogeneous set, and are mainly used to supervise and control the CPU's operations and its working mode. Special-purpose registers are 32-bits long, except for the processor status (PSR) and the module (MOD) registers, which consist of only 16 bits. However, special registers are used as memory pointers and the NS32032 CPU has only 24 address lines, so register bits 31 to 23 are always forced to zero.

The program counter (PC) always points to the beginning of the instruction currently being executed and is incremented only when this has been completed by the CPU. The program counter is directly affected by a variety of jump, branch, call and return instructions, and by several exceptional events, such as interrupts and traps.

The NS32032 can operate in two basic modes. In supervisor mode all the CPU instructions can be executed, even those that heavily affect the processor's behaviour. In the user mode, however, some critical instructions are not allowed, that is, they are privileged and must be executed only by trustworthy system programs. The current CPU working mode, user or supervisor, is selected by the U bit in the 16-bit processor status register (PSR), the structure of which is shown in Figure 7.4. When U is set, the processor is running in the user mode and each attempt to execute a privileged instruction will cause a suitable trap (see Section 7.7.2). Obviously, the user is not allowed to change the value of the U bit to gain access to protected operations. The L, F, Z, N and C bits in the status register are the typical flags used in each microprocessor and are affected by logical and arithmetic operations. When set, L means that the second operand is less than the first datum in comparison instructions; Z is a zero flag; F signals possible overflows in arithmetic computations; N has the same meaning as L, but is used with signed integer operands; C is a carry flag signalling carry or borrow events, which is needed in extended precision computations.

Figure 7.4 shows that users can access the least significant byte of the processor status register; this also includes a trace bit (T), which enables/disables the step-by-step CPU working mode. When T is set, a trace trap is automatically generated by the NS32032 on completion of each instruction; in this way, the user can examine the effects of each processor operation before resuming execution of the program.

The upper byte of the processor status register is intended for privileged users only. It contains three other significant bits besides U: the I bit, for example, allows maskable interrupts to be enabled or disabled (see Section 7.7.1), while the P bit is used in conjunction with T to ensure correct trace results when programs are interrupted or trapped (Section 7.7.2). As the NS32032 supports two different stack pointers (SP1 and SP0), as shown in Figure 7.3, the stack bit (S) in the status

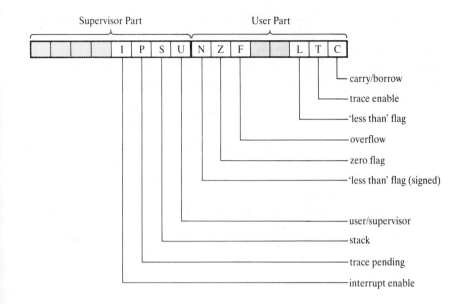

Figure 7.4   Processor status register organization.

register selects which register, SP0 or SP1, is to be used for current stack operations.

In general, the user stack pointer (SP1) is associated with the running user's task and is switched by the operating system between the different application processes. The interrupt stack pointer (SP0) is used, however, when interrupts or traps occur, to save the processor status. It is therefore primarily intended to manage exceptional events in the system software. Because the CPU selects SP0 or SP1 for stack operations, depending on the value of S, the stack bit is automatically cleared (SP0 is chosen) on each interrupt or trap occurrence. While the user cannot normally access the interrupt stack by resetting S, users of privileged programs can gain access to the user stack by forcing S to one; this is important in operating system routines implementing the task context switching, for example.

The frame pointer (FP) in Figure 7.3 is another special-purpose register in the NS32032 architecture. It supports efficient procedure activations, as required by modern high-level languages (HLL). In fact, HLL procedure calls cause the system to dynamically allocate a suitable memory area that contains two kinds of information: parameters and local variables for the procedure and, possibly, saved registers and the return address. The frame pointer is usually loaded with the base address of this area by means of a special enter instruction at the procedure entry point, so that data in the frame area can be easily retrieved and accessed.

The module register (MOD) is intended to support the organization of large programs into modules, each one consisting of a set of logically related variables and procedures. A user task can therefore be seen as a sequence of module activations, each module being described by a suitable module descriptor contained in a module table stored in main memory. The module register points to the descriptor for the module currently being executed; because the register is only 16-bits long, the module table must be contained in the first 64 Kbytes of memory. Each module descriptor is 16-bytes long and contains pointers to global variables, to the program entry point and to a special link table for accessing data and procedures external to the module itself.

The static base register (SB) in Figure 7.3 is usually loaded with the pointer to data statically allocated for the current module (that is, globals); the pointer is obtained from the module descriptor and is automatically updated when control is transferred from one module to the other.

The interrupt base register (INTBASE) in Figure 7.3 holds the base address of another special system table containing descriptors for interrupt and trap-handling procedures. More than one table can be used, and table relocation is possible by changing the content of this register.

The configuration register (CFG) is not normally available to users, because it informs the NS32032 about the hardware configuration used in the system. This register is therefore loaded with a suitable value when the system is initialized by means of a special instruction; it is usually never modified. As Figure 7.3 shows, the configuration register contains only four bits. The I bit tells the CPU whether maskable interrupts are vectored; in other words, it declares the presence or absence of external interrupt control devices. The F, M and C bits were introduced for co-processors: F signals whether the floating-point unit is available or not; M is devoted to the MMU; and C is intended for a possible user-defined slave processor, as explained in Section 7.11.

As well as the CPU registers, the NS32032 programmer can gain access to the special slave processor registers in a completely transparent way. A set of floating-point and/or MMU registers is available when the microprocessor is used in conjunction with the NS32081 and NS38082 units.

7.5 Addressing modes

7.5.1 Operand addressing

The NS32032 supports several different modes for specifying the effective address (EA) of an operand. Some of them are typical of all microprocessor families, including early 8- and 16-bit CPUs. Others can be found only in advanced architectures (the new 16- and 32-bit generations) and are particularly useful for high-level languages and the manipulation of complex data types, as explained in Chapter 1. The NS32032 designers have also introduced an additional addressing mode called external, which is unique to this microprocessor. It is intended to support modular programming, making it more efficient.

Data can be stored in the CPU registers (register operands) or in instructions (immediate addressing). Moreover, the programmer can specify operand addresses by means of registers (register indirect mode) or directly in the program code (absolute addressing).

The NS32032 top-of-stack addressing corresponds to the auto-increment and autodecrement indirect modes of Section 1.5.5, and is used to save/restore data in or from the current stack.

In addition, indexing, in the NS32032 scaled index mode, can be used with any other addressing technique, except for immediate references and/or another scaled index.

The NS32032 architecture also supports the base displacement indirect addressing mode (see Section 1.5.6). When a general-purpose register is used to form the operand effective address, the associated mode is said to be 'register relative', while the phrase 'memory mode' is used when one of the pointer registers PC, SP, SB or FP is used as a base address. When scaled indexing is used with the register relative and memory modes, the base displacement indexed indirect mode of Section 1.5.11 is implemented. Three different displacement sizes can be recognized by the CPU, which uses the displacement's most significant bits to distinguish between different lengths, as shown in Figure 7.5.

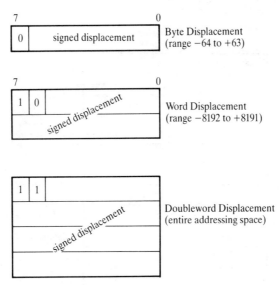

Figure 7.5   Signed displacement encodings in the NS32032 architecture.

The base displacement indirect displacement indirect and base displacement indirect displacement indexed indirect modes are supported by the NS32032 memory relative and scaled indexed memory relative modes, respectively.

The external addressing modes are peculiar to the NS32032. External addressing corresponds to the base indirect displacement indirect displacement indirect and base indirect displacement indirect displacement indexed indirect modes described in Chapter 1, depending on whether indexing is or is not used when computing the effective address of the operand.

Modern programming languages such as Ada often encourage modularity; that is, where large programs are structured in a set of smaller modules designed and developed independently. The external addressing mode is a powerful hardware support enabling a module to gain access to external variables and procedures which belong to other entities compiled independently. During program execution the module

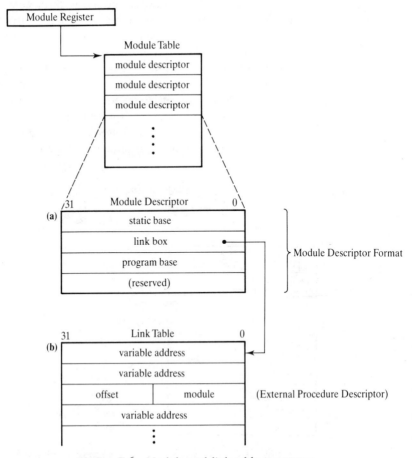

Figure 7.6 Module and link table structures.

register points to the current module descriptor in the system-wide module table. As shown in Figure 7.6(a), each module descriptor contains three pointers: static base, link base and program base. The static base points to the memory area where static variables and constants are located for the current module, while the program base is used to address the first instruction byte in the module. As a module can have several entry points – that is, it can consist of different procedures, such as an Ada 'package' – the program base is needed to find them. The link base points to the module link table, the format of which is depicted in Figure 7.6(b). The table can contain two types of item: external variable absolute addresses (32-bits long) or external procedure entry points consisting of a 16-bit module field and a 16-bit offset inside the external module program area. The link table therefore supports the sharing of variables between different modules and transfers control from one module to the other (see Section 7.6.6). External operand addressing causes the CPU to access the link table by adding a user-defined first displacement $d1$ to the link base. The variable address is computed by adding a second displacement $d2$ to the link entry. This situation is illustrated in Figure 7.7. External references require two accesses in main

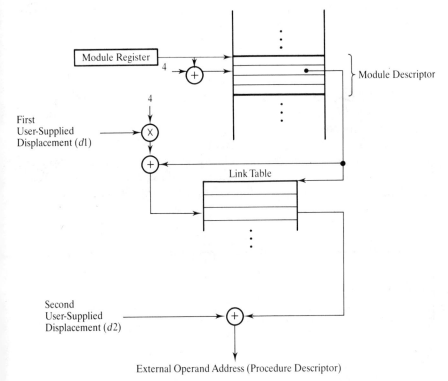

External Operand Address (Procedure Descriptor)

Figure 7.7 External addressing mechanism for accessing variables and procedures.

memory to obtain the effective address of the operand, but this overhead is not significant because external references seldom occur during a program execution.

Table 7.2 summarizes the NS32032 addressing modes and the time required to compute an operand's effective address in different cases. The first two columns in Table 7.2 list the possible addressing modes for the NS32032 using the notation introduced in Chapter 1 and that adopted by the manufacturer, respectively, while the third column shows how the effective address is computed. Each level of parenthesis means a step of indirection. The final column gives the effective address evaluation time (TEA) expressed in number of machine cycles; when this computation requires one or more address components to be read directly in main memory, TEA also includes the time, Trd, which is the time the CPU needs to read a doubleword from the external storage. Trd depends on the memory speed, on whether the doubleword is aligned on an even address boundary and on whether an MMU is present in the system. In scaled indexed addressing, the total effective address computation time is given by the sum of two factors: the first (TEAb) is the time required to evaluate the effective address in the base mode (EAb), while the second is a constant ranging from five to ten cycles, depending on the scale factor (byte, word, doubleword or quadword) used.

7.5.2   Instruction format

The NS32032 instruction format is split into a basic and an optional part. Figure 7.8 shows that the basic part can be one to three bytes long, and contains the opcode and up to two general address mode fields (GAM), each consisting of five bits. Every GAM field encodes information about the addressing mode used for the related operand and possibly about the base register to be used in the effective address computation. When scaled indexing is specified in the GAM field, the optional part of the

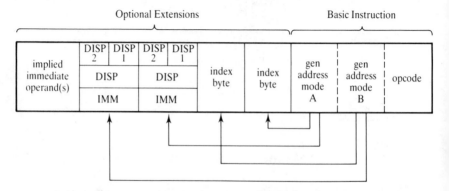

Figure 7.8   NS32032 general instruction format: basic and optional parts.

Table 7.2 NS32032 addressing modes.

Type	Addressing Mode / National Semiconductor Notation	EA Computation	Computation Time (clock cycles)
Register direct	Register	$EA = Rn$	2[1]
Immediate	Immediate	$EA = $ next word(s)	4[1]
Memory direct	Absolute	$EA = ($next word(s)$)$	4
Base displacement indirect	Register relative	$EA = (Rn) + d1$	5
Base displacement indirect	Memory space	$EA = (FP) + d1$ $(SP) + d1$ $(SB) + d1$	5 5 5
Relative	Memory space	$(PC) + d1$	5
Base displacement indirect displacement indirect	Memory relative	$EA = ((FP) + d1) + d2$ $((SP) + d1) + d2$ $((SB) + d1) + d2$	$7 + $ Trd $7 + $ Trd $7 + $ Trd
Autoincrement and autodecrement indirect	Top of stack	$EA = $ Top of stack	2/4
Base indirect displacement indirect displacement indirect	External	$EA = $ pointer[2] $+ d2$	$11 + 2*$Trd
Indexing[3]	Scaled index	$EA = EAb + (Rn)*$scale factor	TEAb $+ $ 5/7/8/10

[1] Operand fetch included.
[2] Pointer is found at link table entry number $d1$.
[3] Applicable to all addressing modes except immediate.

instruction includes one or two additional index bytes; each specifies the general register to be used as the index and the base addressing mode, while the scale factor is encoded by GAM. The resulting optional bytes contain one or two displacements or one immediate datum, as required by the addressing mode specified by GAM. Some instructions require other displacements or immediate data besides those implied in the addressing mode; this additional information is appended to the optional part of the instruction, as shown in Figure 7.8.

7.6 Instruction set

The NS32032 microprocessor supports a complete instruction set of manipulating each hardware-recognized data type. From the user's point of view, perhaps the most attractive characteristic is the high degree of symmetry of the National Semiconductor CPU instructions: in almost all cases, the programmer can use any addressing mode to specify the selected operands. Furthermore, the same kind of operation is always supported for longword, word and byte data. For this reason, in the following mnemonics for instructions accepting different operands, sizes will be introduced using the notation INSTR*i*, where INSTR is the operation mnemonic and *i* is the suffix B, W or L, depending on whether it is a byte, word or longword operand.

The NS32032 instructions can be grouped into six classes:

- data transfers,
- integer and packed decimal arithmetic,
- logical and shift operations,
- bit and bit-field manipulations,
- strings and arrays, and
- program flow and processor control.

However, when the CPU is used in conjunction with other slave processors, the instruction set is automatically extended to include floating-point operations, MMU register manipulations or custom co-processor operations, for example. These additional instructions will be discussed in the section on NS32032 co-processors.

7.6.1 Data transfer instructions

Transfer instructions allow the programmer to move a source operand in several ways. By selecting the source and destination addressing modes, it is possible to implement register-to-register, register-to-memory,

memory-to-register, and memory-to-memory data movements. This is done by using the MOV*i* instruction. A move quick variant (MOVQ*i*) allows a small immediate value in the range -8 to $+7$ to be loaded in a general operand, saving code and memory space. Two other transfer instructions are move with sign extension (MOVX*i*) and move with zero extension (MOVZ*i*); these allow integer values to be lengthened while being moved.

The move multiple (MOVM*i*) instruction allows efficient transfers of small blocks of operands stored in contiguous locations in main memory; unlike string operations (Section 7.6.5), this operation does not require any register presetting. When started by the CPU, it cannot be interrupted, so the block dimension, specified by the user, must not exceed 16 bytes.

Another transfer operation is ADDR (move effective address). In this case, the 24-bit effective address of the source operand is computed and loaded in the destination operand. This is particularly useful when accessing external data and procedures, because the logical address of an external variable or an external routine descriptor can be obtained by using the external addressing mode to access the source operand.

7.6.2 Integer and BCD arithmetic instructions

The NS32032 supports instructions for arithmetic computations with both signed and unsigned (two's complement) integer operands. For example, the ADD*i* and SUB*i* operations allow the programmer to sum and subtract a pair of operands and to obtain the correct result regardless of whether the operands are signed or unsigned. Furthermore, the add with carry (ADDC*i*) and subtract with borrow (SUBC*i*) instructions also involve carry bit C from the program status register, so that extended precision arithmetic operations can be carried out. An add quick variant (ADDQ*i*) is also available to sum small values with a general operand. The arithmetic group also includes operators for complementing (NEG*i*) and for computing the absolute value (ABS*i*) of the source operand.

Multiplication is performed via the MUL*i* and MEI*i* instructions. MUL*i* returns a result with the same length as the original operand, whereas MEI*i* (multiply extended integer) computes the product with twice the number of bits in the factor. MEI*i* interprets the input operands as unsigned integers, so that extended precision multiplications can be easily performed.

There are three kinds of instruction for dividing an integer dividend by a second operand: DIV*i* computes the result as the nearest integer that is less than or equal to the exact quotient; QUO*i* yields the nearest integer whose absolute value is less than or equal to the absolute value of the exact quotient. Both DIV*i* and QUO*i* interpret the input operands as signed integers and give different results when the quotient is negative. The third instruction, the divide extended integer (DEIi) instruction divides a double length unsigned integer, such as a quadword, doubleword or word, by a single length unsigned operand, to produce a quotient and a remainder. It is useful for executing extended precision computations. Remainders from the DIVi and QUOi processes can be obtained via the MODi and REMi operators, respectively.

Packed decimal arithmetic instructions include add and subtract operations implemented by ADDPi and SUBPi. Here, the carry bit of the processor status register (PSR) is always involved in the computation, to allow additions and subtractions of decimal strings with any number of digits.

It is convenient to include the integer compare instructions in this arithmetic group. These consist of the CMPi, CMPQi and CMPMi operators. CMPi and CMPQi compare the source and destination operands – the second datum is small when CMPQi is considered. They set the condition code bits in the processor status register according to the operation result. Moreover, the non-interruptable instruction CMPMi compares two small blocks of data whose length ($\leq$ 16 bytes) is specified by the programmer. In this case, the condition bits are set to indicate which block contains the greater value or whether the two blocks are equal or not.

7.6.3   Logical and shift instructions

The logical group consists of a number of instructions needed to execute Boolean operations on general operands. For example, the ANDi, ORi and XORi operators allow the user to perform the bit-wise logical 'and/or' and 'exclusive-or' functions between a pair of input operands. The NS32032 designers also introduced two instructions to copy the bit-wise complement of a source datum in the destination (COMi) and to clear all the destination operand bits set in the source operand (BICi), thus supporting efficient masking operations.

All the logical operators work correctly on Boolean values, except for COMi. Hence, a special instruction (NOTi) is also provided for complementing Boolean data; this can change the value of the least significant bit in the source operand, leaving the other bits unaltered. As high-level languages often require that Boolean variable values be derived from relational operations, the save condition as Boolean (Scond$i$) instruction is used when a Boolean value must be generated, based on a condition code test.

Boolean comparisons can be obtained from integer compare operators, since the NS32032 system follows the convention that true ($= 1$) is greater than false ($= 0$), as required by several high-level languages.

Shift and rotate instructions consist of the ASH*i*, LSH*i* and ROT*i* operators. ASH*i* performs the arithmetic shift of the second operand in the direction and for the number of bits specified by the first operand; LSH*i* executes logical shifts in a similar manner. Shifts are left when the source or first datum is positive, and right when the specified value is negative. ROT*i* is used to obtain clockwise and/or counterclockwise rotations of the destination operand.

7.6.4   Bit and bit-field instructions

A number of NS32032 operations have been designed to support direct-bit and bit-field manipulations. Hence, the programmer can use instructions to test (TBIT*i*), test and set (SBIT*i*), test and clear (CBIT*i*) and find the first bit set (FFS*i*) in a register or in a memory operand. Both the SBIT*i* and CBIT*i* operators are divisible, so they are not suitable for implementing semaphore variables in multiprocessor environments. In contrast, the two indivisible instructions, SBITI*i* and CBITI*i*, were introduced to obtain low-level mutual exclusion. In fact, when executed, SBITI*i* and CBITI*i* issue the interlock CPU output signal, so that an external arbiter can lock the shared bus, to grant exclusive access to the shared data to the requesting processor, for example (see Chapter 3).

The invert bit (IBIT*i*) instruction complements single bits, while the convert to bit pointer (CVTP) operator computes the address of an accessed bit by using its base and offet components.

Bit-field instructions include operations to insert (INS*i* and INSSI*i*) and extract (EXT*i* and EXTS*i*) a variable-length, unaligned bit field into or from a specified operand. There are two forms of insert and extract: short and array oriented. The short form does not require any preloading of the general-purpose register and is useful when the offset of the bit field is fixed. This happens in accessing the field components of a packed record, for example, as shown in Figure 7.9(a). The array-oriented form, on the other hand, allows the bit-field offset to be specified by a general register and is suitable for manipulating individual elements of a packed array, for example, as in Figure 7.9(b).

7.6.5   Array and string instructions

The NS32032 HLL support also consists of special instructions for array and string processing. In particular, the CHECK*i* operation performs a limit check to verify whether the source operand falls in the range specified by a second operand. When the test is positive, the CPU adjusts the user-supplied operand by subtracting the lower limit from it and places the result in any general-purpose register specified by the user. Conversely, when the check fails, the F condition bit is set in the processor status register to cause either a branch or a trap (see Section 7.7.2). Hence, CHECK*i* is particularly useful to designers of compilers for implementing run-time checks when array elements are addressed. Wrong accesses, those outside the specified bounds, are immediately trapped, while the check result, when positive, can be directly used as an index, through the NS32032 scaled index addressing mode.*

The INDEX*i* instruction is used with multidimensional arrays, to compute a single, one-dimensional index, based on the values of the different indices supplied by the user. This instruction is intended to be used iteratively, as it allows the accumulation of the sum of the product of its old contents in the destination register, multiplied by the length of the current dimension, plus the index related to the dimension itself; in this

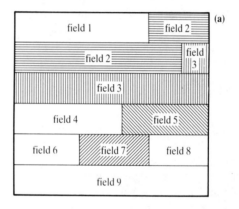

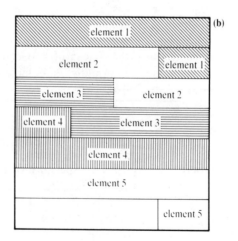

Figure 7.9 Packed record and packed array organization in main memory.

way, $n - 1$ iterations are needed when an n-dimensional array is considered.

Together with array operations, the NS32032 also supports some string instructions, which speed up the execution of typical functions, such as copy, search or compare, and save memory space at the same time. Strings are sequences of integer elements all having the same length (byte, word or doubleword), stored consecutively in main memory. Since strings can also be very long, the string instructions can be suspended by interrupts and resumed when the asynchronous event has been served by the CPU. String instructions can operate on one or two strings at the same time, and use general registers to access the involved operands. For this reason, before a string instruction execution, R0 must always be loaded with the maximum number of elements to be processed, while R1 and R2 contain the address of the first element in string one and that in string two when needed. MOVS*i* allows string one to be copied to string two, while CMPS*i* executes a string comparison of the two input operands. In addition, SKPS*i* is used to scan the elements in the input operand, looking for a user-specified condition to be verified.

There are also options that can be specified with the string instructions. The translation option, for example, causes the string instruction to translate each byte element in the first string before using it. For this purpose, R3 must be loaded with the base address of the translation table containing the new or translated values; that is, it is addressed using the old element values as indices. Translation versions of MOVS*i*, CMPS*i* and SKPS*i* are MOVST, CMPST and SKPST, respectively. Strings can be processed starting with the last element and ending with the first by a backward option that causes string pointers R1 and R2 to be decremented instead of incremented. Finally, the 'until match' and 'while match' options allow the user to load R4 with a termination value, tested during string processing; in this case, the instruction is executed until each element of the string matches or does not match the value in R4.

7.6.6 Program flow and CPU control instructions

There are several instructions allowing conditional and unconditional changes in the program flow: jump (JUMP) and branch (BR), for example, are both used to jump to a new address. While JUMP permits the destination address to be specified using a general addressing mode, BR allows a more compact coding form to implement a branch in relation to the program counter. Another version of branch (BRcond) has been introduced to allow those conditional branches that depend on some condition code bit value. Yet another instruction (CASE*i*) has been introduced to simplify the implementation of multiway branches in high-level languages, such as the Ada and Pascal **case** instructions, or the C language **switch** statement. CASE*i* loads the program counter with the sum of its old contents plus the signed value of a user-specified operand. Thus, it follows that jump tables with variable lengths can be accessed efficiently with a single machine instruction when the scaled indexed addressing mode is used in conjunction with CASE*i*.

Another special branch instruction is ACB*i*, which replaces an index operand with the sum of its content plus a user-specified value in the range -8 to $+7$. When the result is zero, the instruction branches to the specified destination, otherwise the program continues sequentially.

Local procedures can be activated by the jump-to-subroutine (JSR) and branch-to-subroutine (BSR) instructions. These are equivalent to JMP and BR except that they save the calling program's return address in the current stack. Returns from local subroutines are achieved via the RET operation.

Procedures external to the current module can be invoked by using module mechanisms. The NS32032 supports two instructions for calling an external routine (CXP and CXPD) and a special function (RXP) to return the control to the calling program. When either CXP or CXPD is executed, the CPU saves the module register (MOD) into the current stack, so that the pointer to the calling module descriptor can be correctly restored when the external procedure returns. The return address is also pushed on to the stack. The module and pointer (SB) registers are then loaded with the called module parameters, to set up the new addressing environment for the invoked routine. When CXP is used the procedure entry point is specified via an offset in the link table of the current module, which locates the element containing the procedure descriptor (see Section 7.5.1). In contrast, CXPD specifies the descriptor as a general operand and this simplifies references to procedures passed as parameters to other programs. RXP restores the module and SB register contents and returns control to the caller once the external procedure has been executed.

There are also instructions dedicated to the efficient saving/ restoring of registers. These are useful for implementing fast context switching, both in monoprogrammed (that is, to serve an interrupt-driven event) and multitasking systems. SAVE and RESTORE are used to push and pop the programmer-specified set of general registers on to or from the current stack with a single machine operation. However, a pair of instructions – ENTER and EXIT – have been introduced to set up and abandon the operating context for a procedure. ENTER is usually executed as the procedure's first operation, since it saves the frame pointer register (FP) into the stack and allocates the selected number of bytes from stack to store the variables local to the procedure, for example. It then loads the frame pointer register to the stack area just created. ENTER can also push a set of general registers on to the stack in the same way as SAVE. EXIT, however, is used to end a procedure, possibly by restoring the general registers and the frame pointer register contents when the procedure stack area has been de-allocated.

The program control group also includes instructions to raise software-programmed exceptions on particular conditions. The supervisor call trap (SVC) invokes system services by means of the well-known trap mechanism (see Section 7.7.2). The flag trap (FLAG) and breakpoint trap (BPT) can also be used to activate exception handlers – on an overflow condition, when the F bit is set in the processor status register or on a breakpoint condition, respectively.

Trap and interrupt handling are usually performed by reliable system software and should not be normally left to users. Exception handlers are therefore executed in supervisor or privileged mode, even though they can be activated by normal tasks. For the same reason, the return-from-trap (RETT) and return-from-interrupt (RETI) instructions are protected operations that can be executed only in supervisor mode.

The CPU architecture usually forbids users from executing other users' privileged instructions. The set configuration register (SETCFG) and the load and store processor register (LPR*i* and SPR*i*) operations, for example, are protected instructions when referring to the processor status or INTBASE registers. Users can, however, set or clear bits belonging to the processor status register's least significant byte by using BISPSR*i* and BICPSR*i*, but these operations must be executed by supervisor programs when acting on the most significant bits of the register.

Finally, the NS32032 also provides no-operation (NOP), wait-for-interrupt (WAIT) and diagnose (DIA) instructions. WAIT suspends the instruction processing for an interrupt, while DIA is only intended to support hardware breakpoint circuits.

7.7 Exceptions

The NS32032 architecture supports two classes of exceptional event, which can alter the normal instruction execution flow: traps and interrupts. Traps include all the exceptions that can occur during an instruction execution and are caused by abnormal conditions met during the processing cycle. Interrupts, on the other hand, are due to external events occurring asynchronously and are not generally related to the instruction currently being executed.

When an exception occurs, whether an interrupt or a trap, the CPU starts a sequence of operations to set up the correct environment for the exception-handling procedure. These can be summarized as follows:

(1) The contents of the program counter, status register and current stack pointer are adjusted, depending on the particular type of trap or interrupt.

(2)   The processor status register is temporarily saved (a copy is made inside the CPU) and the U bit is cleared (supervisor mode), together with T and S, to reflect the exception-processing condition.

(3)   The return address is computed and stored inside the CPU.

(4)   The exception vector is obtained, either from an external device or is supplied automatically by the NS32032. The vector is an offset component needed to retrieve the address of the exception handler descriptor in main memory.

(5)   The processor status register is saved into the interrupt stack together with the contents of the module register and the return address.

(6)   The program counter is loaded with the address of the procedure dedicated to the exception processing, and the normal instruction execution cycle is resumed after the module (MOD) and static base (SB) pointer registers have been set with the correct pointers to the new environment.

The exception recognition and acknowledge sequence is shown in Figure 7.10. Each trap or interrupt has an associated service routine whose descriptor in the external addressing format is contained in a system-wide table called the **interrupt dispatch table** (IDT). The table's base address is contained in the INTBASE register, so that tables can be easily relocated in main memory and very sophisticated systems can make use of more than one table. The exception vector in the fourth step of the sequence just outlined is used as an offset and added to INTBASE to form the address of the routine descriptor. Then, as in the external addressing mode, the CPU uses the procedure descriptor to load the module register and to gain access to the associated module descriptor in the module table. The program base pointer is then added to the procedure offset to form the service routine address loaded in the program counter. In addition, the new contents of the static base pointer (SB) register is read from the module descriptor.

The interrupt dispatch table contains entries for each kind of trap and interrupt recognized by the CPU. Figure 7.11 shows the organization of this table, which consists of 16 entries: the first three are dedicated respectively to the non-vectored, non-maskable and abort interrupts, while entries 3–10 are reserved for traps. The descriptors 11–15 are not used at present. Other entries are dedicated to the vectored interrupt descriptors when the CPU is used in conjunction with an external interrupt controller.

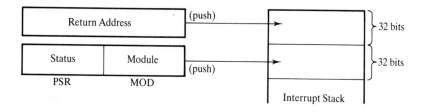

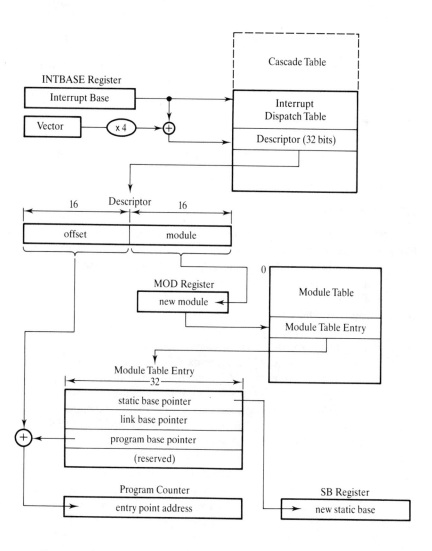

Figure 7.10 Interrupt servicing sequence: status saving and handler addressing.

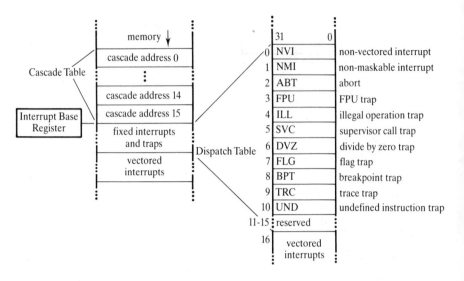

Figure 7.11   Interrupt table organization in the NS32032 system.

7.7.1 Interrupts

The NS32032 architecture supports three different types of interrupt. Non-maskable interrupt requests are submitted via the $\overline{\text{NMI}}$ line depicted in Figure 7.2 and cannot be disabled; hence, they are used to signal the occurrence of urgent and possibly catastrophic events, such as power failures. On the other hand, maskable interrupts, which use the $\overline{\text{INT}}$ line, can be disabled when necessary and prioritized with the aid of external devices. The ABT interrupt is activated by driving the $\overline{\text{RST}}/\overline{\text{ABT}}$ CPU pin and is used to abort a bus cycle and the execution of the associated instruction. This is needed in systems where the NS32032 is used in conjunction with an external MMU, when an error such as a page fault or privilege violation is detected by the co-processor. During the abort interrupt acknowledge sequence, the CPU saves the address of the aborted instruction in the stack, so that the interrupt handler is able to return control for its correct execution after managing the exceptional condition. Since instructions are prefetched by the CPU, aborted bus cycles can be related to instructions that will not be really needed or executed by the NS32032. For this reason, the abort interrupt occurs only when the aborted prefetched code must be executed, while prefetching is stopped as soon as a bus fault is signalled on the $\overline{\text{RST}}/\overline{\text{ABT}}$ line.

When an interrupt occurs, the CPU completes the current instruction, or iteration for string operations, and then starts an interrupt acknowledgement cycle. In this phase, a vector value is read from the CPU address space to compute the address of the service routine. When interrupts are not vectored, and the I bit in the configuration register is reset, the value so obtained is discarded and the NS32032 uses the first descriptor in the interrupt dispatch table to access the interrupt handler. In contrast, interrupt vectorization allows the system designer to implement different interrupt levels, each one having its own handler and associated priority.

Interrupt vectorization requires one or more additional interrupt controller devices, such as the NS32202, capable of supporting up to 16 interrupt request lines. These are served according to a number of different programmable strategies based on priority mechanisms. In this case, the CPU uses the vector supplied by the NS32202 during the interrupt acknowledge cycle as an offset in the dispatch table to find the associated routine descriptor.

The NS32202 controllers can be cascaded, as shown in Figure 7.12, to obtain a system consisting of up to 256 interrupt levels. For this purpose, an additional table of cascaded interrupts must be established in main memory, as shown in Figure 7.13, containing the addresses for the slave devices in Figure 7.12, and placed in a negative direction from the location given by the INTBASE register. The interrupt acknowledge sequence is more complex when cascaded controllers are used. In fact, the CPU now obtains a negative vector value in the range -1 to -16 from the master NS32202, instead of a positive offset. This value is used to access the cascade table and to get the address of the interrupting slave controller. Then a read operation is performed by the CPU at the slave

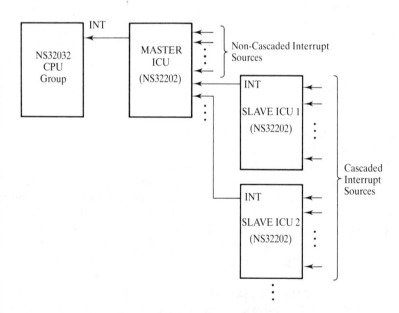

Figure 7.12 Cascaded interrupt controllers.

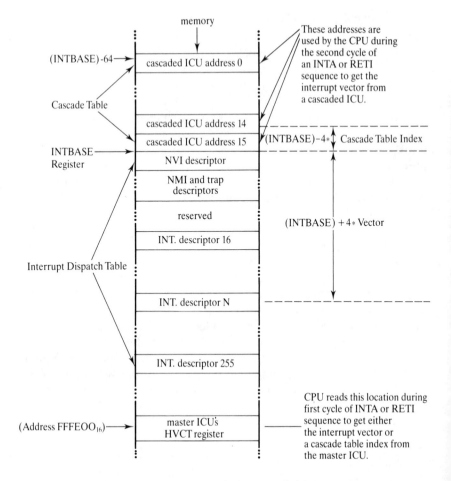

Figure 7.13 Vector table for cascaded interrupts.

address and an unsigned 8-bit value is returned to the NS32032. From now on, the sequence continues as usual: the dispatch table is addressed and the service routine descriptor is obtained.

Interrupt returns must be performed by means of the RETI instruction. This instruction is similar to the return from trap operation, but also informs interrupt controllers in the system that the service has been completed. RETI, however, does not pop any parameter from the stack, since the interrupt mechanism cannot be activated by a procedure call, so no data can be passed through the stack by the caller to the called service routine.

Interrupts and traps are served with different priorities by the CPU when more than one exception occurs during an instruction execution. Table 7.3 summarizes the priority levels defined in the NS32032 system.

Table 7.3   Interrupt and trap priorities in the NS32032 system.

NS32032 Simultaneous Interrupts and Trap Priorities
(1)   Traps other than trace (highest priority)
(2)   Abort
(3)   Non-maskable interrupts
(4)   Maskable interrupts
(5)   Trace traps   (lowest priority)

7.7.2   Traps

There are several situations that can generate a trap during an instruction. For example, the divide by zero (DVZ) and floating-point unit (FPU) traps arise when the CPU detects an attempt to divide an integer by zero, or the FPU meets a computation exception during any floating-point opration. Other exception conditions include the occurrence of an undefined code (UND) when a non-implemented opcode is met in the instruction processing or illegal instruction (ILL), which is raised whenever a user attempts to execute a privileged operation.

The programmer can also raise software-programmable traps via the FLAG and supervisor call (SVC) instructions. In the former case, the exception handler is activated, depending on whether the overflow bit F is or is not set in the processor status register, while SVC allows system or privileged services to be invoked by the normal programs in a controlled and safe way.

The NS32032 architecture includes two other traps to simplify system debugging and to allow the use of the microprocessor in emulators. The breakpoint trap occurs when the BPT instruction is executed, and the trace (TRC) handler is activated when each instruction is completed, if tracing is enabled. Trace handling is accomplished by mechanisms that differ slightly from the other traps. In fact, tracing is enabled by setting the T bit in the processor status register. At the beginning of each instruction, the CPU copies the value of T into the trace-pending P bit of the processor status register, then the trace handler (TRC) is activated at the end of the instruction if P is set. This is necessary as the trace handler is served by the CPU with the lowest priority, and all interrupts and traps occurring during a traced instruction are processed before the trace handler. The P bit is reset during the trace handler execution and is used as a flag reminding users that the instruction just executed has or has not already been traced. All the exception service routines should manipulate the P bit so that each instruction can be traced only once when executed and the trace handler is really activated for each instruction to be traced.

Returns from traps are obtained via the RETT machine operation. This restores the contents of the processor status register, the module register, the program counter and the static base pointer (SB) register to their previous values and de–allocates a programmer-defined number of bytes from the original stack. This is particularly useful when traps are used as supervisor calls and parameters are passed through the stack to the service routine; in this case, the input data are automatically discarded when the invoked system service ends.

7.8   Co-processors

The NS32032 can be used in conjunction with a number of external co-processors designed to carry out specialized tasks efficiently, such as floating-point computations and memory management. Hence, the system designers included in the CPU architecture some mechanisms to implement a standard and uniform hardware interface for each co-processor that had been introduced into the system. From the programmer's point of view, the set of units constituting the NS32032 and its related co-processors functions like a single, powerful microprocessor, supporting all the CPU and slave processor registers and instructions.

Each co-processor is interfaced to the NS32032 by conventional data and address buses and the four status lines ST0–ST3 (see Figure 7.2). In addition, the external co-processor must be able to drive the CPU $\overline{AT/SPC}$ input line. The CPU recognizes a co-processor operation by decoding the first byte of the basic instruction part (see Figure 7.8), which also contains the co-processor identifier. If the selected co-processor is present in the system, and the associated bit is set in the configuration register, the CPU starts the execution sequence, otherwise an undefined opcode trap occurs. In this way, the system programmer is able to simulate co-processor operations in software, by writing a suitable trap-handling routine.

The NS32032 starts a co-processor instruction by broadcasting the implied co-processor identifier to all the external units on the system data bus. These detect the broadcast cycle by decoding the status information presented on the status lines ST0–ST3. From now on, the co-processor selected by the identifier will be active and will cooperate with the CPU to execute the instruction. Then the NS32032 sends the remaining two bytes of the basic part of the instruction to the co-processor as well as transferring all the operands needed in the operation. In fact, the co-processor obtains operands from the CPU and returns the operation results to its master. At the end of the operand transfer, the co-processor is able to carry out the invoked operation, while the NS32032 proceeds to fetch instructions, or waits for the co-processor's answer, when the internal instruction queue is full. The end of the co-processor's processing phase is signalled via the $\overline{AT/SPC}$ line; then the CPU reads the co-processor's status word to check whether the operation was successful or not. If the operation is successful, results are transferred from the co-processor to the CPU and the instruction execution ends correctly; otherwise a suitable trap is invoked to manage the erroneous condition.

7.9 Memory management

The powerful instructions and mechanisms implemented by modern microprocessors could not be used efficiently if special supports for memory management were not included in the CPU architecture. In fact, advanced designs such as the NS32032 are intended for complex applications where several system and user tasks share the same computing and storage resources. As outlined in Chapter 4, some hardware aids must then be provided for the operating system software to supervise and control the main memory utilization.

7.9.1 NS32082 MMU

The NS32032 supports memory management in conjunction with an external NS32082 MMU. This is interfaced to the CPU by means of the co-processor standard interface and provides mechanisms for logical-to-physical address translation, access rights checks, virtual memory management and program debugging.

The NS32082 extends the system programming model to the set of registers shown in Figure 7.14, offering the designer an additional group of special-purpose instructions. In particular, operators are provided to read and write the MMU registers (SMR and LMR), to validate pointers (RDVAL and WRVAL), and to move data from the supervisor to the user space and vice versa (MOVSUi and MOVUSi). However, each MMU instruction is privileged, so that it must be executed in supervisor mode or a trap will occur.

Figure 7.15 shows the logical interconnection between the CPU and the MMU. The multiplexed address/data bus connects both the NS32032 and NS32082 units and the logical address lines in the system are the same as the physical lines. These are time-shared between the CPU and the slave processor. The CPU verifies whether an external address translation is provided by sampling the $\overline{AT/SPC}$ line during reset. When addresses are translated by the MMU, the NS32032 puts a 24-bit logical or address value on the bus lines, as in Figure 7.15, but does not provide any strobe signal to the physical memory devices, since the logical address

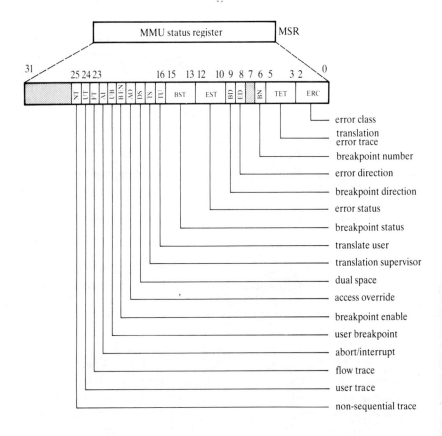

Figure 7.14 MMU programming model and status register format.

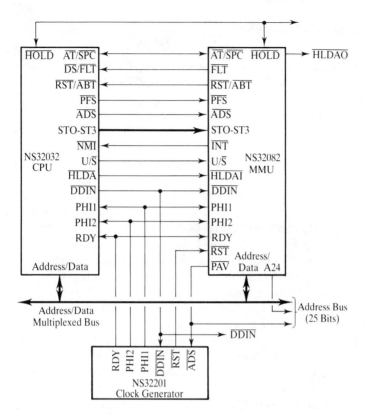

Figure 7.15 CPU and MMU interconnection in the NS32032 system.

is stored inside the MMU. This performs the logical-to-physical translation and then drives the bus address lines with a 25-bit physical value, and supplies the correct strobe signal ($\overline{PAV}$) to the memory devices. Note that the physical space width is twice that of the logical space. This can be useful in large systems where several overlapped logical spaces assigned to different tasks are mapped into a single physical space.

During the translation period the CPU is idle, so this phase must be kept as short as possible to ensure satisfactory overall memory access times. The translation algorithm makes use of special tables stored in main memory and the MMU is able to access the physical memory directly during the translation period, since the NS32082 is a DMA co-processor.

7.9.2   Address translation

Translation mechanisms map the logical address space into a physical space consisting of 32 768 pages, each of which is 512 bytes long. Hence, the CPU's 24 logical address bits are structured in three subfields: the nine least significant bits are used as a page offset to locate a byte inside the page, while bits 23–16 (first logical index field) and 15–9 (second logical index field) are used to retrieve a 16-bit page selector. For this purpose, the MMU uses a two-level mapping algorithm based on tables containing 32-bit entries. The format used for each table entry is shown in Figure 7.16: the bank select bit (BS) and the 15-bit page frame number field (PFN) are concatenated with an index computed from a bit field in the logical address to build a pointer for a page of physical memory. The remaining bits support virtual memory and access rights checks.

The mapping is performed in three steps: first a page table is addressed using the eight most significant bits of the logical address. The address is formed by adding the contents of the three least significant bytes in a page table register (PTB) to the logical address bits 23–16, as shown in Figure 7.17(a). Since the first logical index field is used in this phase, each page table can contain up to 256 entries. The second step uses the bank select bit and the frame number field of the page table entry and the second logical index field to locate another entry in a pointer table (Figure 7.17(a)). The addressing mechanism for the pointer table is the same as for the page table, except that the former can contain at most 128 entries, not 256. Finally, the new bank select bit and frame page number are used to point to the physical memory page.

This mapping solution offers a number of advantages. For example, each user or system task can have its own address space; more than one page table can be maintained for each process in the system and tables can be easily swapped during context switching, simply by changing the contents of the page table register. For the same reason, tables can be easily relocated in main memory by modifying either the page table

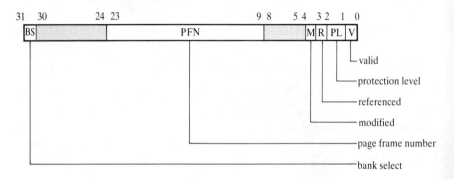

Figure 7.16   Page table and pointer table entry format.

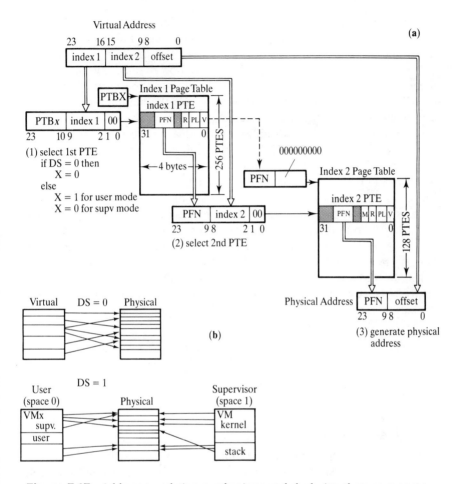

Figure 7.17 Address translation mechanisms and dual virtual space support.

register, or a table entry address field. The two-level mapping scheme allows different user tasks to share the same physical space containing common data or procedures, implementing system services, for example, since each page table can contain an entry for a shared pointer table, associated with the common physical pages. In this way, shared pages can be relocated with the minimum overhead, since it is necessary only to change entries in a pointer table without modifying any page table associated with the user tasks.

Some MMU registers accessible to programmers are used to affect and control the address translation operations. As Figure 7.14 shows, there are two page table registers (PTB0 and PTB1) that can also be used by the MMU. When set, the dual-space bit (DS) in the MMU status register (MSR) forces the NS32082 to use PTB1 for each address specified in user mode, and PTB0 for memory accesses in supervisor mode. When DS is reset, both supervisor and user addresses are translated by PTB0. This situation is illustrated in Figure 7.17(b).

The address translation mechanism can be enabled and/or disabled by means of the translate user (TU) and translate supervisor (TS) bits in the MMU status register. The former controls the mapping of addresses in user mode, while the latter refers to the supervisor mode. When the mapping mechanisms is disabled, the MMU interprets the logical addresses coming from the CPU as physical addresses.

Error conditions met during the MMU operations indirectly notify the CPU and raise a suitable interrupt exception. The supervisor program can obtain information about errors by reading the MMU status register. For this purpose, the ERC field shown in Figure 7.14 encodes the error class (translation error, trace or break interrupt), while the TET bits are needed to distinguish between different exceptions in address translation, such as protection level errors or invalid entries found in page or pointer tables. In addition, the error-direction bit (ED) tells the system which part (read or write) of an indivisible read–modify–write cycle caused the translation error.

7.9.3   Translation cache

The translation algorithm can require up to 20 clock cycles to be executed, because several memory accesses are needed to read the table entries. In the MMU architecture, the NS32082 designers have included a cache memory that can be addressed by contents and consists of 32 entries to reduce this overhead. Each entry is used to store the 15 most significant bits in the virtual address and the page frame number for the physical page. When the logical address is output by the CPU and stored in the MMU, the internal cache is addressed, and, if a hit occurs, the physical address portion can be used immediately. In contrast, the pointer table entries are fetched on each cache miss and a new translation entry is loaded in the cache. The program locality principle usually yields a good success rate, so that translation tables are seldom accessed.

Cache entries can be invalidated by writing in the MMU error/invalidate address (EIA) register. In this case, the virtual address specified by the programmer is removed from the cache, together with its current translation. This is useful, for example, when several logical spaces can exist in a system associated with different tasks. The same logical address therefore corresponds to more than one physical page.

7.9.4 Memory protection

Besides translation facilities, the MMU architecture also supports memory protection and access rights checks. For example, Figure 7.16 shows that each page table entry contains a protection level (PL) field. This encodes the access rights restrictions for the index table, or memory page, pointed out by the frame page number field. The values assumed by the PL field and its associated meanings are summarized in Table 7.4. During the translation phase, the MMU checks the PL field to verify if the read or write operation is legal for the executing task. When an attempt to violate the access rights is detected, a translation error occurs and the CPU bus cycle is aborted.

Table 7.4 Protection level encodings.

Protection Level	Meaning	
Encoding	User	Supervisor
00	No access	Read only
01	No access	Full access
10	Read only	Full access
11	Full access	Full access

The protection mechanism is also controlled by the MMU status register (see Figure 7.14). When set, the access override (AO) bit is used to override the protection level of all addresses. In this case, access rights checks are not performed and the user can access protected memory areas that usually can be read or written to only in supervisor mode.

Other mechanisms have been introduced to avoid a user being able to circumvent the protection scheme, by passing a pointer for a protected page to a supervisor task during a service request. For this purpose, the system programmer can use two MMU instructions to validate addresses to be used in a read or write operation: RDVAL and WRVAL. In such cases, the MMU verifies whether the address supplied by the CPU could cause a privilege violation when translated in user mode, and returns the result of this test to the NS32032 by setting or clearing the F bit in the CPU program status register.

7.9.5 Virtual memory management support

The NS32082 offers the programmer support for virtual memory management. Each page and pointer table entry in Figure 7.16 contains a valid bit, V, used to signal whether fields in the entry are correct or not. The V bit is checked by the MMU during the address translation phase: if V is reset, the bus cycle is aborted and an ABT interrupt is sent to the CPU. In this way, demand-based paging systems can be implemented by resetting the V bit in a page table entry, when no physical page is linked to the logical address. An attempt to access a missing page will cause a page fault exception and a suitable handling routine will be activated.

Two other fields are included in each page table entry: referenced and modified bits, R and M. M is only used in tables pointing to physical pages. These bits are intended to aid the operating system in paged memory management. M is set whenever a write operation is performed to the associated page, so that a system task can distinguish pages that need to be copied back to the mass storage when they are swapped from the main memory. R can be used to find memory pages to be replaced, on a least-recently-used basis, for example, since this bit is set by the MMU whenever the associated page is accessed, and can be periodically cleared by the operating software.

7.9.6   Program debugging support

The NS32082 architecture also includes mechanisms to simplify program debugging. Figure 7.14 shows that two breakpoint registers (BPR0 and BPR1) and one breakpoint counter (BCNT) allow program breaks when the user-specified memory locations are accessed. The format of each breakpoint register is shown in Figure 7.18. The 24 least significant bits contain the breakpoint address that the MMU compares with the virtual addresses supplied by the CPU during the program execution, or with the translated physical addresses used to access memory pages. The other bits are used to specify the breakpoint conditions. Hence, VP allows the virtual or physical address space to be selected, while AS is used to distinguish between virtual addresses translated by PTB0 and PTB1. The breakpoint execution (BE), breakpoint read (BR) and breakpoint write (BW) bits are used to enable or disable the breakpoint mechanism when the CPU attempts to access the associated location for fetching instructions, or reading and/or writing data. The count enable bit (CE) is used with the BCNT register to break programs only when the breakpoint has been reached a predefined number of times. When CE is set, BCNT is decremented by one on each breakpoint occurrence, but no action is taken by the MMU until the count register content is zero. Breakpoints are signalled to the NS32032 by driving the $\overline{\text{NMI}}$ line shown in Figure 7.2, causing a non-maskable interrupt exception.

Some bits in the MMU status register are used to control the breakpoint functions (see Figure 7.14). The BEN bit enables or disables the MMU breakpoint support, while UB specifies breakpoints for

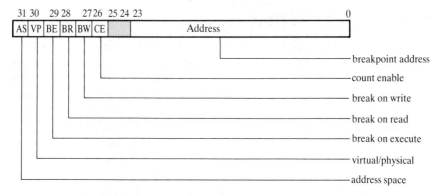

Figure 7.18 Breakpoint register format.

supervisor accesses. BN is a status bit indicating the breakpoint address register (BPR0 or BPR1) of the current program break, while the breakpoint direction (BD) bit indicates whether the read or write part of a read–modify–write operation caused the last break exception.

Besides breakpoint facilities, the NS32082 has support for tracing program flow. The program flow registers (PF0 and PF1) in Figure 7.14 are used by the MMU to record the addresses of the two most recently executed non-sequential instructions and can be read by the CPU. The sequential count registers (SC0 and SC1) consist of the lower and upper parts of a single 32-bit register. When a non-sequential instruction is executed, the MMU copies its address into PF0 after saving the register content in PF1. In addition, the content of SC0 is copied into SC1 and a value of zero is stored in SC0. SC0 is then incremented by one on each sequential instruction executed by the CPU. It is easy to see that PF0 and PF1 always contain the addresses of the two most recently executed instructions that caused a change in the program flow; SC0 and SC1, however, hold the numbers of sequential instructions that have been executed after those accessed by PF0 and PF1. A trace handler can thus use this information to reconstruct the program flow and to present trace reports to the user.

The tracing mechanism is controlled by the FT, UT and NT bits in the MMU status register (see Figure 7.14). The flow trace bit (FT) enables or disables the MMU tracing operations, while a set UT bit suspends tracing when the CPU performs memory accesses in supervisor mode. NT, on the other hand, allows the non-sequential tracing interrupt to be enabled or disabled. In fact, when NT is set, a non-maskable interrupt is sent to the CPU by the NS32082 whenever a jump, branch, call or return instruction is executed, so causing the activation of a tracing routine.

7.10   The NS32081 floating-point co-processor

When used in conjunction with the NS32081 floating-point co-processor, the NS32032 offers an extended instruction set including floating-point operations. There are two floating-point operand sizes: the single and double basic formats, according to the IEEE P754 Standard. Thus, single-precision reals have a 23-bit mantissa and an 8-bit exponent, while a double-precision mantissa and exponent are 52 and 11 bits long, respectively.

7.10.1   Registers

The programming model introduced in Section 7.4.1 and shown in Figure 7.3 must be extended to the registers shown in Figure 7.19 when the floating-point unit is present in the system. There are eight 32-bit floating-point registers (F0–F7) intended to provide fast access to the real operands most frequently used. When double-precision operands are required, the registers are paired and each pair works as a single 64-bit accumulator.

The user can also access the floating-point status register (FSR) shown in Figure 7.19. This contains both status information and control bits for the floating-point unit operating mode. For example, the RM field is used to select the rounding mode used by the slave processor during the computations. There are four different rounding methods: rounding to the value nearest to the exact result, rounding towards zero, or towards positive or negative infinity.

The UEN bit is used to enable underflow traps by the floating-point unit and occurs whenever the result of an operation has an absolute value too small to be represented in the normalized format. Similarly, the inexact result trap (IEN) bit is used to raise an exception when the computed data cannot be expressed in the format specified for the destination operands. The other bits in the floating-point status register record exceptional conditions met during floating-point unit operations. IF is a flag having the same meaning as IEN; that is, the computation result cannot be represented in the destination format. However, IF does not cause any trap to be activated when it is set. UF, on the other hand, monitors any underflow condition without causing any exception to be taken. The trap-type (TT) field is cleared whenever a floating-point instruction is successfully completed. In contrast, abnormal conditions, such as overflow, underflow, divide by zero and so on, are encoded in TT when occurring in a floating-point unit operation. Finally, the SWF field can be read and written to by the user but its contents are never hardware interpreted, either by the CPU or by the floating-point unit.

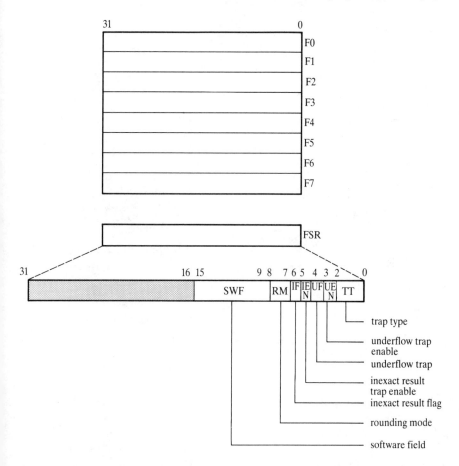

Figure 7.19 Floating-point unit programming model and status register format.

7.10.2 NS32081 co-processor instructions

Table 7.5 summarizes the additional floating-point instructions offered to the NS32032 programmer. There are two versions for most operations, corresponding to single- and double-precision computations: the notation INSTRf is used for the mnemonic INSTR, where f can be equal to either F (floating point, single precision) or L (floating point, double precision). The floating-point group includes both arithmetic and data transfer instructions. Table 7.5 shows that addition, subtraction, division and multiplication are supported in addition to the compare, negate and absolute value operators. Unlike other floating-point co-processors, the NS32081 does not provide any facility for computing transcendental or trigonometric functions.

Table 7.5   Floating-point instruction summary.

Floating-Point Instruction Mnemonic	Meaning
ADDf	Add
SUBf	Subtract
MULf	Multiply
DIVf	Divide
NEGf	Negate
ABSf	Absolute value
CMPf	Compare
LFSR	Load FPU status register
SFSR	Store FPU status register
MOVf	Move without conversion
MOVFL	Move converting from double to single precision
MOVif	Move converting from integer to floating point
ROUNDfi	Move converting from floating point to nearest integer
TRUNCfi	Move from floating point to integer, truncating
FLOORfi	Move from floating point to largest integer less or equal

Each kind of format conversion is obtained by other instructions in Table 7.5. For example, floating-point data can be transformed into integers by rounding the input value to the nearest integer (ROUNDfi), towards zero (TRUNCfi) or towards negative infinity (FLOORfi).

Finally, two instructions have been introduced allowing the floating-point status register to be read (SFSR) and written to (LFSR).

7.11   Custom co-processors

The same mechanisms supported by the CPU to achieve cooperation with the National Semiconductor co-processors are also offered to users to define their own custom co-processors. The presence or absence of a custom device in the system is signalled to the CPU by the C bit in the configuration register (see Figure 7.3).

Custom co-processors are interfaced to the NS32032 by the same I/O lines mentioned in Section 7.8 and the general co-processor interface protocol is also used by the CPU. The CPU is able to recognize custom instructions whose operating code interpretation is left to the user. In fact, when a custom operation must be executed, the NS32032 simply transfers user-defined operands to the custom processor and then reads the operation results from the co-processor when a pulse is received on the $\overline{AT}/\overline{SPC}$ line (see Figure 7.2); this represents the completion of the instruction.

Custom instructions can belong to different classes. They are roughly similar in construction to the floating-point instructions of Table 7.5. Hence, compare, move and format conversion operators are automatically recognized by the CPU, together with the two-operand operations whose meaning is user specified.

7.12   Conclusion

The NS32032 is a modern 32-bit microprocessor with a high degree of symmetry in its instruction set and for addressing operands.

The CPU architecture includes all the basic supports for high-level language programming and for the implementation of sophisticated operating system functions.

The NS32032 basic data types, addressing modes and instruction set are well balanced and allow the design and implementation of powerful microprocessor-based systems for a wide range of applications.

As in other advanced microprocessors, exceptional events such as interrupts and traps are managed by the NS32032 by means of uniform mechanisms that allow quick and efficient exception recognition and processing. External co-processors can be easily interfaced to the NS32032 to cooperate with the CPU in carrying out specialized tasks.

The NS32032 can be used in conjunction with the NS32082 memory management unit to develop virtual memory systems, to implement separate access domains for task and procedures and to simplify program development by means of the memory management unit program debugging supports.

Finally, the NS32081 floating-point co-processor is able to extend the processing facilities offered by the NS32032 with floating-point operations according to the IEEE P754 Standard.

EXERCISES

7.1 A program must be developed that scans a terminal buffer for the carriage return character and produces the length of the string preceding the first occurrence of the carriage return in the terminal buffer. Discuss the main advantages or disadvantages of a solution that does or does not use the NS32032 string instructions.

7.2 Draw the flowchart for a program that implements semaphore primitives P and V in a multitasking system based on the NS32032. Must it use the SBITI*i* and/or CBITI*i* instructions? Why? Does the answer depend on the number of processors in the system?

7.3 Describe the stack and CPU register contents before and after the execution of the CXP and RXP instructions.

7.4 Draw the flowchart for a routine that performs context switching, including the status save/restore operations. Is it necessary to save/restore the context of the numerical co-processor? When and how should these operations be done?

7.5 How can the square root of a floating-point number be computed using the NS32081?

7.6 Design a procedure to compute the value *a* of the hypotenuse in a right-angled triangle, given the values *b* and *c* of its other two sides; *a*, *b* and *c* are floating-point numbers in single precision. Use the NS32081 floating-point unit and assume that a routine for square root computation is available.

7.7 Discuss the NS32082 address translation mechanisms. Which control structures are involved in the translation process?

7.8 How can private and global data or program areas be implemented using the NS32082 translation mechanisms?

7.9 Draw the flowchart of a routine intended to handle page faults in a system containing the NS32082. Which exceptions must activate this routine? Which control structures need to be tested and/or updated? Must the MMU move to or from user address space instructions to be used? Why?

7.10 Draw the flowchart for a program that manages non-maskable interrupts caused by the NS32082. On each NMI occurrence, a message must be inserted in a buffer consisting of (a) the reason for the interrupt and (b) the value of the MMU registers containing information about the exceptional event.

7.11 Design a simple trace handler for a system containing both the NS32032 and NS32082 units. The handler must be able to work in two ways: when instructions are executed in user mode, tracing must be activated on each instruction completion; while only changes in the program flow must be traced in supervisor mode. (*Hint*: Use both the CPU and MMU trace supports.)

7.12 Assume that a NS32032 development system also contains the NS32081 and NS32082 units. Design a breakpoint handler to save the CPU, FPU and MMU registers in a suitable memory area when the user program reaches a breakpoint. Breaks must be raised whenever a given instruction is executed or when a memory location is written the *N*th time.

CHAPTER 8

The INTEL iAPX286 System

OBJECTIVES

The aims of this chapter are as follows:

- to illustrate the basic organization of the iAPX286 CPU and its interface to the external world;

- to introduce the main iAPX286 characteristics concerning data types, addressing modes and instruction set;

- to discuss memory management mechanisms of the iAPX286 and, in particular, the virtual address space organization, the virtual-to-physical address translation process, and all the memory protection checks involved in the access to both data and code areas, including those on the machine privilege state;

- to show how the iAPX286 architecture processes exceptional events, such as interrupts and traps, and how supports for exception handling have been incorporated in the CPU;

- to analyze the main features of the 80287 floating-point co-processor.

8.1	Introduction	8.8	Privileged machine states
8.2	CPU architecture	8.9	Task control information
8.3	Basic data types		and switching
8.4	Registers	8.10	Interrupts and traps
8.5	Addressing modes	8.11	The arithmetic co-
8.6	Instruction set		processor
8.7	Memory management and	8.12	Conclusion
	protection		

8.1 Introduction

The iAPX286 is an Intel microprocessor intended for high-end applications, in powerful workstations, for example, and for advanced real-time controls. To support these applications, several important features have been introduced in the iAPX286, features not present in its predecessors, the iAPX86/88 and iAPX186/188. The most relevant of these mechanisms are the hardware or microcode supports, which manage virtual storage with swapping, for implementing protected execution environments, as well as managing tasks in multiprogramming systems.

The microprocessor's design is quite different from previous CPUs in the same line, so to ensure compatibility with those previous models, it has two modes of operation: a real address mode, which employs the iAPX286 as a super-iAPX86 or iAPX186; and a protected mode, which uses all the features peculiar to the iAPX286. Since the real address mode of operation is simply an enhancement of previous microprocessors' capabilities, this chapter will mainly focus on the characteristics of the iAPX286 functioning in the protected mode.

Memory management mechanisms form a major part of the distinctive features introduced in the iAPX286, both for allowing virtual memory management with swapping, and for implementing checks on the correct memory access. However, the MMU is implemented on the same chip as the CPU, unlike many similar microprocessors. This implementation is possible because the chip adopts a memory management philosophy very different from those used by other manufacturers.

The main problem in memory management is in the allocation of segment or page descriptors to achieve efficient address translation without limiting the number of such descriptors. This problem is avoided in the iAPX286 because the management of segment descriptors is performed by mechanisms not completely transparent to the programmer. As memory management is performed inside the CPU, special registers are used to hold the descriptors of four segments: one for the code, one for the stack and two for the data. Thus, whenever it is necessary to switch to another segment, the appropriate register is reloaded.

Although this approach can achieve a system performance equal to or better than that based on transparent system management, it does, however, introduce a distinction between intra- and inter-segment references at the programmer level, which could affect the implementation and reuse of large software systems.

Another peculiar feature of the iAPX286 is the extensive set of hardware-implemented checks on the accuracy of memory accesses. The basic protection mechanisms are based on segment limit checking, and separating the task address spaces and privileged machine states. The protection mechanisms implemented also address the problems connected with pointer validation and correct call or return procedures.

As there is no external chip dedicated to memory management, the chip set required to build a powerful processing system includes the main CPU, an 80286, and a numerical co-processor (80287).

8.2   CPU architecture

8.2.1   Internal organization

The CPU of the iAPX286 system is the Intel 80286, whose internal block diagram is shown in Figure 8.1. It is composed of four main blocks: a bus unit (BU), an instruction unit (IU), an execution unit (EU) and an address unit (AU). One of the CPU's major features is the use of a buffer queue in the communication lines between the bus unit and the instruction unit, and between the instruction unit and the execution unit or the address unit. This tends to enhance the execution speed for straight code by allowing an overlap of the fetch, decode and execution of the instructions.

The prefetch queue, between the bus unit and the instruction unit, can store up to six bytes with the next piece of code. (For more details about the operations of the prefetch queues see Chapter 4.) The instruction unit decodes the instructions and places the results in a decoded instruction queue, three instructions deep. The execution unit processes the operands according to the decoded instructions extracted from the decoded instruction queue, and also computes their virtual addresses, which will later be translated into physical addresses by the address unit. This unit represents a real MMU implemented on the same chip as the CPU, which leads to faster operations because inter-chip transmission delays are avoided; on the other hand, the limited area allowed for implementing this function limits some of the functions that can be performed.

8.2.2   CPU signals

The 80286 CPU has 63 external signals, including three V_{ss} connections for the system ground and two V_{cc} connections for a +5 V power supply. In addition to power supply leads, a CAP connection filters the output of the internal substrate bias generator. The other 57 signals are devoted to the following functions.

A.   D0–D15

These are data bus signals used to input data during memory, I/O and interrupt acknowledge cycles, and to send data during the memory and

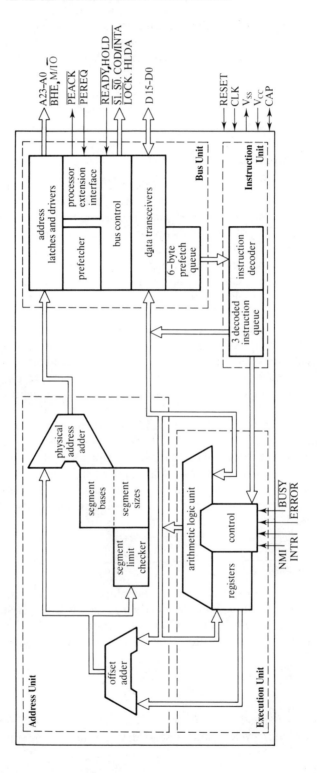

Figure 8.1 Internal block diagram of the 80286 CPU.

I/O cycles. Transfer of both 16-bit words and 8-bit bytes is possible; with 8-bit bytes, either D0–D7 or D8–D15 are used, depending on whether the address is even or odd.

B. A0–A23

Address bus lines used to output the physical address of the memory or I/O location referenced by the bus cycle are represented by the A0–A23. The full set of 24 lines is used to address the memory, but only A0–A15 are used when I/O devices are addressed.

C. $\overline{BHE}$

The bus high enable ($\overline{BHE}$) signal indicates whether or not the current bus transfer involves a single byte with an even address. As the addresses of 16-bit words are always even, odd addresses indicate a byte transfer by default; an even address may indicate the transfer of either a whole word or a single byte with an even address. When the $\overline{BHE}$ signal is set to 1 it indicates an even address.

D. $M/\overline{IO}$

The state of this output signal indicates whether the current bus cycle accesses a memory location (high voltage) or an I/O device (low voltage).

E. $COD/\overline{INTA}$

This signal distinguishes instruction fetch from memory data read cycles. It also distinguishes between interrupt acknowledge and I/O read cycles.

F. $\overline{S0}$–$\overline{S1}$

This pair of output signals is used in conjunction with $M/\overline{IO}$ and $COD/\overline{INTA}$ signals to indicate the type of bus cycle performed, according to the values shown in Table 8.1.

G. $\overline{LOCK}$

The $\overline{LOCK}$ signal indicates that the CPU is performing an indivisible operation, such as that required to implement mutual exclusion (see Section 3.5). When this signal is activated, no other device can perform a cycle, either on the local or the common bus in a multiprocessor configuration. The instruction XCHG (see Section 8.6.1) automatically activates this signal during its execution. Another way of activating the $\overline{LOCK}$ signal is to use a specific prefix before an instruction whose indivisibility should be guaranteed.

Table 8.1   Control signal encoding.

COD/$\overline{\text{INTA}}$	M/$\overline{\text{IO}}$	$\overline{\text{S1}}$	$\overline{\text{S0}}$	Bus Cycle Initiated
0 (low)	0	0	0	Interrupt acknowledge
0	0	0	1	Reserved
0	0	1	0	Reserved
0	0	1	1	None; not a status cycle
0	1	0	0	IF A1 = 1 **then** halt; **else** shutdown
0	1	0	1	Memory data read
0	1	1	0	Memory data write
0	1	1	1	None; not a status cycle
1 (high)	0	0	0	Reserved
1	0	0	1	I/O read
1	0	1	0	I/O write
1	0	1	1	None; not a status cycle
1	1	0	0	Reserved
1	1	0	1	Memory instruction read
1	1	1	0	Reserved
1	1	1	1	None; not a status cycle

H. $\overline{READY}$

This signal tells the CPU that the addressed memory or I/O device is ready to complete the current bus cycle. The bus continues to cycle until the $\overline{READY}$ signal is activated. This signal allows the system to work with devices of different speeds, without any hardware modifications.

I.   HOLD AND HOLDA

This pair of signals implements the simple protocols required to transfer the control of the local bus from the CPU to another bus master and vice versa. When the HOLD signal is activated, the CPU terminates any bus cycle in progress and grants control of the bus to an external bus master by activating HOLDA. As long as HOLD is active, the bus is under the control of the external bus master; the CPU regains controls when HOLD is de-activated and the HOLDA signal is switched by the CPU.

J. INTR

This is a single input that receives requests for a maskable interrupt. As only one input is provided for this purpose, an 8-bit interrupt identifier is read during the interrupt acknowledge cycle to obtain information about the interrupting device.

K. $\overline{NMI}$

Requests for non-maskable interrupts are received by this CPU input, but no interrupt identifier is read externally when this interrupt is acknowledged.

L. PEREQ AND $\overline{PERACK}$

This pair of signals extends the memory management and protection mechanisms of the CPU to the data transfer of the co-processors. The activation of the PEREQ signals tells the CPU that a data transfer for the co-processor is requested; the $\overline{PERACK}$ signal is used to tell the co-processor that the requested operand is being transferred (see also Section 8.11.3).

M. $\overline{BUSY}$ AND $\overline{ERROR}$

This pair of signals is also used for the dialogue between the CPU and the co-processor. When active, the $\overline{BUSY}$ signal indicates that the operation launched on the co-processor is still in progress. An active $\overline{BUSY}$ signal stops the CPU activities if a WAIT instruction is executed (see also Section 8.11.3), but the operations are resumed as soon as $\overline{BUSY}$ is de-activated by the co-processor. An active $\overline{ERROR}$ signal activates a special interrupt that tells the CPU that an error has been detected during the execution of a co-processor operation.

N. RESET

This input is used to cancel all CPU operations and re-initialize or restart the system operations.

O. CLOCK

This input provides the fundamental timing for the CPU.

8.2.3 Memory organization

The main memory of the iAPX286 comprises a linear collection of elementary addressable units, each one corresponding to an 8-bit byte. The total memory addressable by a single programmer varies according to the selected mode of operation; in the real address mode, the memory is composed of 2^{20} bytes, while in protected mode, the address space visible to the programmer is 2^{30} bytes. Note that in the protected mode, the memory physically addressable by the CPU is composed of only 16 Mbytes because only 24 pins of the chip are dedicated to the address signals. The main physical memory may be expanded to 32 Mbytes if separate address spaces are implemented for code and data, by using a suitable method of decoding the output of status signals during bus cycles. Thus, the gigabyte address space provided to each programmer in protected mode should be regarded as virtual address space; as programmers can use the same virtual addresses for their own programs, the iAPX286 mechanism for translating virtual into physical addresses can support different memory spaces, one for each program running in the system.

Memory addressing is based on segmentation concepts (see Chapter 4), since the whole address space is organized into segments whose length ranges from 1 to 64 Kbytes. The maximum number of segments allowed is 16 in real address mode, or 16 Kbytes in protected mode.

8.3 Basic data types

The two basic data structures in the iAPX286 are a single byte and a 16-bit word, and they may be read or written in a single bus cycle. However, several instructions are available to manipulate data larger than 16 bits. The data types manipulated directly by the iAPX286 are as follows.

- **Signed integers**: 8- or 16-bit positive or negative numbers represented in two's complement. When the arithmetic processor is used, 32- and 64-bit integers are also supported.

- **Unsigned integers**: Positive integer numbers represented with 8- or 16-bit values. All the bits represent the magnitude of the number.

- **Pointer**: 32-bit quantities that designate an address. They are composed of two 16-bit parts – a **selector** component, which selects the segment number, and an **offset** component, which indicates the offset within the segment.

- **Strings**: Contiguous sequences of bytes ranging from 1 to 64 Kbytes.

- **ASCII bytes**: Bytes holding the representation of the ASCII code of a character.

- **Unpacked BCD**: Bytes that represent a single decimal digit.

- **Packed BCD**: Bytes storing the values of a pair of decimal digits. Each half-byte holds a digit, with the most significant digit stored in the high-order half-byte.

- **Floating point**: This data type is only supported when the arithmetic processor 80287 is used. 32-, 64- and 80-bit real numbers are available using the IEEE 754 Standard representation (see Chapter 2).

Separate multiplication and division instructions are provided for signed and unsigned integers, while the same addition and subtraction instructions are used for both types. However, different conditional jump instructions detect overflows in the two cases.

The unpacked BCD and ASCII representations of a single decimal digit differ in the high-order half-byte, which is always zero for the unpacked BCD, but three for the ASCII representation of the corresponding character. The addition and subtraction of BCD numbers, both packed and unpacked, is performed by using the corresponding instructions for integer numbers, followed by adjustment instructions.

8.4 Registers

The register set available to the programmer constitutes 14 registers, including those for general use, address computation and control use. Figure 8.2 shows the organization of the register set with the corresponding grouping in the three classes mentioned.

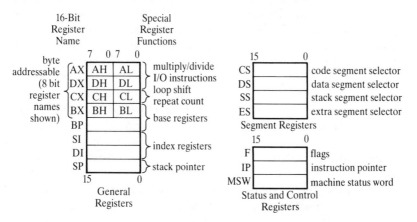

Figure 8.2 Internal register organization.

8.4.1   General registers

The general registers consist of eight 16-bit registers. These are used for storing data and addresses manipulated by the program. The registers AX, BX, CX and DX may also be used as eight independent 8-bit registers, as also shown in Figure 8.2.

Although all the general registers can normally be used inter-changeably to store the operands of the different instructions, some addressing modes refer implicitly to some general register. Their use is conditioned by the possibility of using those registers for accessing the operands through specific addressing modes. For example, the BX and BP registers – referred to as base registers – hold the base address of data structures, while SI and DI – index registers – store offsets within a data structure. SP is even more specialized as it holds the offset of the top of the stack within the stack segment.

8.4.2   Segment registers

The four segment registers hold the selector of four distinct segments that define the current addressable space of the program. To access a word or byte in a segment it is necessary first to load one of the segment registers with the selector of the segment.

Each segment register performs the address computation for a particular kind of segment. For example, the CS register stores the selector of the code segment currently used, while the SS register identifies the current stack segment. The DS and ES registers hold the selectors of two data segments, which can be directly addressed without loading any segment register. Two data segment registers are provided to allow easy movement of data between different data segments.

Memory addressing is performed by implicitly using the segments whose selectors are currently stored in the corresponding segment registers. Hence, the instructions are fetched using the selector stored in CS, the stack operations use the contents of SS for address computations, while the contents of DS are a default value for the segment selector of the operands.

To achieve more flexibility in operand addressing, the iAPX286 allows the programmer to specify explicitly one of the other segment registers to be used in the address computation of instruction operands. In this way, it is possible to manipulate operands stored in any of the segments whose selectors are currently stored in one of the segment registers.

However, the visibility of the memory is always constrained by the window of four segments defined by the contents of the segment registers, as shown in Figure 8.3. If it is necessary to address a memory cell in another segment, the programmer must first load the segment register of the appropriate type – code, stack or data – with a new selector. This then addresses the desired memory location. Given the locality properties shown by almost all programs (see Chapter 4), the segment register reloading operations seldom occur. However, this addressing method can cause problems, such as a routine that can be called by other routines stored in the same segment, as well as in other segments.

The segment selector has different formats and different roles depending on whether the iAPX286 is in real address mode (RA) or in virtual mode (VM). In real address mode, the selector constitutes the 16 most significant bits of the starting address of the segment: the least significant is zero. Address computation in real address mode is therefore performed following the scheme shown in Figure 8.4, where the offset is

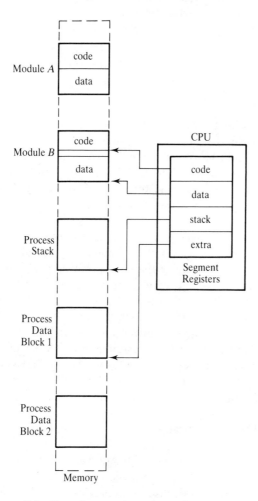

Figure 8.3 Use of segment registers for memory access.

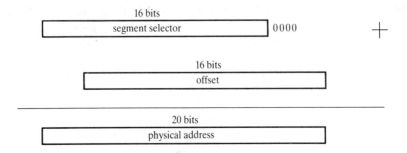

Figure 8.4 Physical address computation in the real address mode.

a 16-bit number computed according to the specific addressing mode chosen for the current instruction. In virtual mode, the segment selector has a more complex layout: its contents indicate a segment of 16 Kbytes in the virtual address space.

8.4.3 Control registers

The IP register holds the offset of the next memory cell in the program to be fetched. As all the addresses in the iAPX286 are composed of a segment selector and an offset, a single program counter does not exist. The CS:IP pair of registers defines a 32-bit program counter.

The layout of the flag register is shown in Figure 8.5. CF indicates whether a carry or a borrow was generated by the last operation, according to the instruction performed. PF gives the even parity bit for the low-order byte of the last result computed. AF is an auxiliary carry/borrow flag indicating whether the least significant BCD digit gave rise to a carry or borrow during the last operation performed. SF and ZF are set when negative or zero results are produced, respectively, and they are reset whenever these conditions are not found. The IF flag enables the external maskable interrupts, while the TF flag enables the single step mode, which automatically produces an internal interrupt when each instruction is completed. In this way, it is possible to pass control to a debugging routine provided by the user. If set, DF determines the direction of a string instruction. All the string instructions operate backwards, from the last to the first element of the string, but if DF is reset, the string operations are performed from the first to the last element. The OF flag indicates an overflow condition and the last two flags, IOPL and NT, refer to the protected mode. IOPL indicates the minimum level of privilege required for performing I/O operations, while NT indicates whether a return from the current task is expected.

In the protected mode, the modification of IOPL, NT and IF are subject to checks on the privilege level. These checks inhibit operations

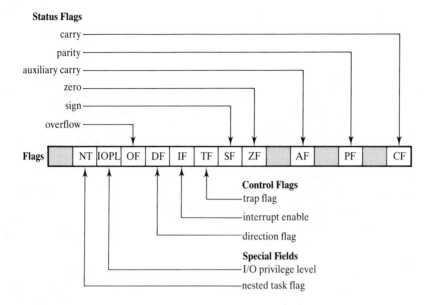

Figure 8.5 Contents of the flag register.

performed by unproven programs. TF cannot be modified directly in the flag register: it can only be altered by loading the whole flag register. Hence, TF can be modified by saving the flags on to the stack, modifying TF and restoring the flag register. TF is also reset by the occurrence of a single step interrupt.

8.5 Addressing modes

The iAPX286 instructions can operate on zero, one or two operands. The two-operand instructions only allow one operand to be stored in a register or memory location, while the others must be either immediate or stored in a register. The only exception to this rule is represented by instructions operating on strings, which manipulate operands, which are both stored in memory.

The mechanism for computing the address for any memory reference always involves one of the segment registers of the CPU. Each type of memory reference is associated with a specific segment register implicitly used when the address for that reference is computed. Only operand addressing allows a different segment register to be explicitly specified; thus, it is possible to reference operands in the code segment, in the stack segment or in the extra segment, by introducing a special single-byte prefix for the instruction. This overrides the implicit rule and is called the **segment override prefix**. However, the implicit rule for segment selection cannot be overridden when the memory reference is a stack or string operation.

Eight addressing modes are used in the iAPX286. However, since a reference to the memory requires the selection of an offset and a segment register, according to the implicit or explicit rules just described, the discussion on addressing modes that specify operands in memory will be limited to the offset computation.

The register operand is stored in either a 16- or 8-bit register, which can be general purpose, base or index. Some specific instructions can also access the segment and flag registers. Immediate operands, in comparison, are themselves part of the instructions. In the direct address, however, it is the 16-bit offset of the operand that is part of the instruction. The offset of the operand in the register indirect mode is stored in SI, DI or BX, with no limitation or implicit rules on the use of the three registers.

These addressing modes are quite simple and common to many microprocessors. However, the following modes are useful for addressing operands in more complex data structures. As the names of the modes do not correspond with those in Chapter 1, manufacturers' names for modes are explained in Table 8.2. The reader will therefore be able to refer to the general discussion on addressing modes to assess their possible use.

Table 8.2   Correspondence between manufacturers' name and addressing modes.

Type	Addressing Mode Intel's Notation	Operand Addressing
Register operand	Register operand	$G[g]$
Direct address	Direct address	$M[M[PC]]$, $PC := PC + 1$
Immediate	Immediate	$M[PC]$, $PC := PC+1$
Register indirect	Register indirect	$M[G[g]]$
Base displacement indirect	Based Indexed	$M[G[g] + d]$
Base indexed indirect	Base indexed	$M[G[g1] + G[g2].sht.N]$ $(N = 0)$
Base displacement indexed indirect	Base indexed with displacement	$M[G[g1] + d + G[g2].sht.N]$ $(N = 0)$

Note: Operand addressing does not take into account the addition of the suitable segment register contents.

8.5.1 Base

The operand offset here is obtained by adding the contents of either the BI or BX registers to a displacement, which is part of the instruction itself. This addressing mode therefore corresponds to base displacement indirect.

8.5.2 Indexed

The indexed operand offset is obtained by adding the contents of either SI or DI to a displacement, which is also part of the instruction. This addressing mode differs from base only in the registers involved in the offset computation.

8.5.3 Base indexed

The offset of this operand is computed by adding the contents of a base register (BP or BX) to the contents of an index register (SI or DI). This addressing mode is therefore equivalent to a base indexed indirect mode with no shift of either register.

8.5.4 Base indexed with displacement

This operand offset is computed by adding the contents of a base register (BP or BX), the contents of an index register (DI or SI) and a displacement, which is part of the instruction itself. This mode is equivalent to the base displacement indexed indirect mode, with no shift of either register.

8.6 Instruction set

8.6.1 Data transfer instructions

The general-purpose instruction for data transfer is MOV. Because all the instructions in the iAPX286 must have at least one operand in a register – with the exception of string instructions – MOV can be used to transfer data between registers, or from registers to memory, and vice versa. Two separate instructions, IN and OUT, are provided to transfer words or bytes to or from I/O devices. To execute IN or OUT correctly, the CPL privilege code in the program must be no greater than the IOPL field in the flag word (see also Section 8.9). This only allows I/O operations for routines with a sufficiently high privilege level.

However, some special data movements cannot be executed by

using the MOV instruction; all the data transfer to and from the stack are implemented by dedicated instructions, for example, since the autoincrement/decrement addressing modes are illegal in other instructions. Simple PUSH and POP instructions are included in this class, along with POPF and PUSHF, which are used to pop and push the flag register from or on to the stack. The two instructions POPA and PUSHA are used to pop and push the whole register, and they can be useful for implementing task switching, since they immediately implement the register save/restore operations (see Section 3.4).

To load segment registers dedicated instructions are needed; for example, the two segment registers DS and ES can be loaded with a pair of 16-bit words stored in memory by using the LDS and LES instructions. Another register manipulated with dedicated instructions is the flag register, which may be loaded from the register AH, using SAHF, or copied into the register AH, using LAHF.

The instruction XCHG is of particular interest – it exchanges the contents of a specified register with the contents of an addressed memory location. During its execution the $\overline{\text{LOCK}}$ signal is activated and the instruction is indivisible. XCHG may therefore be used to implement the test-and-set instruction introduced in Chapter 3 as a support for mutual exclusion. It is necessary here to set the register to 1s and exchange it with the memory location that stores the state of the resource. When the instruction is executed, the resource is set to busy, and after the XCHG instruction it is possible to find what the state of the resource was before XCHG was executed.

Table lookup operations may be easily implemented using the XLAT instruction. This uses the contents of the register AL as an index to the table whose starting address is in the register pair DS:BX; the byte in the table addressed by AL is itself copied into AL.

8.6.2   Integer and BCD arithmetic instructions

The four basic arithmetic operations are implemented in the instruction set. Addition may be performed by the normal instruction ADD, by the instruction addition of carry (ADC) or by the special instruction increment by one (INC). Similarly, subtraction may be performed by using SUB, borrow (SBB) or decrement by one (DEC). Another arithmetic instruction is NEG, which changes the sign of the operand.

Two separate multiplication instructions, MUL and IMUL, are provided for multiplying signed and unsigned integers, respectively. In both cases, 8-bit operands with 16-bit results and 16-bit operands with 32-bit results are legal. The multiplication instructions require that one operand be stored in AL or AX, according to whether the operand is a byte or a word, and the result is stored in AX, or in the pair AX:DX, depending on whether the result is 16- or 32-bits long.

The same distinction between signed and unsigned integers may be found for division: both instructions divide the AX register or the pair AX:DX by an 8- or 16-bit divisor, and the result is stored in AL or AX, depending on the length of the quotient. The remainder is stored either in AH or in DX. The instruction IDIV is used for unsigned operands, while DIV operates on signed integers.

BCD arithmetic, both packed and unpacked, is implemented by providing adjustment instructions. These make it possible to use integer arithmetic instructions to perform the corresponding BCD operations. The result is then corrected by the adjustment instructions. This is valid for addition and subtraction, while for multiplication and division the adjustment must be performed before the integer operation. Adjustment instructions are therefore implemented for addition (AAA for unpacked and DAA for packed data), subtraction (AAS for unpacked and DAS for packed data), multiplication (AAM for unpacked data) and division (AAD for unpacked data).

Two instructions are implemented to extend the sign of a register, so that they can operate with operands of different length: CWD extends the sign of the operand stored in AX to DX, while CBW extends the sign of AL to AH.

8.6.3 Logical and shift instructions

This class of instructions includes the four classical instructions, bit-wise logical OR, AND, NOT and EXOR, operating on both byte and word operands. The TEST instruction is also used to set the flag values according to the value of the instruction operand.

The shift and rotate instructions can perform multiple shifts and rotations, depending on the value of one of their operands. However, the execution time increases with the number of positions the data need to be shifted or rotated.

The operations implemented are: left arithmetic/logic shift (SHL/SAL), and right arithmetic (SAR) shift and right logical shift (SHR), with insertion of zeros in the most significant bits. Rotate instructions allow simple right and left bit rotations, ROR and ROL, respectively, together with right and left rotations through the carry flag, RCR and RCL, respectively.

8.6.4 Instruction prefixes

One characteristic peculiar to the iAPX286 instruction set is the possibility of using leading prefixes for the instructions. These can have special effects on the execution of the instruction itself. Basically, three types of one-byte prefix are allowed:

- segment override;
- repetition;
- lock.

The first prefix explicitly specifies the segment register to be used for addressing the memory operand of the instruction; the explicit indication overrules the implicit segment register use described in Section 8.2.4. The segment override prefix is automatically generated by the assembler, whenever the programmer explicitly indicates a segment register in the operand addressing mode.

The repetition prefix is only allowed before a specific subset of data movement and comparison instructions. The prefix REP placed before one such instruction causes the repetition of the prefixed instruction until the value stored in the register CX is zero. Other prefixes – for example, REPE/REPZ and REPNE/REPNZ may be used with some comparison instructions to stop the repetition of the prefixed instruction when CX reaches zero or a comparison does or does not fail. REPE may thus be interpreted as repeat while zero flag set and REPNE as repeat while zero flag reset.

Repetition prefixes allow the programmer to obtain string operations by loading the string length in the CX register before the execution of the prefixed operation. The prefixed can only be used with certain instructions because such instructions must perform a data transfer or comparison and decrement CX as well.

The LOCK prefix may be used to implement indivisible read–modify–write memory operations in multiprocessor configurations. During the execution of the prefixed instruction, the external hardware signal ($\overline{\text{LOCK}}$) is active; while it stays active, $\overline{\text{LOCK}}$ prevents connection with the shared memory being lost. As explained in Section 3.5, this condition is essential for the correct implementation of elementary indivisible operations on shared variables. The LOCK prefix can only be used when the privilege code of the program is no greater than the IOPL field in the flag word.

As more than one prefix is allowed on the same instruction, it is possible to perform locked string instructions. Here, the LOCK prefix is only valid for each operation on a single element of the string, as long locking periods can harm multiprocessor systems. For similar reasons, external interrupts may be recognized at the end of each iteration composing a string instruction.

8.6.5 Array and string instructions

The operations on string operands in the iAPX286 are implemented with special instructions in conjunction with a suitable repetition prefix. The common characteristic of such instructions is that they are able to perform their operation on a single string element, and to increment or decrement the source (SI) or destination (DI) index register according to whether the direction flag (DF) is zero or one. The registers are incremented by one for strings of bytes, or by two for strings of words. In addition to the increment or decrement of the two index registers, storing the pointers within the strings, the instructions described in this section also decrement the contents of the counter register (CX).

The movement of strings is implemented by the MOVS instruction, which copies the contents of the location referenced by SI into the location whose address is obtained by combining the ES segment register with the offset stored in DI. If a REP prefix is used with MOVS, the instruction copies the source string into a destination string, with a length specified by the contents of the counter register CX.

The CMPS instruction compares the operand whose offset is in SI with the operand whose address is given by the pair of registers ES:DI. This instruction leaves both operands unchanged, but sets their flags. If a REPE prefix is used, CMPS compares two strings and terminates when the CX register is zero, meaning the string is terminated, or when the zero flag is set, representing a pair of string elements that do not match.

The search for a specific word or byte in a string may be implemented by the instruction SCAS which compares the contents of AL (for byte operations) or AX (for word operations) with the contents of the location whose address is given by ES:DI. With a REPE prefix, SCAS searches for a string element other than AL or AX; the execution stops when the whole string has been examined and CX reaches zero or when the last element has reset the zero flag. The REPNE prefix performs a similar function in searching for a byte or word equal to AL or AX.

String operations are also legal for data transfer with I/O devices. The instructions governing this type of operation are INS and OUTS. Both these instructions move a byte or word from or to the addressed I/O device; the element read by INS is accessed by ES:DI, while the element written by OUTS is referenced by ES:SI. As in other I/O operations, INS and OUTS can only be correctly executed if the current privilege code is no greater than the IOPL field in the flag word. When used with the prefix REP, INS and OUTS can input or output a string of data, whose length is specified by CX. REPE and REPNE prefixes cannot be used, however, since INS and OUTS do not modify the flags.

The STOS instruction stores the contents of the AL or AX registers – for byte or word operations, respectively – into the memory location given by ES:DI. If the REP prefix is used, STOS can block fill CX bytes or words. Similarly, the LODS operation loads the AL or AX registers with the contents of the memory location given by ES:SI, but it does not decrement CX. LODS cannot therefore be used with repetition prefixes. It does, however, increment or decrement the pointer.

The only instruction related to the use of arrays in high-level languages is BOUND. This instruction checks whether the contents of the register specified as the first operand are in the range indicated by the memory words specified as the second operand. If the check fails, trap 5 is activated. BOUND implements subscript bound checks for array elements.

8.6.6 Comparison and program flow instructions

The iAPX286 implements a set of flags, and conditional jumps are performed by setting the flag values and then executing a conditional jump instruction; this tests the flags to decide whether or not the jump should be taken.

One important operation for conditional jumps is the comparison of two operands. This is implemented by the CMP instructions, whose only effect is to set the flags according to the result of the subtraction of the two operands. The result of the comparison may then be used by a set of conditional jump instructions testing the flags. The subtraction performed by CMP is used for signed operands, but it can also be used for comparing unsigned operands, since a separate set of conditional jumps for unsigned numbers is also provided.

Conditional jumps for signed and unsigned numbers test for the greater than, greater than or equal to, less than or equal to and less than operations. In addition to these jumps, used after comparison instructions, it is possible to use conditional jumps on the value of the flags ZF, OF, PF, and SF. A special instruction, JCXZ, may be used to jump when the CX register is zero. This is used to test the CX register itself, which is often used as a counter.

Loop termination can be controlled using three special instructions: LOOP, LOOPE or LOOPZ (these two names are equivalent) and LOOPNE or LOONZ. All three instructions decrement the CX register and test the result. LOOP jumps if $CX \neq 0$; LOOPE/LOOPZ jumps if $CX \neq 0$ and $ZF = 1$; and LOOPNE/LOOPNZ jumps if $CX \neq 0$ and $ZF = 0$. These loop instructions control the loops using the CX register to count the iterations.

Procedure call and return instructions are only implemented in the unconditional form. The return instruction (RET) is also allowed to have a parameter specifying the even number of bytes to be removed from the stack just after the return. This eliminates the parameters pushed when the procedure has been called.

Strictly connected with the procedure call/return there are two further instructions, ENTER and LEAVE. These are used to set the appropriate working frame of a high-level language on the stack (see Chapter 1) when a procedure call or return instruction is issued. The

ENTER instruction has two parameters: the first indicates the amount of storage to be allocated on the stack for the local variables of the procedure; the second indicates the level of nesting of the procedure declaration in the source program, which correctly sets the display field. The effect of ENTER is shown in Figure 8.6, where a main program calls a procedure *A* and needs to allocate the corresponding area for the local variables on the stack, just after the procedure begins. Figure 8.6(a) shows the stack contents before ENTER is executed, and Figure 8.6(b) shows the situation after the execution. The LEAVE instruction may be used to de-allocate space on the stack just before the procedure return and it works in exactly the opposite way to ENTER.

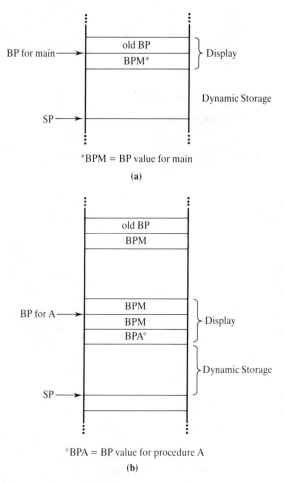

Figure 8.6 Stack contents (a) before and (b) after the execution of an ENTER instruction.

Call instructions may activate a procedure whose code is in the same segment of the caller, or even in a different segment. In the first case, a 32-bit address is pushed on to the stack, while in the second only a 16-bit offset is pushed. Two kinds of return instruction are needed: an inter-segment return, popping a 32-bit return address, and an intra-segment return, popping only a 16-bit return offset. Thus, libraries composed of modules called by external routines or other library modules cannot be implemented without using 32-bit call/return instructions.

A special case of program control transfer is the invocation of special trap handlers to detect exceptions or to implement operating system calls. This is made possible through the INT instructions, which use the number associated with the handler as a parameter to be activated in the interrupt descriptor table. Overflow conditions can, however, raise a trap if the INTO instruction is used just after an arithmetic instruction whose result needs to be tested for a possible overflow.

8.6.7   Privileged and CPU control instructions

When used in protected mode, important information required for operations should be stored in the correct system. For example, the contents of special registers used by the memory protection mechanisms and control flags should be stored, so it is necessary to prevent unprivileged software from incorrectly altering such information. A solution is to allow a program to execute a set of privileged instructions only if its level of privilege is not less than a specified value.

Not all the instructions manipulating flags are privileged. For example, the three carry flag instructions, set (STC), clear (CLC) and complement (CMC), can be executed with any privilege level without causing an exception. Another flag that can be set (STD) and cleared (CLD), regardless of the privilege level, is the direction flag. The instructions used to set and clear the interrupt enable flag, STI and CLI, respectively, can only be executed when the privilege code is no greater than the IOPL field in the flag word.

The IOPL field, in contrast, can be loaded or stored only when the privilege level is greatest. The PUSHF and POPF instructions are thus privileged, as well as the specific instructions for loading and storing the machine status word, LMSW and SMSW, respectively.

The highest privilege level is required to execute instructions manipulating the registers used for memory protection and task switching. These include the global descriptor table (LGDT and SGDT), the local descriptor table (LLDT and SLDT), the interrupt descriptor table (LIDT and SIDT), and the task register (LTR and STR).

Other operations related to access rights manipulation do not require any special privilege level. However, they can only be correctly executed if the operands are visible from the current privilege level. LAR, for example, loads the access rights into a register, LSL, that loads the segment limit into a register, while ARPL adjusts the RPL field (see Section 8.8). The same requirement is valid for the VERR and VERW instructions used to verify whether read or write operations are or are not allowed on a specific segment.

Finally, the HLT instruction, which stops CPU operation until an interrupt or reset is received, can only be executed at the highest privilege level. The WAIT instruction, however, which suspends CPU activity until the $\overline{\text{BUSY}}$ signal is de-activated, does not require any special privilege level to be correctly executed.

8.7 Memory management and protection

8.7.1 Virtual address

The protected mode allows each task to address up to 1 Gbyte. As this address space is larger than the maximum physical memory size (16 Mbytes) allowed in the iAPX286, the system provides a mechanism to map the larger virtual address space into the physical one. Of course, only a subset of the whole virtual address space can be mapped at a given time: the rest of the addressing space resides on mass storage devices, as discussed in Chapter 4. The iAPX286 manages the physical memory according to the segmentation philosophy.

The virtual address is composed of a 16-bit offset within a specific segment with a 16-bit segment selector. The format of a segment selector is shown in Figure 8.7. Note that only the highest 14 bits are used for mapping the virtual address into the physical address, while the RPL field is used by the protection mechanisms and will be discussed later.

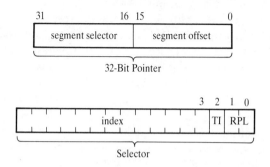

Figure 8.7 Format of a segment selector.

The two possible segments of the virtual address space of an individual task are the global segments, common to all programs running on the same iAPX286, and the local segments, visible only to the current task. This subdivision of virtual space satisfies the two conflicting needs arising in systems running monoprocessing and multitasking in parallel. The independent tasks need separate virtual spaces so that each one can use the whole address space with maximum freedom. This avoids the problem of overlapping the memory areas of two different programs. On the other hand, partial memory overlapping must be implemented for cooperating tasks, which need to communicate by using common data structures. Overlapping on machines supporting only separate virtual spaces is difficult to implement, as it requires the mapping of two separate virtual addresses on to the same physical address. As the physical address can change during execution, because of swapping operations on the portions of different virtual spaces, it is very difficult to keep the two mappings consistent. Thus, overlapping should be implemented directly at the virtual address level.

The solution adopted in the iAPX286 consists of a double-mapping mechanism: one is for the global or overlapped virtual space, which always maps a virtual address into the same physical address whatever the task issuing the address; the other mechanism maps a virtual address into one of several possible physical addresses, depending on the task issuing the address. The distinction between the two mechanisms is made by the CPU using the value of the TI bit in the segment selector. The remaining 13 bits indicate one of the segments in the global or local address space.

8.7.2 Segment descriptors and their organization

The physical address computation is obtained as shown by Figure 8.8. The TI bit selects either the local descriptor table (LDT) or the global descriptor table (GDT). The 13-bit segment number is used as an index within such a table, stored in RAM, to find the descriptor of the addressed segment. This holds the physical address of the first byte of the segment, and the offset field is used to find the referenced memory location within the segment. Each descriptor table stores up to 1024 entries (each one 8 bytes long).

In addition to the base address, each segment descriptor also holds information useful for memory management. The layout of a normal segment descriptor is shown in Figure 8.9. The base address is a 24-bit field, which is followed by a limit field indicating the actual segment size in bytes; this is so the memory protection mechanism can check whether the offset of the virtual address falls within the segment. The format of the other valid byte in the segment descriptor is shown in Figure 8.10, where both the code segment and the data segment cases are illustrated.

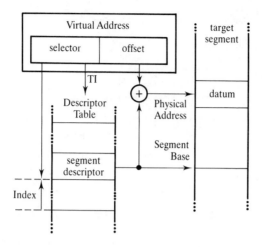

Figure 8.8 Physical address computation in protected mode.

A present or absent (P) flag indicates whether the addressed segment currently resides in the main memory or whether it needs to be swapped in. The addressing of an absent segment activates a special trap, which will be discussed later.

Another flag relevant to memory management is the access (A) bit, which is set on the first access to a segment following a reset operation on that bit. In this way, it is possible to verify if the segment is frequently used or not.

All other flags and fields are used by the protection mechanisms for checking both the type of access and the privilege level.

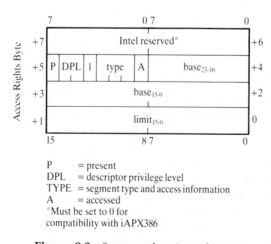

Figure 8.9 Segment descriptor format.

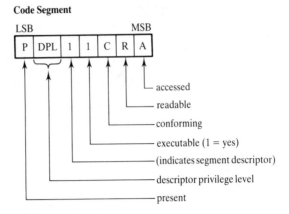

Code Segment

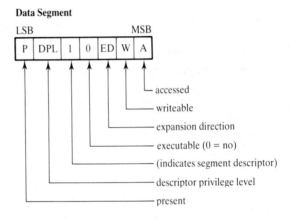

Data Segment

Figure 8.10   Format of the access byte in a segment descriptor.

The segment descriptor tables may also be regarded as segments, so they too need segment descriptors. The local descriptor table (LDT) segment descriptors differ slightly from normal descriptors and their format is shown in Figure 8.11. LDT segment descriptors must all be placed in the global descriptor table (GDT). An access to an LDT whose segment descriptor is stored in another LDT will cause a protection violation. The contents of the LDT, whose descriptors are in the GDT, cannot be modified by mistake. It can only be loaded into a memory management register using the LCTR instruction.

The relationship between the different types of segment and segment descriptors are summarized in Figure 8.12.

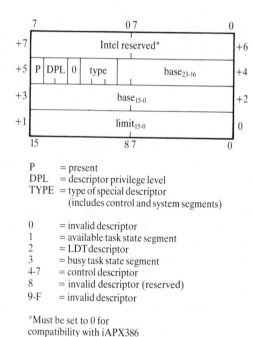

P = present
DPL = descriptor privilege level
TYPE = type of special descriptor
(includes control and system segments)

0 = invalid descriptor
1 = available task state segment
2 = LDT descriptor
3 = busy task state segment
4-7 = control descriptor
8 = invalid descriptor (reserved)
9-F = invalid descriptor

*Must be set to 0 for
compatibility with iAPX386

Figure 8.11 Control segment descriptor format.

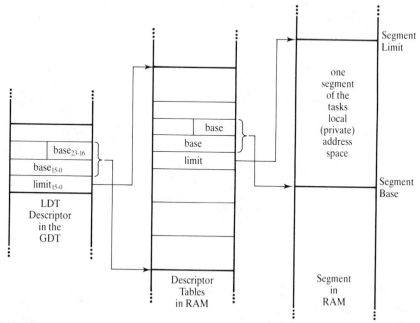

Figure 8.12 Complete process of address computation for local segment references.

8.7.3   Loading segment registers

Not all iAPX286 memory references need to go through the double indexing mechanism of Figure 8.12 to access proper locations, since the microprocessor provides a set of registers for storing the most frequently used information related to the address translation operations. These registers are shown in Figure 8.13. It is worth noting that the four registers CS, DS, ES and SS are the same as those discussed in Section 8.4.2; however, they have a 16-bit visible part, which can be modified by a programmer using the load instruction. Jump instructions can be used on CS only. The contents of the segment registers are always interpreted as a segment selector, according to the format in Figure 8.7.

When the contents of a segment register are altered, the iAPX286 loads the 48-bit hidden part of the register with the significant part of the segment descriptor corresponding to the selector stored in the visible part. To retrieve the required segment descriptor, the contents of either GDTR or LDTR are used to obtain the base address of the GDT or LDT, respectively. The hidden parts of the registers cannot be explicitly manipulated by the program, since they can only be altered by loading a new segment descriptor. This must always correspond to the selector stored in the visible part of the same register.

When a reference is issued to a memory location within one of the four current segments, the CPU can find all the information needed to translate a virtual address into a physical address in the internal registers, without generating any additional memory reference. This allows fast

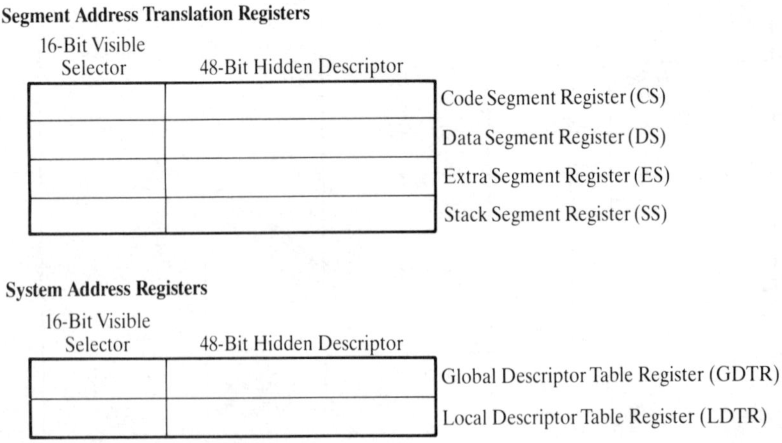

Segment Address Translation Registers

16-Bit Visible Selector	48-Bit Hidden Descriptor	
		Code Segment Register (CS)
		Data Segment Register (DS)
		Extra Segment Register (ES)
		Stack Segment Register (SS)

System Address Registers

16-Bit Visible Selector	48-Bit Hidden Descriptor	
		Global Descriptor Table Register (GDTR)
		Local Descriptor Table Register (LDTR)

Figure 8.13   Full format of segment and control registers.

address translations, as far as the program locality characteristics allow the CPU to use the same segment descriptors.

The LDTR stores the information on the LDT to be used by the current running task. It has a 16-bit visible part, where the LDT segment selector is stored, and a 48-bit hidden part. This latter part holds the base address and the limit of the LDT, whose descriptor corresponds to the selector stored in the visible part; hence, the hidden part cannot be directly manipulated by the programmer.

The GDTR has the same format as the LDTR; however, it is visible only for the highest privilege tasks, which load it with the values of a base address and a limit for the memory area serving as GDT during initialization. Such a register is completely hidden from the tasks at lower privilege levels.

8.7.4 Protection mechanisms

The mechanisms for virtual-to-physical address translation provide a method of implementing protection mechanisms for task isolation and limited type checking.

The isolation of the different address spaces is implemented only for the priviate portion of each task's virtual memory space, because all the memory references are translated by a different local descriptor table (LDT). There is no possibility therefore of accessing the memory area of another task, provided that the LDT descriptors and the LDTR register have been correctly set.

The LDT can be seen as a list of capabilities for the different segments (see Chapter 4). If a segment descriptor is in the LDT of a task, then that task has access capabilities for the segment, specified in the access byte of the segment descriptor. A special case is the segment descriptor with the P flag set to zero; when a reference is issued to this segment, a protection violation trap is generated. This mechanism suspends the execution of the instruction when a reference for a segment not present in the main memory is generated.

The same kind of protection against incorrect memory accesses is not implemented for global virtual space, since all the descriptors for the segments in this space are stored in the same table, the global descriptor table (GDT). This isolation, implemented by using different addressing spaces for the private spaces, disappears when global segments are accessed. This can cause problems if the global segments are used by different groups of tasks for storing common data structures. In this case, the erroneous accesses of a task to the global data structures of another group cannot be recognized.

Since the global virtual space not only holds common areas for different applications tasks, but also segments of the operating system, it is necessary to use some other mechanisms to prevent the corruption of system software code and data structures. Such corruption is usually caused by incorrect accesses generated by the application tasks.

The mechanism used to protect system segments in the GDT is based on hardware-recognized privilege states, which prevent less privileged software from accessing segments of more privileged tasks directly. In this way, global memory segments are protected from erroneous accesses by tasks at lower privilege levels, but it is still possible to execute incorrect accesses to global segments at the same privilege level. To protect the memory areas effectively different applications tasks should not communicate through the common data structures stored in global segments. In other words, an intensive use of the global virtual memory space by tasks with the lowest privilege level endangers program execution.

Before discussing the implications of the privilege state mechanisms in the iAPX286, consider again the protection mechanisms associated with the address translation process. In addition to the intrinsic protection given by the separation of the private virtual spaces, a memory reference issued for a private or global segment fires a set of checks on the legality of the access. If the reference is for a memory location within one of the four segments currently accessible via the CPU segment registers, then the checks performed are those on the offset values. These must not exceed the limit field of the segment descriptors. Checks on the type of access must match them with the type field of the segment descriptor. In this way, it is possible to catch all the accesses beyond the segment size and all the attempts to use segment contents incorrectly. Performing stack operations on read-only segments is one example.

Whenever the program loads a new segment selector into one of the segment registers, or into the LDTR and TR (task register) registers, the corresponding segment descriptor is retrieved and loaded into the hidden part of the register. These operations are subject to a number of additional checks performed automatically by the hardware.

The first check is on the value of the segment index, which must not exceed the limit of the LDT or GDT it is stored in. Furthermore, the hardware checks the type of segment, so that any attempt to load the LDTR register with a non-LDT descriptor, for example, raises a memory protection violation trap. Similar checks are also performed when CS, DS, SS and ES are loaded. The hardware controls whether the type of access allowed for the segment is compatible with the intended use of the register. It is not possible, therefore, to load the CS register with a non-code segment descriptor, or to load the SS register with a code-segment descriptor.

Since some entries in the LDT and GDT may be empty, the checks can also catch attempts to use such segments descriptors illegally.

8.8 Privileged machine states

The privilege state mechanism of the iAPX286 is an extension of the system/user states often found in other microprocessors. There are four privilege levels and four corresponding hardware-recognized machine states. These levels are numbered 0 to 3, 0 being the highest privilege level, 3 being the least; therefore, high privilege level corresponds to low privilege code and vice versa. A privilege code (DPL) is written in the descriptor of each segment in the system, and this determines the restriction on the access to the segment contents.

The basic access rules associated with the privilege levels are as follows:

(1) data segments are accessible only by tasks at the same or higher privilege levels;

(2) subroutines can be called only by tasks at the same or lower levels than the called routine.

These rules are consequences of the basic assumption that software reliability increases when the privilege code decreases. Hence, more privileges are assigned to more trustworthy software. This can manipulate data structures also used by less privileged tasks. On the other hand, calling less privileged and less trusted routines may cause the reliable software to fire the execution of incorrect actions, so these calls are forbidden by the iAPX286 hardware.

As noted in Chapter 4, the introduction of privileged machine states violates the basic principle that each process should have the capabilities strictly required by the task assigned to it. In the iAPX286, the privilege levels protect against software mistakes, because more privileges are assigned to more trustworthy software, so that the unneeded capabilities of this software are never used. However, if errors caused by hardware faults are considered, the execution of more privileged software cannot be considered more reliable; thus, if a wrong segment selector is used at higher privilege levels, then the protection mechanisms are not able to detect the incorrect access.

This partial protection is not a typical characteristic of the iAPX286, but it derives from the introduction of the privilege levels. On the other hand, privilege states are a cheap solution to several protection problems.

8.8.1 Privilege code checking

Privilege codes are stored in several places in control data structures within the system. A DPL privilege code field is present in the segment descriptors; another privilege code, RPL, occupies the two least significant bits of a segment selector; while CPL is the DPL field of the segment descriptors stored in CS and SS. CPL indicates the privilege level of the program currently executed.

When a CPU segment register is loaded with a new value, the hardware performs some controls on the DPL field of the referenced descriptor, in addition to the checks on segment limit and type. In the case of a data segment descriptor, the check is passed only if DPL $\geqslant$ CPL, so that the rule on data accessibility is verified. In the case of a code segment, the check is passed only if DPL = CPL, because inter-level jumps and calls are subject to other checking mechanisms, described later.

Less reliable software can, however, call more privileged routines, and it can pass pointers as parameters to that software. Potentially, this mechanism allows an unreliable task to manipulate a segment outside its access domain, by asking a more privileged routine to manipulate a segment, whose pointer is passed to the privileged routine by the unreliable caller. To avoid this problem, it is necessary to check whether pointers received by a routine are accessible by the caller.

This pointer-validation operation is performed by the iAPX286 hardware on the RPL field in the segment selector. This is part of a 32-bit pointer. The RPL field contains the privilege level of the routine from which the selector originated. In this way, even if the pointer is passed through several procedure calls, it always holds the privilege level of its originator in the RPL field.

When a data segment is loaded in an internal segment register, the RPL is checked against CPL, and if RPL > CPL, then a protection violation trap is activated.

8.8.2   Control transfer operations

Control transfer operations relevant to the protection system are jumps or calls to code segments at the same privilege level, or calls to code segments with lower privilege levels. But jumping to such segments is not allowed.

All the protection mechanisms for checking the accuracy of control transfers in the iAPX286 are based on the so-called **call gate**, which is used to establish whether the requested transfer satisfies the following criteria:

- the transfer destination address is accessible by the task;
- the constraints on the privilege levels are met;
- the transfer destination address is a correct entry point.

In the case of a transfer destination address outside the current code segment, the offset field is meaningless, since only the segment selector is used to retrieve the call gate, whose format is shown in Figure 8.14, from either the local or the global descriptor table. Note that the TYPE field may also indicate other types of gates, such as those used for traps and interrupts. Such gates are used for control transfers not caused by a simple procedure call – their use will be discussed in Section 8.10.

The call gate holds the real destination address of the current control transfer in the usual form of offset and segment selector. Therefore, to reach the destination segment, it is necessary to retrieve the segment descriptor referenced by the segment selector stored in the call gate. Then the entry point address is computed using the offset and stored in the call gate. The base address is stored in the code segment descriptor. The whole addressing process is summarized in Figure 8.15.

Note here that the programmer does not know even the virtual address of the location the program is jumping to. Consequently, this allows a routine used by more than one task to relocate within the global address space, for example, without modifying the programs that need to call that routine.

As call gates introduce an additional level of indirection, their use

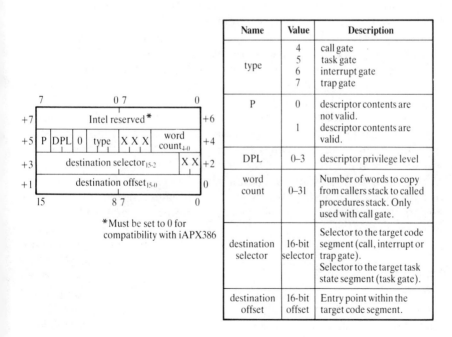

Figure 8.14   Gate descriptor format.

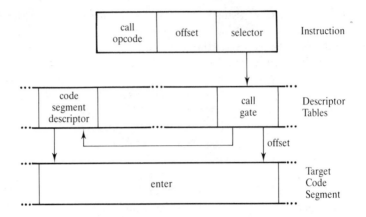

Figure 8.15 Destination transfer address computation using a call gate.

leads to some loss in execution speed; however, they can be used to implement different forms of protected access to certain pieces of code. For example, a routine shared between two tasks should be hidden to all other tasks in the system. Since the corresponding call gates may be in the local address space, a call gate pointing to the shared code is placed in the local address space of each task requiring to call the routine. The code itself, however, can be placed in the global address space, so that it is accessible by more than one task. In this way, all the tasks holding a call gate pointing to the shared routine can call it, while others cannot use the routine, because no call gate for that code exists within their address space, either global or local.

Call gates are like segment descriptors, and so the privilege rule checks also apply to the call gates. To perform a correct control transfer, the maximum value between CPL and the selector RPL must be no greater than the DPL field in the addressed call gate. This mechanism allows the system to establish a minimum privilege level required to jump or call the routine accessed through the call gates. System routines not needed by the user programs cannot therefore be accessed by non-privileged users.

Another check on privilege levels is required to enforce the second type of protection. This check involves the caller's CPL field and the DPL field of the destination code descriptor, but not the call gate descriptor. The correct control transfer must have CPL ≥ DPL. If CPL = DPL (that is, no privilege change is implied by the control transfer), then jump instructions are accepted on the call gate; otherwise only call instructions are allowed to change the current privilege level implicitly.

To preserve system integrity, separate stacks are maintained for each privilege level within the same task; thus, a change of the privilege level caused by a control transfer also leads to a stack switch. Such a situation could cause problems, because one of the commonest techniques of passing parameters to a subroutine, especially for compiler-generated code, is to place them on to the stack. This problem is solved in the iAPX286 by specifying the number of words (0 to 31) to be copied, upon a call, from the old stack to the new one. This number is stored in the WORD COUNT field of the gate descriptor. Using this mechanism, the old values of SS, SP, CS and IP are saved on to the new stack, in addition to a number of words copied from the top of the old stack, as specified by WORD COUNT. The caller's CPL is also saved in the two least significant bits of CS.

Upon the execution of a return instruction, the hardware checks whether the current CPL is lower than or equal to the RPL of the caller's CS, saved next to the top of stack. If so, the return is considered correct, otherwise a protection violation trap is activated.

If the DS and ES registers hold upon procedure return descriptors with a DPL lower than the new CPL, meaning they are more privileged than the caller, they are loaded with a null segment, so that any further attempt to use them will cause a general violation trap. This check prevents data manipulated by privileged routines being accessed by less privileged software, through segment descriptors left in the registers after the completion of a privileged routine.

8.8.3 Conforming segments

Special types of segment, called **conforming segments**, are allowed in the iAPX286 to implement procedures that can be executed at the same privilege level of the caller, instead of owning their CPL. Of course, some checks are not applicable to such segments. For example, procedures in conforming segments can be called by programs at any privilege level, and they are executed without changing the CPL and the stack. Similar exceptions to the protection rules are allowed if the conforming segment is readable; in this case, its contents can be accessed by any privilege level. Conforming segments are indicated by a dedicated bit in the segment descriptor and represent the only exception to the basic rules governing the protection mechanisms implemented.

8.9 Task control information and switching

8.9.1 Task state descriptor

To obtain a real protected execution environment, it is not enough for the protection mechanisms to only cover the accesses performed by different tasks on data or code segments; they need to be extended to control task execution and switching. To achieve this, the iAPX286 uses control data structures to store all the control information required for correct task managing. Their structure is similar to the other control structures adopted to protect access to data and procedures.

The main structures used are the task state segment (TSS) and the associated segment descriptor, whose format is shown in Figure 8.16. The P bit is used to signal whether or not the descriptor holds valid information, whereas the DPL field controls the access to the descriptor. The type field may be either 1 or 3, depending on whether the corresponding task is active. This indication is used to avoid nested activations of the same tasks, since the tasks are considered non re-entrant. Base and limit fields have the usual meaning.

The contents of a TSS are shown in Figure 8.17. Each one is composed of a static portion, which can never be changed during the task's life, and a dynamic portion, whose contents are generally changed by task-switching operations. The static part stores the information, which should be protected against illegal manipulation; hence, the static fields of the TSS are those indicating the segment and offset of the stack to be used when the task is in the three most privileged states. The selector of the task's local descriptor table is also static. All these data are essential to perform correct operations, because the information in the local descriptor table is used to separate the local data space of the current task from the addressing spaces of all the other tasks in the system. The stack pointers of privilege levels 0 to 2, on the other hand, are essential for the correct behaviour of the privileged software.

The dynamic portion of the TSS is used, essentially, to save the state of the task when its execution is suspended; thus, the TSS in the iAPX286 takes the role of the process descriptor, introduced in Chapter 3, where all the register and other information required for an

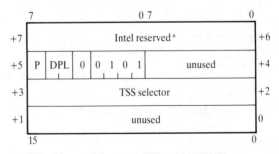

*Must be set to 0 for compatibility with iAPX386

Figure 8.16   Task state segment descriptor format.

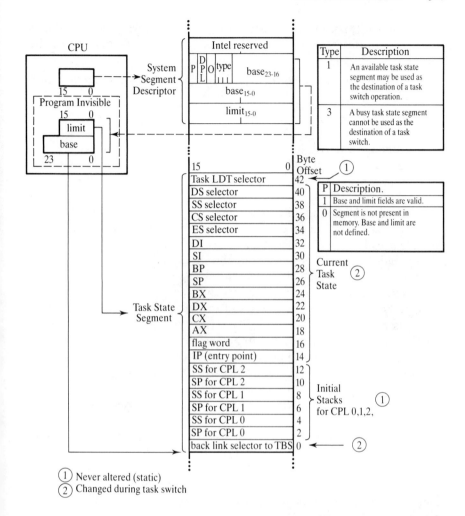

Figure 8.17 Task state segment format.

eventual correct resumption are stored. One particular field is represented by the back link, which is used to return the CPU control to the
calling task, when the current task terminates.

8.9.2 Task switching

A task-switching operation is fired when one of the following events
occurs:

● a jump or call instruction is executed, and the destination selector
refers to a TSS;

- a return from interrupt instruction is executed when the NT flag is set – in this case, the control is passed to the task pointed by the back link field of the terminating one;
- the destination selector of a jump or call instruction refers to a task gate;
- an interrupt occurs.

Although call and jump instructions may be used to activate a new task, they have different effects. If a call instruction is used, then a return from the new task is expected, but if a jump instruction is used, no return is expected.

If the task switching is performed through a task gate, the controls performed are identical to the checks fired when a subroutine is called through a call gate. No constraint exists for the privilege levels of the calling and called tasks, however, because each task is considered autonomous. The format of a task gate is as outlined in Figure 8.14.

After the checks on accessibility and the existence of a new task, the state of the outgoing task is saved in the appropriate area, reserved within its own TSS; the new task is then marked 'busy'. Its descriptor is placed in the TR register so that the new TSS is readily accessible using an internal CPU register. Finally, the state of the new task is restored from the appropriate area in the new TSS. The back link field in the TSS of the incoming task is also set to point to the TSS descriptor of the outgoing task, if the task switching has been fired by a call instruction, an interrupt or a trap.

The iAPX286 can perform a task switch in a single instruction, including the save and restore operations of the state of the outgoing and incoming tasks. However, the state automatically saved or restored by a call or jump to another task only refers to the internal CPU registers. A complete task state should also include the internal state of the arithmetic co-processor, if present.

After a task switch, an internal flag is set so that when the current task attempts to perform an operation involving the arithmetic co-processor a processor extension not-present exception (7) is automatically activated. The service routine of such a trap should internally maintain the information about the last task that used the arithmetic co-processor. This can help identify the task the current co-processor context belongs to. If the last co-processor owner is identical to the current task, then no action need be performed, because the current contents of the co-processor refer to the same task attempting to use it. Otherwise, the co-processor state must be saved in the TSS of the task that last used it. The format of a TSS shown in Figure 8.17 only has the fields mandatory for a correct implementation. There are no limitations on increasing such a descriptor area to include a block of words used for saving the state of the computation in the arithmetic co-processor or for saving any other information needed by the user. The only difference between these additional areas and those shown in Figure 8.17 is that the areas in the figure are automatically handled during a task switch, while the additional areas should be explicitly managed by privileged software.

The internal flag indicating that a task switch has occurred is reset when the exception generated by the first co-processor operation has been activated. Hence, any further operations involving the co-processor will be executed normally, so that system performance is no longer affected.

This mechanism circumvents harmful effects, which could arise as a consequence of a task switch. The most trivial example of such an effect is the corruption of the contents in the co-processor register; but much worse is the effect of numeric exception, such as an overflow, caused by an operation of the outgoing task. This is sensed during the execution of the incoming task. In this case, a task is forced to serve an interrupt referring to the execution of another task, while the outgoing task, which is the logical recipient of the exception, will never be aware that an error occurred in a co-processor operation.

When a task terminates, the IRET instruction should be executed. If the nested task (NT) flag is set, then a task switch passes control to the task whose TSS descriptor is referenced by the back link of the current task's TSS. If NT is cleared, a normal return from interrupt is performed, by using the current contents of the stack. A task activated by a call instruction or by an interrupt or trap occurrence has the NT flag set, initially, by the task-switching operation.

Tried and tested software is allowed to modify the back links of the different TSSs in the system. This kind of operation is necessary if the user needs to override the implicit task-scheduling rules implied by the use of back links to activate tasks. In particular, if a software scheduler, such as that presented in Chapter 3, is implemented, then it must alter the back links in order to execute the task it selects.

8.9.3 Task scheduling

Scheduling a new task for execution on the CPU may be initiated by a number of different events. A task may leave the CPU either because it terminates, or because it has to wait until a particular condition is met. If, for example, it tries to extract data from an empty mailbox, then just before being suspended, it will call a special operating system routine. This adjusts the back link of the current task to point to the first task in the ready list. In this way, a simple IRET instruction transfers the CPU control to the appropriate task referenced by the back link.

The current executed task can also be forced to release the CPU when it activates a task with higher priority; for example, when it sends a message to a mailbox with tasks waiting to be carried out. In this case, the operating system routine used to activate the task inserts the corresponding descriptor in the ready list according to the priority. If a waiting task exists, with a higher priority than the current task, the back link is adjusted to point to the head of the ready list and an IRET instruction passes the CPU control to the new task. If the activated task has a lower priority, the only operation required is the insertion of the corresponding TSS in the ready list.

Task rescheduling can also be initiated by interrupts and traps. Activation of the corresponding handler initially causes a task switch, which is hardware scheduled; thus, if appropriate interrupt masking is implemented, then the handlers are scheduled correctly. Moreover, each handler can activate or re-activate tasks with higher priority than the interrupted task. In such cases, the handler calls an operating system routine which takes the activated tasks and places their descriptors in the ready list, according to their priority. The same operation is performed, in the case of nested interrupts, on the TSS of the other handlers interrupted, which are also placed in the ready list. Finally, the back link of the current task is set to point to the head of the ready list, so that an IRET instruction will transfer the CPU control to the next highest priority active task.

8.10   Interrupts and traps

8.10.1   Interrupt and trap gates

Interrupts and traps in the iAPX286 can be regarded as special mechanisms used to activate tasks: interrupts are caused by special signals from external hardware to notify the CPU that an important event has occurred in the external world; traps, on the other hand, are events caused by the execution of an instruction, which can explicitly request the trap activation or cannot correctly be completed.

External interrupts are caused by the activation of either the INTR or NMI signal. The difference between these two signals is that it is possible to mask the effects of the activation of INTR by clearing the IF flag in the CPU, while the interrupts caused by NMI are always serviced by the CPU. Thus, the NMI interrupt is normally activated on the occurrence of important, sometimes catastrophic, events, such as a power failure.

When an enabled interrupt or trap occurs, a specific software routine, referred to as a handler, performs the appropriate actions required by the event signalled by the specific interrupt or trap. Since many different sources for interrupts and traps exist, each of them is assigned a number, from 0 to 255, used as an identifier for the activated handler.

A special table, called the interrupt descriptor table (IDT), holds the interrupt, trap or task gates corresponding to the interrupt and trap handlers. Interrupt and trap gates have the format shown in Figure 8.14, and their role is analogous to that of the task gates. However, important differences do exist, since the activation of the handler by using a task gate causes a full task switching. Activation through an interrupt or trap gate, however, causes a transfer of control to the handler, without saving the state of the interrupted task. Therefore, trap and interrupt gates respond more quickly to events requiring simple actions, while task gates automatically perform the save or restore operation on the CPU registers.

Another important difference is that the handlers activated by a trap or interrupt gate must have a privilege level no lower thän the interrupted task, and their code and stack segments must be placed in the GDT table.

Finally, a difference also exists between trap and interrupt gates: handler activation through an interrupt gate clears the IF flag, so that the activation of further maskable interrupt handlers is inhibited; but if the same handler is activated by a trap gate, then it can be interrupted by the occurrence of other maskable interrupts. All the handlers can be interrupted by traps.

8.10.2 Interrupt and trap handling

All the trap, interrupt and task gates are stored in the interrupt descriptor table, whose descriptor is stored in the IDTR register in the CPU. This descriptor contains the base address and maximum offset of the interrupt descriptor table, so that it is possible to check whether the addressed gate is or is not within the table. The limit field must be at least 255, since 32 interrupt and trap handlers are used for the system-defined exceptions and interrupts. The remaining 224 identifiers are for user-defined interrupts and traps. Whenever an interrupt or trap, whose number is outside the interrupt descriptor table limit, is activated, a general-protection trap is raised. This receives an error code with the format shown in Figure 8.18.

As the handlers activated by trap or interrupt gates do not cause a task switch, they are serviced within the same space as the interrupted task. To protect the system against the incorrect use of such gates, they are treated almost like call gates. In particular, when an instruction such as INT*n* is executed, explicitly requesting a trap, the corresponding handler is activated if the program CPL is numerically no lower than the DPL field. The DPL field is stored in the corresponding gate used to access the handler. The privilege level of the handler, however, must be no lower than that of the CPL.

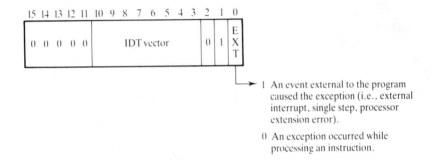

Figure 8.18   Error code for wrong IDT addressing.

When the handler activation causes a privilege transition, the used stack is taken from the current TSS by selecting the SS and SP values reserved for the new privilege level. As with the subroutine calls, this causes a stack switch, and as with call gates, the old values of CS, IP, the flag register, SP and SS are pushed on to the new stack. No parameters are explicitly passed to handlers, but some traps and interrupts use an error code to indicate the specific cause of the interruption. In this case, the error code is pushed on to the new stack. If the handler activation does not cause a privilege transition, then a normal call is performed, with the error code pushed on to the old stack.

All the handlers terminate by executing the IRET instruction. If the handler was activated through a task gate, the nested task flag is set and the IRET causes a switch to the task pointed out by the back link of the current TSS. Otherwise, a simple return-from-interrupt operation is performed. However, it is possible to have a task switch as a consequence of an IRET performed by a handler activated by a trap or interrupt gate, if the nested task flag has been previously set. In this way, it is possible to implement the scheduling activities described earlier.

8.10.3   Reserved vector numbers

All the traps raised by the failure of one of the checks performed by the iAPX286 during the execution of an instruction, as well as the interrupts generated by the arithmetic co-processor, are identified by reserved numbers. A complete list of the system-defined interrupts and traps is given in Table 8.3. This table also shows whether or not each trap or interrupt can be resumed or restarted once the handler terminates its execution. The table also shows whether an error code identifies the specific cause of the trap or interrupt.

Table 8.3 System-defined interrupts and traps.

Vector Number	Description	Restartable	Error Code
0	Divide error exception	yes	no
1	Single step interrupt	yes	no
2	NMI interrupt	yes	no
3	Breakpoint interrupt	yes	no
4	INTO detected overflow exception	yes	no
5	BOUND range exceeded exception	yes	no
6	Invalid opcode exception	yes	no
7	Processor extension not available exception	yes	no
8	Double exception detected	no	yes (always 0)
9	Processor extension segment overrun interrupt	no	no
10	Invalid task state segment	yes	yes
11	Segment not present	yes	yes
12	Stack segment overrun or not present	yes	yes
13	General protection	depends on the error code	yes

A. DIVIDE ERROR

This trap is activated whenever a DIV or IDIV instruction is executed and the result is too large to be represented, or if the divisor is zero. This trap repeats the instruction that caused the exception, after the trap handler has terminated.

B. BOUND RANGE EXCEEDED

This trap is activated if the BOUND instruction is executed to check an array index against its bounds and the check fails. This trap also repeats the instruction that caused the exception once the handler has completed its operations.

C. SINGLE STEP

The single-step trap allows the single-step execution of a program under test, and is activated after each instruction when the TF flag is set. This trap transfers control to a handler, which begins its execution with the TF flag cleared. When the handler terminates, the control is transferred to another task, possibly the one interrupted. If the TF flag of the new task is set, then, after the first instruction, another single-step trap will occur, otherwise the task will continue its execution normally.

D.   INVALID OPCODE

When an invalid opcode is detected by the instruction decoding unit, the invalid opcode trap is activated. The exception is raised when either the opcode or the addressing mode field in the instruction includes an illegal pattern of bits. The trap is only activated if an attempt is made to execute the invalid instruction. It is not activated if the illegal pattern of bits is merely extracted from memory.

E.   DOUBLE FAULT

This trap is activated when two different protection violations occur during the execution of a single instruction, and is not restartable. If another exception is generated during the execution of the handler associated with this trap, then the iAPX286 shuts down and no further exceptions or instructions are processed. The CPU must then be reset unless an NMI interrupt is issued. A task gate must be used for this trap to maintain proper handling.

F.   PROCESSOR EXTENSION SEGMENT OVERRUN

This interrupt signals to the CPU that during the operations of a co-processor a read or write operation was attempted for a memory location whose offset exceeded the segment limit. All the specific information on the cause of this interrupt are stored in the co-processor. To stop the CPU attempting to use the co-processor without resetting the interrupt condition, no WAIT or escape instruction can be executed – except for FNINIT – until the co-processor is reset or the interrupt condition cleared.

G.   INVALID TASK SEGMENT

This trap is activated if a task cannot be switched, because one of the protection checks fails, or if there is some table limit violation, either for the TSS and the associated descriptor or for the selectors to be loaded in the internal registers. The error codes accompanying this trap are shown in Table 8.4.

Table 8.4 Error codes pushed on to the stack when an invalid segment exception occurs.

Reason	Error Code
The limit in the TSS descriptor is less than 43	TSS id + EXT
Invalid LDT selector or LDT not present	LDT id + EXT
Stack segment selector is outside table limit	SS id + EXT
Stack segment is not a writeable segment	SS id +EXT
Stack segment DPL does not match new CPL	SS id + EXT
Stack segment selector RPL ≠ CPL	SS id + EXT
Code segment selector is outside table limit	CS id + EXT
Code segment selector does not refer to code segment	CS id + EXT
Non-conforming code segment DPL ≠ CPL	CS id + EXT
Conforming code segment DPL>CPL	CS id + EXT
DS or ES segment selector is outside table limits	ES/DS id + EXT
DS or ES are not readable segments	ES/DS id + EXT

H. NOT PRESENT

Any attempt to use absent segments or control descriptors gives rise to this trap. The instruction that generates this trap can be resumed from the point where the exception occurred, once the handler has terminated its operations. This type of trap is essential for the implementation of memory management policies, such as demand paging or automatic segment swapping.

I. STACK FAULT

This trap is activated whenever a stack overflow or underflow occurs, and it is fully restartable like the not present trap – this characteristic is mandatory for implementing automatic page or segment swapping because the stack may encompass several different segments. Thus, stack growth or shrinking can give rise to stack segment violations. These are handled by this trap, but can be made transparent to the user because of the restartability, which allows the handler to switch the stack segments, with no consequences to the program execution.

J. GENERAL PROTECTION

Any protection violation not covered by the previous traps gives rise to a general protection exception. The specific cause is indicated by an error code. If the error code has the bit 0 cleared and the bits 2 to 15 hold a non-zero number, then the exception is restartable. Bit 1 in the error code indicates whether the selector is in the IDT or LDT/GDT, while bit 2 distinguishes between LDT and GDT when the selector is not in the IDT.

8.11   The arithmetic co-processor

8.11.1   Internal architecture

The 80286 CPU, whose instruction set is illustrated in Section 8.6, can process only integer or small BCD operands efficiently, but the application sometimes requires many floating-point computations. This problem can be solved by using the 80287, which is an arithmetic processing unit capable of extending the CPU capabilities for mathematical processing.

The arithmetic co-processor may be seen as a separate CPU, whose internal organization and instruction set are tailored for the specific purpose of executing arithmetic operations efficiently. The block diagram of the 80287 is shown in Figure 8.19. Note that it adopts the same design philosophy as the main CPU, since the bus management and processing functions are performed asynchronously by two different units: a bus interface unit (BIU) and a numerical processing unit (NEU).

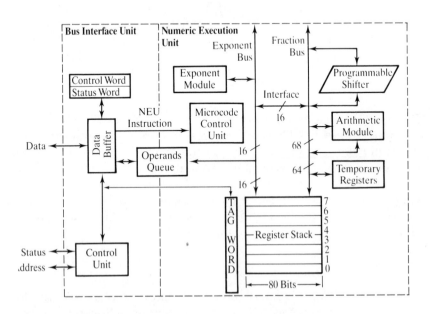

Figure 8.19   Internal block diagram of the 80287.

The numerical processing unit constitutes the register stack and the different subunits performing different types of processing. Exponent operations on floating-point numbers or operand shifting are examples. The execution of all the instructions involving register–stack manipulation and arithmetic computations are performed in this unit.

The bus interface unit manages all external communications, and, in particular, it receives and decodes the instructions for the co-processor. It moves data to and from the chip and also executes instructions that do not need to use the internal register stack or the ALU. All these operations can be performed in parallel with the computations carried out in the numerical processing unit.

The bus interface unit also controls the signals that interface the co-processor with the CPU. This is mainly carried out through the BUSY signal, which is activated when the numerical processing unit starts the execution of a new instruction. It is de-activated when the instruction is completed. The BUSY signal is checked by the CPU when the WAIT instruction is executed. The CPU then suspends program execution until it receives a signal from the co-processor indicating the completion of the instruction.

This protocol between the CPU and the arithmetic co-processor allows the user to mask the time required to perform the co-processor instruction as much as possible, by executing other pieces of code in parallel with the CPU. For example, a program can launch an arithmetic operation on the co-processor, by executing a suitable instruction. Then, if the result of the arithmetic operation is not immediately needed by the subsequent operations, the same program can continue executing instructions on the CPU, while the co-processor performs the arithmetic operation. When the program needs the result of the arithmetic operation, a WAIT instruction is executed by the CPU, stopping the program until the result is available. The parallel operations of the CPU and the co-processor are illustrated by the flowchart in Figure 8.20, where the parellel branches indicate parallel operations. It is possible to avoid the execution of the WAIT instruction when the programmer knows *a priori* that the branch executed by the CPU will always take longer than the parallel branch.

8.11.2 Registers

Internally, the 80287 has eight 80-bit data registers, each one associated with a 2-bit tag field. This field is used to identify whether the register contents are to be considered valid, infinite, zero or empty.

The data registers are not directly addressable, like the general registers in the CPU, but are managed by the 80287 as a real data stack. The registers are therefore addressable only in the top-of-stack relative

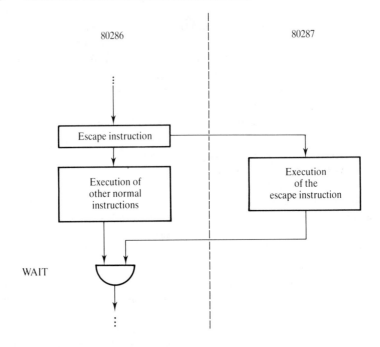

Figure 8.20   Example of parallel processing with the 80287.

mode (indicating that the *i*th register from the top-of-stack is accessed).
The current top-of-stack register is the one with a displacement of zero,
and its number is stored in the status register.

All the data in the registers are represented as floating-point
numbers, with the format indicated by the register fields in Figure 8.21.
This fits the definition of double-extended format specified by the
IEEE 754 Standard (see Chapter 2). Although the internal representation is identical for all the data, the 80287 can manipulate 16-, 32- and
64-bit integers. It also manipulates 32- and 64-bit floating points (corresponding to the single- and double-base formats of the IEEE 754) and
18-digit + sign packed BCD numbers. The conversion between the
external and internal representations is performed automatically, whenever an operand is loaded into the 80287, or when a result is stored in the
system memory. Hence, the conversions are transparent to the user.

The status and control words are used to read the co-processor
status and control the different operating options. Both these registers are
shown in Figure 8.22. The least significant bits of the status word are flags
that signal the occurrence of an exception, which is notified to the CPU
by sending the reserved interrupt signal. The ES flag is set if at least one
exception flag is set, providing a general exception flag. The bits C0–C3
hold the condition codes obtained as a result of the different operations.

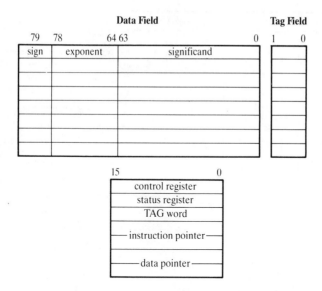

Figure 8.21 Internal registers of the 80287.

The TOP field holds the number of the data register representing the current top of the stack, while the B flag is an internal copy of the external BUSY signal. The control word holds all the different enable bits for the detection of the different types of exceptions, as well as the control fields used to define the type of rounding, precision control and infinity used in the computations.

The TAG register holds the tags of all the data registers, while the remaining two registers – instruction and data pointer – are used to store data and instruction addresses when an interrupt is generated by the 80287.

8.11.3 Instruction set and data addressing

The 80286 CPU and 80287 arithmetic co-processor may be seen by the programmer as a single programmable unit, since the instructions requiring the intervention of the co-processor may be inserted in the normal program flow like any other instruction. The only distinctive feature of the co-processor instructions is a special pattern of leading bits in the opcode referred to as escape (ESC).

Whenever an escape instruction is found by the CPU, the appropriate opcode and operand are passed to the co-processor, while the co-processor passes the result of the operation to be stored in memory back to the CPU. All the data and instruction transfers to and from the

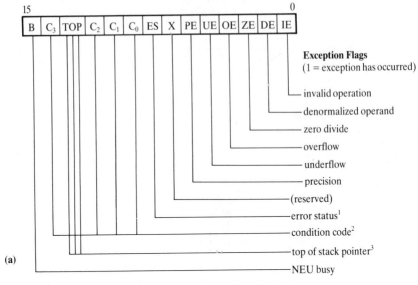

(a)

[1] ES is set if any unmasked exception bit is set, cleared otherwise.
[2] See Table 8.5 for condition code interpretation.
[3] Top values
000 = register 0 is top of stack
001 = register 1 is top of stack
⋮
111 = register 7 is top of stack

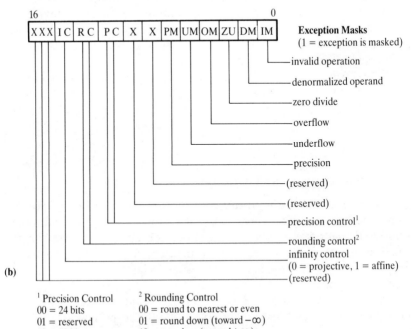

(b)

[1] Precision Control	[2] Rounding Control
00 = 24 bits	00 = round to nearest or even
01 = reserved	01 = round down (toward $-\infty$)
10 = 53 bits	10 = round up (toward $+\infty$)
11 = 64 bits	11 = chop (truncate toward zero)

Figure 8.22 Control and status registers.

arithmetic co-processor are therefore performed through the CPU, and in particular by the processor extension interface unit, which is similar to a DMA control unit. This implies that an additional bus cycle is required to access data and instructions, because the information is read or written by the CPU, but it must also be transferred between the CPU and the co-processor. However, since the memory management functions are all performed inside the CPU, this mechanism protects the co-processor memory references.

The CPU also has access to the internal registers of the 80287 via a reserved portion of the I/O space dedicated to the arithmetic co-processor.

The set of legal addressing modes in the arithmetic co-processor includes all the modes used by the CPU for addressing an operand in memory, but the internal registers can only be addressed as relative to the current top of the stack. At most, one operand can be in memory at one time, and when one is, the only addressable register is the top of the stack. The other registers may be used to hold operands only when the other operand is on the top of the stack. This imposes a practical limit to the use of the 80287 as a non-stack machine.

A. DATA TRANSFER INSTRUCTIONS

The instructions for moving operands and constants to and from the 80287 operate between a memory location and the top of the stack – denoted by ST0 – or between ST0 and another register in the stack. The instructions for operand transfer (FLD, FILD and FBLD) push any type of operand on to the stack from memory or from a register. To store the ST0 contents in a memory location in any legal data format, or in a register in the stack, with a pop of the stack that increments the number of the register currently at the top, it uses FSTP, FISTP or FBSTP. There is also the possibility of storing the ST0 contents either as an integer or real value in memory, or in a register without pop using FST, FIST or FBST. Constants can only be loaded in the ST0 by using specific instructions, each one corresponding to a constant. The set of constants that can be loaded with such instructions include 0.0 (FLDZ), 1.0 (FLD1), 2.0 (FLDPI), and the constants required to convert natural and decimal logarithms into binary (FLDL2E, FLDL2T), and back again (FLDLN2, FLDLG2). Finally, the data transfer class of instruction exchanges the contents of ST0 with one of the registers in the stack (FXCH).

B. COMPARISON INSTRUCTIONS

The comparison instruction sets the condition codes C0–C3 according to Table 8.5. When operating on two operands, comparisons can be performed between ST0 and a register or external operand.

Table 8.5 Condition codes set by comparison instructions.

Instruction Type	C_3	C_2	C_1	C_0	Interpretation
Compare, test	0	0	X	0	ST > Source or 0 (FTST)
	0	0	X	1	ST < Source or 0 (FTST)
	1	0	X	0	ST = Source or 0 (FTST)
	1	1	X	1	ST is not comparable
Remainder	Q_1	0	Q_0	Q_2	Complete reduction with three low bits of quotient
	U	1	U	U	Incomplete reduction
Examine	0	0	0	0	Valid, positive unnormalized
	0	0	0	1	Invalid, positive, exponent = 0
	0	0	1	0	Valid, negative, unnormalized
	0	0	1	1	Invalid, negative, exponent = 0
	0	1	0	0	Valid, positive, normalized
	0	1	0	1	Infinity, positive
	0	1	1	0	Valid, negative, normalized
	0	1	1	1	Infinity, negative
	1	0	0	0	Zero, positive
	1	0	0	1	Empty
	1	0	1	0	Zero, negative
	1	0	1	1	Empty
	1	1	0	0	Invalid, positive, exponent = 0
	1	1	0	1	Empty
	1	1	1	0	Invalid, negative, exponent = 0
	1	1	1	1	Empty

Notes: ST: top of stack; X: value is not affected by instruction; U: value is undefined following instruction; Q_n: Quotient bit n.

Simple comparison of real numbers is performd by FCOM; the same operation with a pop of the register stack is implemented by FCOMP. The instruction FCOMPP compares the two registers on top of the stack and then pops both of them.

Comparison between integers is implemented by FICOM and FICOMP: the latter executes a register pop not performed by the former. Examination of the contents of a single operand such as the register ST0 is performed by FTST. This compares the top register with zero and sets the condition codes. FXAM, in contrast, sets the condition codes as reported in Table 8.6, according to the value stored in ST0.

Table 8.6 Condition codes set by FPREM instruction.

Dividend Range	Q_2	Q_1	Q_0
Dividend < 2 ∗ modulus	C_3	C_1	Q_0
Dividend < 4 ∗ modulus	C_3	Q_1	Q_0
Dividend ≥ 4 ∗ modulus	Q_2	Q_1	Q_0

C. ARITHMETIC INSTRUCTIONS

This class of instructions includes the four basic arithmetic operations (FADD, FSUB, FMUL and FDIV) for integers and real operands. In these instructions, one operand must be ST0, while the second may be either in memory or in an internal register.

In addition to the basic instructions, a small set of unary operations are possible only on ST0. These include operations such as square root (FSQRT), absolute value (FABS), change of sign (FCHS), rounding to integer (FRNDINT) and component extraction (FXTRACT). The instructions for scaling (FSCALE) and partial remainder computation (PREM) also operates on ST0 and the next to top of the stack register.

D. TRANSCENDENTAL FUNCTIONS

Two trigonometric functions are allowed by this class of instructions: the tangent computation (FPTAN) of ST0 and the arctangent computation (FPATAN) of ST0/ST1. The logarithm functions include the computation of the binary logarithm of the absolute value of either ST0 (FYL2X) or |ST0 + 1| (FYL2XP1). In both cases, the logarithm is also multiplied by the contents of ST1, so that it is possible to obtain a natural or decimal logarithm if a suitable constant has been previously loaded into ST1. Finally, it is also possible to compute the power of $2^h - 1$ (F2XM1), where the contents of ST0 are used for h.

E. CONTROL INSTRUCTIONS

This class includes all the instructions used to manage the 80287. Thus, it is composed of instructions for loading (FLDCW) and storing (FSTCW) the contents of the control register. The status word can only be stored (FSTSW).

Other instructions are provided to save and restore the state (FSAVE and FRSTOR) and the environment (FSTENV and FLDENV) of the computations as a consequence of a task switching. Further instructions clear the exceptions (FCLEX), increment and decrement the register stack pointer (FINCSTP and FDACSTP) and initialize the 80287 (FINIT).

8.11.4 Exceptions

The execution of escape instructions can create different types of illegal condition. Some are generated by the 80287, while others are typical situations also detected in normal instructions. Normal exceptions are those caused by operand or code addressing outside a segment limit, or protection violations occurring during the escape instruction. These exceptions are detected directly by the CPU, because all the memory references pass through the processor extension interface unit.

The exceptions detected by the co-processor are those related to arithmetic computations and include the following:

- the invalid operation: this exception corresponds to the occurrence of some special conditions such as 0/0, $\infty-\infty$, stack overflow and underflow, and attempts to use operands with non-numerical values. These are recognized by special bit patterns;

- an overflow: caused by a result too large to be represented in the desired format, the result is 'set-to-infinity';

- an underflow: caused by a non-zero result too small to be represented in the desired format. The result is represented in denormalized form;

- a zero divisor: this exception is generated when a zero divisor is used with a non-zero and non-infinity dividend. The result is 'set-to-infinity';

- a denormalized operand: at least one of the operands is represented in denormalized form;

- the non-exact result: the corresponding flag is set and the exception raised, if not masked, when the result is not representable in the prescribed format.

All the listed exceptions are maskable by using flags in the control word. If enabled, the occurrence of any exception causes the activation of the ERROR signal used to interrupt the CPU. The specific exception should then be read in the status word by the interrupt handler.

8.12 Conclusion

The main feature distinguishing the iAPX286 from the other microprocessors illustrated in this book is its peculiar memory management and
protection system. The first difference when compared with other
microprocessors is that no external specialized unit is used to implement
all the operations required by virtual-to-physical address translation and
access rights check. Vice versa, these functions are performed by on-chip
circuits. Another important difference is that the translation tables are
partially under program control, since the CPU can address, at any given
time, only the segments whose selectors are stored in the four segment
registers visible to the programmers. This may complicate to some extent
the segment management, because it is no longer transparent to the
compiler or human programmer, but it could lead to a good use of the
four registers used for memory management.

The iAPX286 implements four machine privilege levels, as
compared to two in other microprocessors, with a very powerful set of
checks, implemented by the instruction microprogram, which are able to
enforce all the major protection rules indicated in Chapter 4. In
particular, even the trap and interrupt-handling mechanisms are amenable
to the same protection framework used for task management and
procedure calls.

The register organization and instruction set have, however, poor
orthogonality properties, because several registers (such as CX) play a
special role in some instructions. It seems that this choice is mainly aimed
at preserving the compatibility with previous microprocessors manufactured by Intel (namely, the iAPX88/86/188/186), as it is possible to run
the iAPX286 in real address mode so that it becomes a super-iAPX86.

In conclusion, the strength of the iAPX286 is due to its operating
system supports for memory protection and task management, implemented by the microprogram; vice versa, the irregular register and
instruction sets, and the restricted set of data types supported, constitute
a weak point of this microprocessor, although they are due to
compatibility reasons.

EXERCISES

8.1 Assume that the following tasks need to be run on an iAPX286
system:

- operating system (64 Kbytes);
- seven applications programs each requiring 150 Kbytes.

Is it possible to store and address in main memory all such tasks in
the real address mode? What about in the protected mode?

8.2 Assume that the tasks of the previous exercise are structured in the following way:

	Segment number	Type	Size
Operating system	1	code	20 Kbytes
	2	code	10 Kbytes
	3	stack	16 Kbytes
	4	data	16 Kbytes
	5	read only data	2 Kbytes
Application tasks	1	code	80 Kbytes
1 to 4	2	stack	20 Kbytes
	3	data	50 Kbytes
Application tasks	1	data	40 Kbytes
5 to 7	2	read only data	10 Kbytes
	3	stack	20 Kbytes
	4	code	30 Kbytes

Show the limit and access fields for each entry in the GDT and LDT, as well as the full contents of the GDTR register.

8.3 Assuming the memory allocation of the previous exercise, determine whether the following segment selector is correct:

0000000000100011

Does the answer depend on the task using such a selector?

8.4 Is it possible to execute a code stored in a segment, which manipulates data held in two different segments? Is it also possible to access data in the code segment? Write a program to execute the addition of two 18-digit + sign packed BCD numbers, without using the 80287.

8.5 Write a program that scans a terminal buffer looking for the carriage return character and produces the length of the string preceding the first occurrence of the carriage return in the terminal buffer. (*Hint*: Use an appropriate repetition prefix.)

8.6 Describe the stack contents before and after an inter-segment and an intra-segment call (without privilege switching). Can an inter-segment return be correctly used to conclude a procedure activated by an intra-segment call, and vice versa?

8.7 Which of the following accesses gives rise to a protection violation exception:

- access to a data segment whose DPL $\geq$ CPL;
- jump to a code segment whose DPL > CPL;
- jump to a task gate with the new CPL greater than the old CPL;
- call through a call gate whose DPL is lower than the caller's CPL.

Answer the same question assuming that the referenced segment is conforming.

8.8 Write a routine to perform context switching, including the status save/restore operations. Is it necessary to save/restore the context of the numerical co-processor? When and how should this operation be done?

8.9 Draw the flowchart of a routine intended to handle page faults. Which exception(s) must activate this routine? Which control structures need to be tested and/or updated?

8.10 Write a program implementing task rescheduling occurring as a consequence of a send operation on a mailbox.

8.11 Repeat Exercise 8.10 but assume that the rescheduling has been fired by interrupt occurrences.

8.12 Implement the hyperbolic functions using the 80287.

8.13 Write a program that takes a buffer of 100 80-bit floating-point numbers (10 bytes), grouped in 50 consecutive pairs, performs the multiplication of each pair and stores the 50 results in a second buffer. (*Note*: Try to take the maximum advantage from the possibility of overlapping the operations in the 80286 and 80287.)

CHAPTER 9
THE INTEL iAPX432 SYSTEM

OBJECTIVES

The aims of this chapter are as follows:

- to introduce the main architectural characteristics of the iAPX432 system;

- to discuss the concept of an object and to show how objects are addressed by means of capabilities in the iAPX432 system;

- to discuss the iAPX432 basic supports for program execution and for implementing separate task/procedure addressing environments;

- to present the iAPX432 facilities for user-defined object types;

- to introduce the mechanisms designed for allowing transparent multiprocessing, inter-process communications, mutual exclusion, and process scheduling and dispatching;

- to discuss the hardware-recognized objects for memory management and virtual memory support;

- to present the main features of the iAPX432 architecture for implementing fault-tolerant multiprocessor systems;

- to show how faults are confined by the iAPX432 hardware inside a limited number of well-defined areas and which mechanisms have been provided to allow easy hardware checks and system reconfigurations.

9.1 Introduction
9.2 System architecture
9.3 Objects
9.4 Object addressing
9.5 Program organization
9.6 Objects for procedure execution
9.7 User-defined types
9.8 Multiprocessing support
9.9 Objects for memory management
9.10 The iAPX432 interconnect system
9.11 Fault handling in the iAPX432 system
9.12 Conclusion

9.1   Introduction

The Intel iAPX432 is the most sophisticated multiprocessor system recently put on the market. A tentative comparison between the iAPX432 and other traditional machines, such as the iAPX186 and iAPX286, or the MC68020, for example, would be quite meaningless, since their architectures are completely different. Furthermore, the iAPX432 cannot be regarded as evolving from an earlier generation of microprocessors.

The methods of software design that have been used over the last few years have often been unreliable and inadequate in comparison with the ever-increasing complexity of system hardware. The iAPX432 represents a serious effort to embody the best and most powerful hardware techniques in a chip, to speed up software design, and in parallel to increase its reliability and ease of maintenance.

Several advanced mechanisms, concerning memory organization, data manipulation and support for programming environments, have been implemented in the iAPX432 hardware. Its aim is to achieve satisfactory performance, when protection, reliability and fault tolerance are the primary goals, and to encourage the use of hierarchical and structured software design. For example, the CPU's memory space is segmented and the system efficiently supports virtual memory by using a two-level map mechanism for translating logical to physical addresses.

The iAPX432 is a stack machine. This means that no general-purpose registers exist for the programmer, so only stack or memory-to-memory operations can be carried out by this microprocessor. Moreover, no assembly language is currently available for this machine, since its architecture has been oriented towards high-level languages, Ada in particular [1]. Ada is the only tool that can so far be used to develop an iAPX432 program. Another main characteristic of the iAPX432 is its ability to implement directly in hardware and microcode several operating system functions, such as process scheduling, processor dispatching, inter-process communication and storage allocation. Although similar facilities have already been included in other machines, such as the IBM System 38 [2], the iAPX432 implementation has been accomplished with a very small number of VLSI chips, building up a complex 'micromainframe'. In particular, there are three chips that implement the major components of the iAPX432 system. The **general data processor (GDP)** can be assumed to correspond to the CPU, as it carries out all the typical processing functions, including program decoding, computation and address generation. It is designed on two 64-pin chips. The **interface processor (IP)** is responsible for communication and data transfer between the iAPX432 environment and the external I/O devices, and is designed on a single 64-pin chip.

9.2 System architecture

The block architecture of a generic iAPX432 system is shown in Figure 9.1. From the logical point of view, each processor in the system is connected to the 432 message bus, allowing both the general data and interface processor to access the system's shared memory. However, this logical scheme may be physically implemented in several different ways, as explained in Section 9.10, according to the main design goals: reliability, fault tolerance, and performance. Each interface processor is also interfaced to an external subsystem, generally based on the Intel Multibus architecture.

The iAPX432 structure allows true software-transparent multiprocessor operations. The number of processors in the system can be changed without modifying the existing software, since the software is totally independent of the hardware configuration. No interrupt mechanism is included inside the iAPX432 architcture to enhance the reliability of the software. This is particularly important in real-time applications, where the interrupt technique does not allow full analysis and control of the system behaviour, since it is not reasonable to test all the possible interrupt-timing sequences completely. For this reason, all the events that can occur randomly in time have been taken out of the iAPX432 machine

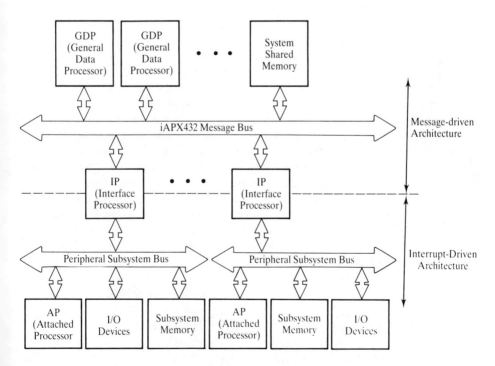

Figure 9.1 The Intel iAPX432 system architecture.

and confined to a peripheral subsystem, where they can be better controlled and managed. All the communications between the iAPX432 processing entities are carried out by means of synchronous message exchanges. The main consequence is that a special-purpose processor, the interface processor, is needed to bridge the gap between the central message-driven 432 system and the external interrupt-driven environment to which the I/O devices are connected.

While other machines can separate the processing functions from the I/O operations efficiently, by means of an I/O processor such as the Intel 8089, for example, the system software can still suffer from errors hidden by the interrupt mechanism. This is not true for the iAPX432.

Another important peculiarity of this system is represented by the set of operands that the processors can handle. Unlike other micro-processors, the iAPX432 CPU can recognize and access both logical and arithmetic operands of different types and sizes, such as Boolean, integer and floating-point numbers, as well as complex memory structures. These represent objects such as processors, processes and ports [3]. Several iAPX432 instructions provide powerful ways of manipulating these objects so that a message can, for example, be sent from a process to a port or mailbox with a single machine operation, instead of using a traditional operating system routine [4]. From this point of view, the iAPX432 encourages an object-oriented programming methodology, by raising the software–hardware interface to a higher level of abstraction.

The interface processor can map a set of memory segments, called windows, belonging to the peripheral subsystem, into a corresponding set of 432 objects placed in the system-shared memory. This is shown schematically in Figure 9.2. In this way, all the data transfers between the shared memory and the external I/O devices are carried out by the interface processor itself, with the aid of the protection mechanisms embedded in the 432 system [5]. In other words, no external CPU can access and modify the system-shared memory in an uncontrolled or unauthorized way. In general, the interface processor can execute almost all the instructions recognized by a general data processor. However, while each general data processor executes a program contained in one or more segments of shared memory, no instruction sequence is fetched from the common memory by the interface processor. On the contrary, the interface processor obtains each instruction to be executed from an **attached processor (AP)**, usually an Intel 8086 connected to the subsystem Multibus and able to operate as the peripheral environment master. The interface processor can therefore be seen as a slave to the attached processor. This issues commands or instructions to the interface processor by writing the opcode and associated operands in the subsystem memory segment that the interface processor uses to get its own instructions. This mechanism is particularly important as it allows the attached processor to extend its instruction set into the interface processor's set. In this way, it gains access to the central system memory via the interface processor.

The interface processor is also responsible for initializing the whole multiprocessor system. When started up, the interface processor does not map the subsystem memory into a set of objects; instead, the peripheral memory is linked to a number of shared memory segments. Thus, the attached processor can execute all the operations required to start the system, including shared memory loading. At the end of this phase, the interface processor is switched to its normal, protected working mode, so that the system is able to perform its programmed tasks.

9.3   Objects

As outlined in the previous section, the iAPX432 can recognize and process several memory structures called objects. Objects are abstract data types [6], each consisting of a collection of information organized in some logical scheme. Moreover, a set of operations is defined for each object to access and modify the data structure. In general, these functions are the only authorized actions that can be performed on the object components. For example, a stack object can be represented by an array of elements in memory and by an index variable containing the number of the top element. Furthermore, some procedures must be given to the users of the stack, such as PUSH (element, stack) and POP (out: element, stack), so that they can use the object.

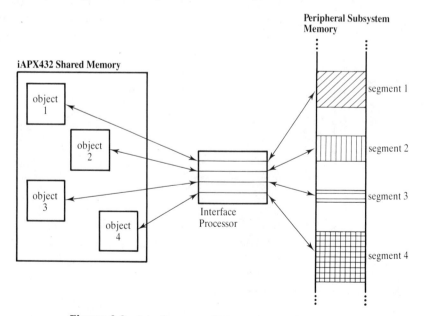

Figure 9.2   Interface processor mapping mechanism.

A crucial point here is that users must not be able to access and modify the stack representation directly. This precaution prevents erroneous or malicious modifications of the data in the object. The object must only be accessed in a controlled and authorized way. From the user's point of view, each object is accessed as one entity – the whole stack in the POP and PUSH operations – while the addressing and manipulation of its parts are hidden.

The iAPX432 hardware handles several kinds of system objects, each of which has a name, a type and, obviously, a representation. The representation consists of one segment of physical memory, structured in a data part and an access part, as shown in Figure 9.3. Some objects, however, can only have the data or the access area. The former may contain whatever type of scalar data can be processed by the user programs, but not capabilities. The access part, in contrast, is a capability list containing only iAPX432 capabilities, called **access descriptors (ADs)**. The hardware can recognize the type of each part that must be accessed at a given time, data or access, so no attempt to interpret data as capabilities or vice versa can be successfully completed.

The objects are processed either by machine instructions or by software, according to their type.

9.4   Object addressing

Each object has an associated **object descriptor (OD)** represented by a 16-byte element. This descriptor contains information about the physical location of the object and its current state. There are several fields in

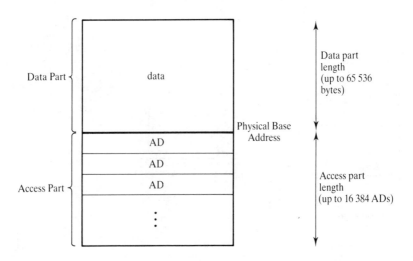

Figure 9.3   iAPX432 object structure.

each object descriptor: Figure 9.4, for example, shows the format of one of the most common, the storage descriptor, used to group all the information about the segment of physical memory representing an object.

During the execution of a user process, the descriptors for the objects that can be accessed and manipulated are contained in an **object table (OT)**. Whenever a new object is created, a new descriptor is moved into the object table. As Figure 9.4 shows, some object descriptor fields store the physical or base address, the data and access part lengths, the DP- or AP-length, and the type (for example, Obj. type) of the associated object. Others contain information about its status. The object descriptor valid (OV) bit, for example, is used to verify whether the descriptor is currently pointing to an object; in other words, operations on the object are allowed only when this bit is set. The data part valid (DV) bit is a flag indicating whether the object also consists of a data part.

Other fields introduced as basic mechanisms are used to implement certain memory management strategies. The accessed (AC) bit is set by the hardware each time a processor reads from or writes to the associated

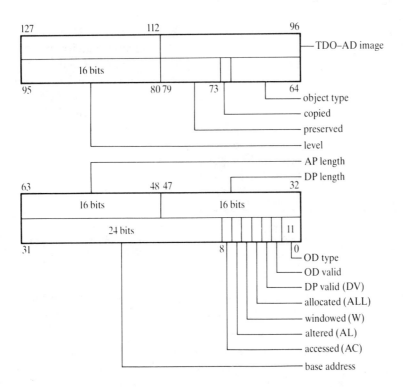

Figure 9.4 Object descriptor general structure.

object. The bit can be reset by the operating system software when virtual memory management is implemented. The altered (AL) bit is set when a processor overwrites a portion of the object. In this case, too, the field can be cleared by system software. Another bit, ALL, is used to signal whether physical storage is allocated with the storage descriptor or not, so that an exception can be raised when an attempt is made to access the object.

The remaining fields in Figure 9.4 are used to enable basic checks on an object during its manipulation. The windowed (W) field is a flag signalling that a peripheral subsystem memory segment is currently mapped in the object by an interface processor. The W bit is updated during this processor's operations. The preserved bits are not used by the hardware after creation of the object descriptor, so they can be used by the system software to store information related to the object status. Finally, three fields control the lifetime of the object (Level, Copied) and support the management of user-defined object types (TDO–AD).

As Figure 9.5 shows, the access descriptors are represented as 32-bit longwords used to name and access objects and segments. When an instruction that manipulates an object must be executed, the user specifies an access descriptor for that object [7].

The access descriptor is located into a capability list, or the access part of a memory segment, by means of an index. The set of access descriptors accessible to a user defines the execution environment, or the collection of objects that can be accessed and manipulated.

An access descriptor, like any capability, contains the information required to retrieve the object descriptor, plus some fields describing the user rights with respect to the object. In addition to the OT associated with each user, there is a single system-wide **object table directory (OTD)**. This contains object table descriptors or object descriptors for all the

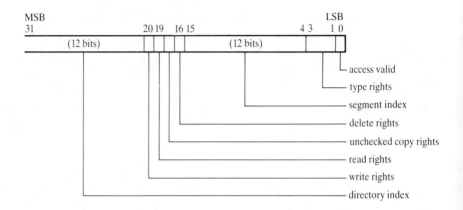

Figure 9.5   Access descriptor format.

object tables in the system. This two-level table structure allows a different object table to be associated with each executing process; hence, a higher degree of protection can be achieved. Object tables can also be regarded as other objects, so relocating or swapping out an object table becomes a simple operation.

The two index fields in Figure 9.5 are used by the iAPX432 hardware to locate an object from the access descriptor according to the scheme shown in Figure 9.6. The directory index locates an object table descriptor inside the object table directory, which contains the base address of the object table where the object descriptor associated with the object resides. This descriptor is then obtained using the object table index field. Finally, the object is accessed using its base address contained in its object descriptor.

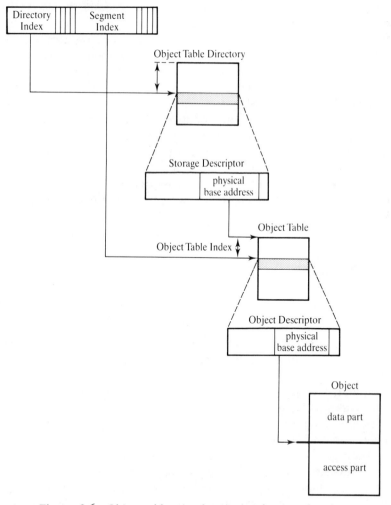

Figure 9.6 Object addressing by means of access descriptors.

In this arrangement, each access to a byte in a segment requires, potentially, four memory references: to the access descriptor, to the object table directory, to the object table and to the object itself. Some on-chip cache associative memories have been implemented to reduce this overhead; thus, an iAPX432 processor can remember the most recently used address translations, and so avoid unnecessary accesses to the access descriptors and object tables.

Particular care must be taken when objects are relocated or swapped out, since some obsolete translations may still be present in the processor caches. For this reason, a mechanism has been designed to flush out the on-chip memories when critical object manipulation is carried out by the system software.

The rights fields in an access descriptor are used by the hardware whenever the object must be accessed, to check whether the instruction being executed is legal. It follows then that the read and write bits are tested during each read or write operation performed on a part of the object. The meaning of the type-right field depends upon the object type: port objects, for example, have send and receive rights coded into these bits. The access valid bit is used by the system to test whether the 32-bit word may be interpreted as a correct access descriptor; that is, whether the access descriptor is currently valid for the object it is addressing. Moreover, a delete bit has been introduced to give or deny the user the right to delete the access descriptor itself. Finally, an unchecked copy-right field is present in each access descriptor to enable or disable compatibility checks when the descriptor is copied. This depends on the object's lifetime. This test can prevent an access descriptor referencing a destroyed object.

In conclusion, every reference to an object from an instruction causes the access descriptor fields to be checked for rights; if an illicit attempt to access the object is detected, a fault occurs.

9.5   Program organization

It is clear that from the programmer's point of view the iAPX432 memory space cannot be addressed as a single, contiguous array of locations, as in most traditional machines, but as a complex network of objects. Furthermore, the system architecture is well suited to support Ada and other advanced high-level languages efficiently, since several Ada features are either implemented directly in microcode or can be easily obtained using the powerful hardware mechanisms.

The package concept, for example, is a basic Ada characteristic [8] that is particularly useful for developing large programs. A package can be defined as a language construct used to group together a set of data (or objects) and the procedures that manipulate them. During program development, several software portions can be conveniently implemented as packages. Moreover, each package can be designed and compiled separately from the other entities, as one of the main Ada characteristics is to allow separate compilations of program modules. The Ada package construct is mapped directly into the iAPX432 **domain object**, which can be seen as a collection of data and procedure objects. The access part of a domain contains the access descriptors for each data structure or procedure accessible in the domain itself.

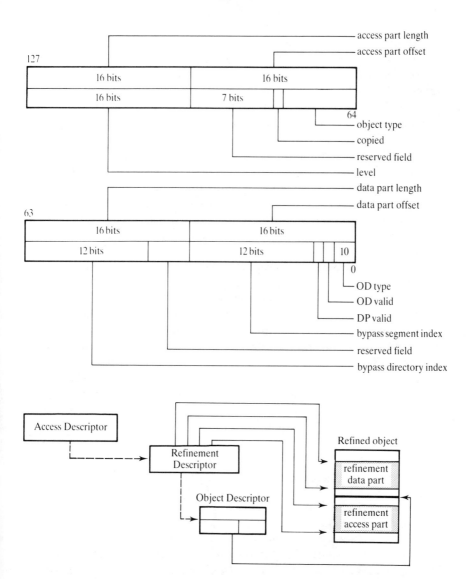

Figure 9.7   Refinement descriptor structure and refinement addressing.

As each Ada package can be arranged into a public and a private part, accessible or invisible to the user, a programmer can protect a set of procedures and data from access outside the module by inserting them in the private package portion. However, the iAPX432 hardware maps the whole package, both public and private parts, into a single domain; but, it does allow the access to be restricted to the protected part of the domain by means of a **refinement** mechanism.

A refinement object, in fact, can be seen as an entity that is physically a part of a larger object, even if the two objects are totally disjointed from the logical point of view. So a user who obtains an access descriptor for a domain gains access to all its data and procedures, while an access descriptor for a previously defined refinement of the domain allows its owner to use only the domain subset contained in the refinement.

The object descriptor for a refinement is slightly different from the general form of an object descriptor. As Figure 9.7 shows, the object descriptor for a refinement contains two bypass index fields, which are used by the hardware to retrieve the storage descriptors of the object containing the refinement. Moreover, information about the offset from the parent object base address and refinement length have been introduced both for the access and data part. Figure 9.7 also shows the refinement access mechanism. However, it is worth noting that accessing a refinement usually requires an additional memory reference to obtain the base object descriptor.

Ada procedures are represented by one or more instruction objects, or data segments containing iAPX432 instructions without an access part. General data processor instructions, on the other hand, are not aligned on certain boundaries (such as byte or word), since they are encoded as bit sequences with varying lengths. Thus, the general data processor instruction pointer always contains a bit displacement in the instruction segment. Since instruction displacements are computed as 16-bit ordinal numbers, the maximum bit displacement is 65 535; hence, each instruction object can be at most 8 Kbytes long. For this reason, some inter-segment branch instructions are provided so that procedures can fill more than one segment.

9.6   Objects for procedure execution

When a procedure is invoked, a local storage for the activated subprogram must be created. In the iAPX432 system, a call instruction causes the hardware to generate a totally disjointed environment to execute the procedure. In general, the called and the calling modules have no access to each other's objects, although a mechanism for passing parameters has been introduced in the machine architecture.

On each procedure invocation, a **context object** is created, containing all the information needed to control its progress. This is true even when the subprogram is recursive; in this case, there can be multiple contexts active at the same time, corresponding to the same procedure.

The format of a generic context object is shown in Figure 9.8. As can be seen, the object data part contains the instruction pointer used to store the bit displacement of the next instruction to be executed. A stack area and its associated pointer have been introduced to allow operand processing, while a context status field has been included to store information affecting the precision and the rounding mode used in floating-point computations. Finally, two additional fields are used to save control data used in tracing operations (trace control data area) and to grant the software a working area (working storage area) not influenced by the hardware.

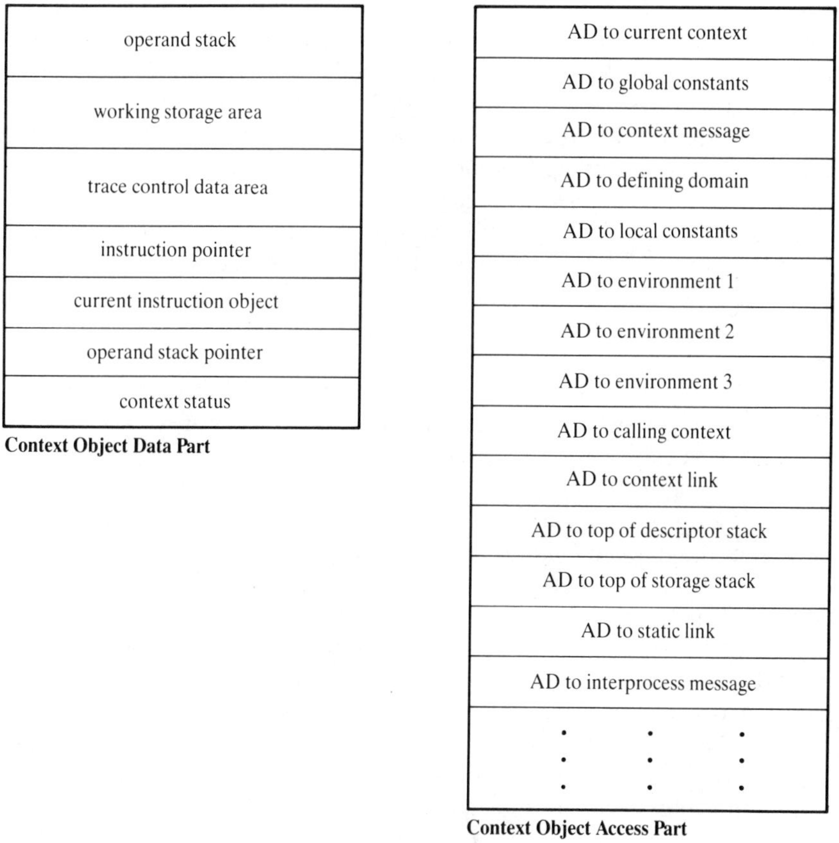

operand stack
working storage area
trace control data area
instruction pointer
current instruction object
operand stack pointer
context status

Context Object Data Part

AD to current context
AD to global constants
AD to context message
AD to defining domain
AD to local constants
AD to environment 1
AD to environment 2
AD to environment 3
AD to calling context
AD to context link
AD to top of descriptor stack
AD to top of storage stack
AD to static link
AD to interprocess message
.   .   .

Context Object Access Part

Figure 9.8 Context object organization.

The structure of the context access part in Figure 9.8 is to some extent more complex, since several access descriptors are used to build up the addressing environment: The first access descriptor is used to access the context itself, while the second one gives access to an object containing the most frequently used data constant in the same package. An access descriptor, introduced for a context message, comes next. The message is a refinement of the calling context which can be used to pass parameters to the called context during the execution of a call context with message instruction.

The local constants access descriptor allows an object containing all the local data constants associated with the current context to be addressed. The access part also contains references used to connect the context to its execution environment. Hence, an access descriptor for the caller has also been provided, to permit the correct execution of return-from-context instructions.

The environment access descriptors are used to address three environment objects, which together with the access part in Figure 9.8 constitute the instantaneous logical address space available to the context. In other words, the context can immediately reach all the objects accessed by the access descriptors in its access part, or in the three access segments addressed by the environment access descriptors. Since each access segment, including the context access part, can contain at most 2^{14} access descriptors, the total logical address space visible to the context consists of $4(2^{14}) = 2^{16}$ objects. However, an enter-environment operation has been introduced in the general data processor instruction set, so that the context is able to use the access descriptors in an access segment directly, by loading its access descriptor into one of the environment slots in Figure 9.8.

When a call context instruction is executed, the iAPX432 hardware fills environment slot number 1 with an access descriptor for the defining domain. This causes context activation, so that the other procedures and data belonging to the same package can be reached if needed. The same access descriptor is saved in the context access part, but in this case the objects in the domain cannot be directly accessed, since only the segment in the environment slots and the context itself are accessible without additional indirection steps.

Figure 9.9 gives an overall view of memory organization during a procedure execution. Arrows are used to show the logical links existing between objects and access descriptors. A dotted line means that the associated access descriptor can be null, so that no object is accessed. The complexity of the network of access descriptors highlights the importance of the enter environment mechanism.

The access part of the context also contains a static link access descriptor, which is used when nested procedure calls must be implemented. Ada and several other high-level languages allow the

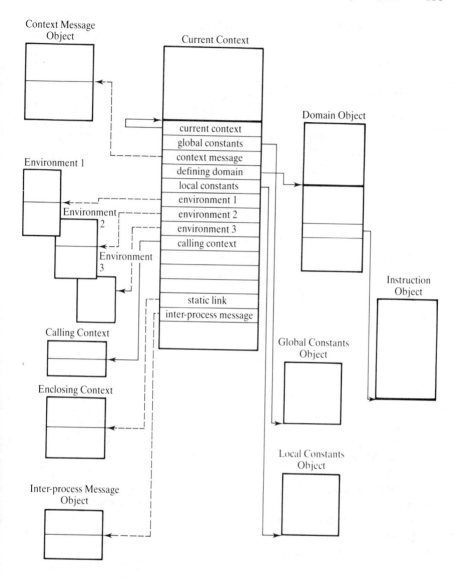

Figure 9.9 Program execution scenario.

programmer to write procedure bodies that textually include other procedures. In general, the innermost subprogram can gain access not only to its own data, but also to variables and constants belonging to each outer procedure. When this happens, the context must be able to reference both objects contained in its caller body, by means of the calling context access descriptor, and in each outer environment that

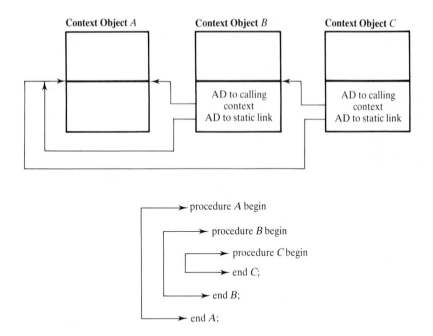

Figure 9.10   Nested procedure support in the iAPX432.

includes the context itself. This situation is shown in Figure 9.10. The solution adopted in the iAPX432 hardware uses the static link field to access local variables in contexts other than the caller's.

Another link field included in the context access part contains an access descriptor used by the system software. Since the invocation of a subprogram is a frequent operation in modular programming, the creation of a procedure instance must be carried out efficiently. To this end, the iAPX432 assumes that a number of free contexts must be assigned to each executing task by the operating system. Thus, each process has a list of pre-allocated contexts, as shown in Figure 9.11, obtained by linking together the objects by means of the context link access descriptor field. When a new context must be activated, the next free element in the list is used, so that the overhead required to create and destroy contexts is significantly lessened.

Finally, two access descriptors (top of descriptor stack and top of storage stack) have been introduced in the context access part to make memory management easier (see Section 9.9), while the last access descriptor (inter-process message) is used to support inter-process communication, as explained later.

Pre-allocated Context List

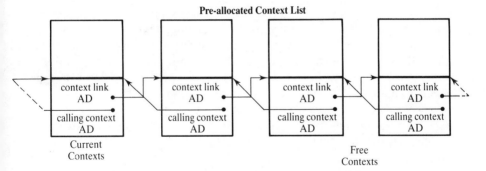

Figure 9.11   Pre-allocated context list structure.

9.7   User-defined types

In general, an iAPX432 user is allowed to create only generic system objects directly. Every other hardware-recognized object can be obtained by invoking a suitable 'create' function in a system-privileged package or type manager designed to control instances of a predefined type. Besides the processor-recognized object types, the iAPX432 system also supports basic mechanisms that define new data types in software and create typed objects dynamically, with the same degree of protection and access control provided for the system objects.

This is useful, for example, when a programmer defines a new type of object, a stack object, say, and wishes other users to be able to create and use instances of the new type without being able to access the underlying representation. If programs are interfaced to the objects or the stacks only by means of a restricted set of procedures (create stack, pop element, push element and flush stack, for example), the representation can easily be modified or changed. It can be converted easily, from an array structure into a linked list, without affecting the user module code. The stack implementation details can be completely hidden to users, so that they are free to develop procedures at a higher level of abstraction, with little or no consideration for the mechanisms required to support data types.

Because several instances of the same software-defined type can be created belonging to different users, references to the objects must be carefully controlled before accessing the associated representations. This is necessary to prevent a user being able, for example, to address and process stacks belonging to other programs, either in error or maliciously. Since the access descriptor is the only iAPX432 addressing mechanism that cannot, in a real system, be altered or forged by the user, each different instance of a user-defined object must be referenced by means of a suitable access descriptor.

On the other hand, however, a conventional access descriptor cannot be passed to users to point to an extended-type object, since, in this way, they could directly access and manipulate the object representation. This problem has been solved by introducing two additional processor-recognized object types into the iAPX432 system: a **type control object (TCO)** and a **type definition object (TDO)**.

When a new software type is defined by a type manager package, a type control object for the new type is passed to the type manager procedure by the operating system. The type control object can be thought of as a key, checked by the iAPX432 hardware whenever objects of the associated type must be created or accessed. In other words, a type control object contains some access rights fields to allow protected operations on the dynamic type instances by the type control object owner; that is, by authorized procedures usually implementing the type manager body. Only the type manager then can physically handle the protected objects. Users refer – but do not access – typed objects by means of access descriptors with restricted rights, or without read and write permissions. In this way, the access descriptor owned by a user program is only a non-corruptable pointer to the user-defined object. The type manager manipulates the object representation after executing an amplify-right privileged instruction, which gives the read and write permissions obtained from the user to the access descriptor.

The typical type control object format is shown in Figure 9.12. It is easy to see that the data part contains some bit fields corresponding to the rights fields included in each access descriptor (for example, type rights, delete, unchecked copy, read and write). When a user exhibits an access descriptor for a typed object, the rights bits are ORed by the type manager with the corresponding fields in the type control object by means of an amplify-right instruction to obtain an active access descriptor for the object. Moreover, the type control object type rights field is used to check whether the type control object itself can be used to perform an operation, such as typed-object creation (create right), typed-object refinement (refine right) and/or access descriptor rights amplification (amplify right).

Other fields shown in Figure 9.12 are involved in object creation and rights amplification operations. The type testing control bit, for example, is checked when the access descriptor rights must be extended, to test whether the type control object can be used to amplify the capabilities of each kind of access descriptor or whether only access descriptors with the same object type field as the type control object can be processed.

The type description object (TDO) was introduced for two main reasons. The first is that a suitable mechanism had to be provided to prevent the user being able to create instances of type *A* and pass the associated access descriptors to a manager for type *B* objects – by

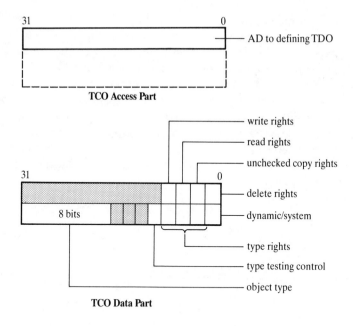

Figure 9.12 iAPX432 type control object format.

invoking a type *B* operation, for instance. In this case, incorrect actions could be performed by the type *B* manager, acting as a Trojan horse, on the wrong type objects, with serious consequences for the system and the integrity of the user's data.

The type description object forbids this kind of violation by typing each user-defined object. In fact, when a new type is defined, a type descriptor object is given to the type manager by the operating system. It is then stored in the user-accessible part of the type manager, and its access descriptor is stored in the associated type control object.

During the creation of a new instance, called a dynamic type object (DTO), an image of the access descriptor for the type descriptor object is copied into the TDO–AD image field of the associated object descriptor (see Section 9.4). From then on, whenever the type manager accesses the dynamic type object, the iAPX432 hardware verifies that the object descriptor TDO–AD image field and the TDO–AD in the type control object refer to the same type descriptor object; that is, the dynamic type object has the same software-defined type as instances controlled by the invoked type manager. However, when the type manager controls the creation of system objects, whose type is hardware defined, the type control object dynamic/system field in Figure 9.12 is reset to indicate that the objects are not user defined, and hence no type descriptor object check must be performed.

The relationships between the different elements implementing the iAPX432 extended-typing mechanisms are shown in Figure 9.13. From a logical point of view, the type descriptor object represents a means of marking dynamic type objects with a unique system-wide label.

The second reason for having a type descriptor object is that it can contain access descriptors for segments and procedures in the type manager domain in its access part, so giving the programmer an efficient way of accessing the type manager services. No processor-interpreted field has been included in the type descriptor object for this reason. User and system programs wishing to access several type managers are not,

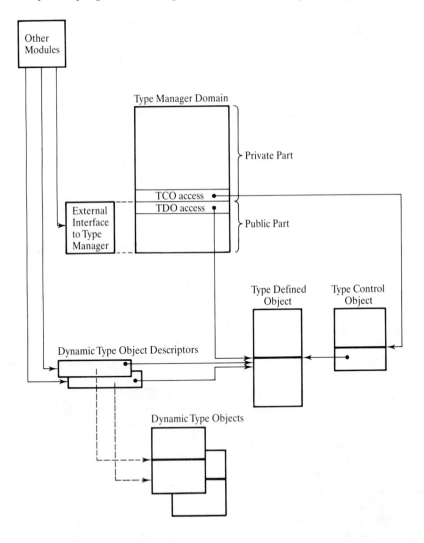

Figure 9.13   Hardware-supported extended-typing mechanisms.

however, forced to maintain an access descriptor for each type descriptor object in the system, since the iAPX432 supports a retrieve-TDO operation for obtaining the dynamic type definition object for a dynamic type object from an access descriptor for the dynamic instance. On the other hand, a type manager must be designed carefully. Hence, the type control object obtained by the operating system during the new type creation must be stored in the private part of the type manager body not accessible to the user. Moreover, the read and write rights must be removed in each access descriptor for a dynamic type object returned to the user when a create typed object operation is executed.

9.8   Multiprocessing support

As outlined in previous sections, the iAPX432 can support true transparent multiprocessing, since the machine behaviour is totally independent of the number of general data processors incorporated into the system. Processors, in fact, can be added to or removed from the system with no changes in user software, affecting only the overall performance.

In a typical iAPX432 system, a number, i, of user tasks is executed in parallel by $j < i$ general data processors, and the hardware supports special mechanisms to switch task contexts and to bind processes to processors on the fly.

Each user program to be executed in parallel with others is represented by an iAPX432 **process object**. A process object contains information required to control the task status and its progressing, to access objects and procedures needed during the computation, and to allow inter-task communication and synchronization.

Most of the information used by conventional multitasking operating system software to build the virtual processor image allocated to each user is managed directly by the iAPX432 hardware. Figure 9.14 shows the process object structure. The first four access descriptors are used by the process to access its addressing environment. The physical storage object in particular is used to allocate memory for objects created by the process during its life (see Section 9.9).

The process object table header and the process global access descriptors are used to refer to the table of objects accessible to the task and a software-definable global object, which can be accessed by each context in the process. The remaining access descriptors in the process object are used to implement the basic mechanisms for process dispatching and inter-process communications. Additional descriptors have been introduced to manage exceptions efficiently when the process crashes because of software or hardware errors.

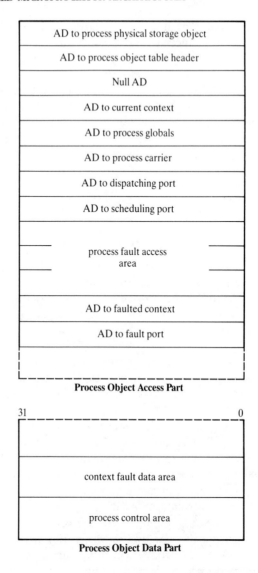

AD to process physical storage object
AD to process object table header
Null AD
AD to current context
AD to process globals
AD to process carrier
AD to dispatching port
AD to scheduling port
process fault access area
AD to faulted context
AD to fault port

Process Object Access Part

31   0

context fault data area
process control area

Process Object Data Part

Figure 9.14   iAPX432 process object organization.

9.8.1   Process communication and synchronization

Concurrent processes can communicate by means of a message exchange mechanism implemented via **port objects**. An iAPX432 port can be considered as a mailbox to or from which tasks can send or receive messages. Several senders can append information to a port for multiple receivers, thus implementing a complex many-to-many communication scheme.

The structure of a port object is shown in Figure 9.15. Fields in the data part and access descriptors in the access part are primarily used to control two queues – of messages and processes – managed by the port object. In fact, when a process tries to obtain a message from an empty port, where no other task sent a message to the port, it is queued to the port itself, waiting for a message to be received. Similarly, when a message is sent to a communication port and no task is ready to receive it, the information packet is appended to the port message queue until a process executes a receive instruction from that port.

While the process queue is unlimited, the message list is software limited. Each message queued to a port has a corresponding access descriptor in the port access part. The port message queue structure is described in the message queue entry area in Figure 9.15. This is an array of message descriptors organized in two linked lists, one for free descriptors and the other for currently used entries or waiting messages. For each entry in the array, both used and free, a corresponding descriptor exists in the port access part. Pointers to the head of the waiting message queue and of the free entry list are also included in the

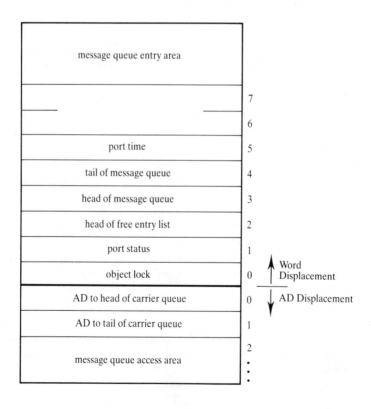

Figure 9.15 iAPX432 port object structure.

port data part. Message and process queuing or dequeuing is automatically performed by the iAPX432 hardware during port operations.

In practice, processes waiting to complete their send or receive port operation, because the message queue is full or empty, are not themselves queued to the port. In fact, an additional system object called a **carrier object** is used to implement the port mechanism. Each process has an access descriptor for an associated carrier in its access part (see Figure 9.14). The carrier is used to transfer message access descriptors from the port to the process, or vice versa, and to block the process itself in the waiting queue when the invoked port operation cannot be completed at once.

The format of a carrier object is shown in Figure 9.16. When a message is sent to a port, the message access descriptor is copied from the process carrier into the first free slot in the port access descriptor message area; then the process continues its execution. If the port message buffer is full and no further message access descriptors can be inserted in the port message area, the process carrier is inserted in the port carrier queue. This blocks the task execution, and an access descriptor for the port is copied into the carrier current port access descriptor slot. When a message is received from the port, the AD to blocked message in the first queued carrier is copied into the freed port message access descriptor slot. Then the process carrier is sent to a second port, specified by a suitable access descriptor in its access part, where the associated process will again be dispatched.

The AD to the next carrier in Figure 9.16 and the access descriptors to the top and bottom of the carrier queue are used to implement the carrier queue as a linked list. During a receive operation, a message access descriptor is copied from the port access part to the carrier incoming message access descriptor slot. However, if no message is waiting at the specified port, the carrier is once again queued and the carried process stopped. Even though two different process queues are handled in a port (processes waiting to append messages to the port and processes waiting to get messages from the port), only one carrier queue is physically implemented in each port. This is because at least one of the two lists must be empty at any given time.

There are many practical situations in which process blocking is not convenient if the send or receive operation cannot be completed immediately. Consider, for example, a monitoring task that displays messages obtained from several data-collecting processes via a number of different ports. An unsuccessful receive from a port could block the monitor process, thus preventing further, possibly urgent, messages being read from the other ports.

For this reason, the iAPX432 supports two further kinds of nonblocking message exchange, in addition to the blocking send and receive. Conditional send and receive instructions allow the user to specify a

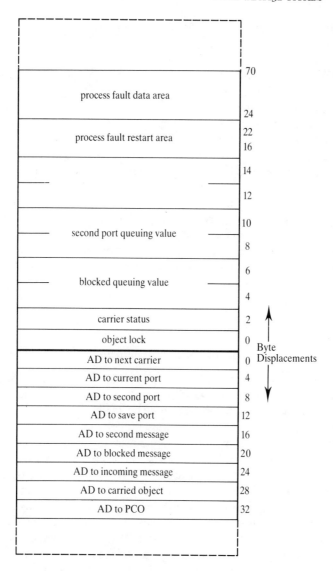

Figure 9.16   iAPX432 carrier object structure.

Boolean parameter set by the hardware according to the result of the operation. If the send or receive function can be completed without blocking, the Boolean variable is forced to true; however, if the port message queue is full or empty, the Boolean is set to false. The process carrier is not appended to the port, however, so the execution of the associated task is not stopped.

Another way to avoid processes being stopped during message exchanges is to use surrogate send or receive operations. In this case, an auxiliary or surrogate carrier is used instead of the process carrier. This moves message access descriptors between the port message area and the carrier itself. In this way, when the port message queue is full or empty the surrogate carrier is appended to the port without blocking the process. When the surrogate send/receive can be completed, the corresponding access descriptor is copied into the auxiliary carrier, and this is forwarded to a second port specified by the user, where the process will look for the received message and/or the surrogate carrier to be used in further operations. When a surrogate carrier reaches its second port, the user must execute a receive operation to get the carrier from the port and then read the carried message, when a surrogate receive is considered. The AD to second message in Figure 9.16 is used for this purpose: it represents a reference to the carrier itself, or to a carrier refinement used as a message descriptor in queuing or dequeuing the carrier to or from the second port. The blocked message and incoming message access descriptors, in comparison, are used during a blocking send or during a receive operation, respectively.

9.8.2   Process scheduling and dispatching

Other important topics in multitasking systems are process scheduling and process dispatching. The iAPX432 hardware provides basic mechanisms for binding processes to processors. The logical scheme involved is very similar to that implemented for inter-process communication and makes use of the same kind of objects: ports, carriers and processes.

An iAPX432 microprocessor is represented by a **processor object**, whose access part contains an access descriptor for the current processor dispatching port. This is where processes ready to run are assigned to CPUs, in the same way that messages are exchanged among processes by communication ports. In this case, however, message access descriptors are replaced by process carrier access descriptors, while processes and process carriers are replaced by processors and processor carriers, respectively. Hence, a processor waiting for a task can be queued to an empty dispatching port via its associated carrier. Ready-to-run processes can wait for a general data processor service in the dispatching port message queue.

A process can be queued at a dispatching port for several reasons: for example, when a blocking send or receive operation that suspended the task execution can be completed, the process carrier is sent again to the second or dispatching port so that the task becomes ready to run. Moreover, when some high-level scheduling conditions have changed – for example, a time-slice period has expired, a new process is activated or the process itself is rescheduled – the process carrier is appended to the dispatching port.

Processors access the dispatching port and can be blocked waiting for processes ready to run via their own processor carriers.

While dispatching is strictly related to short-term scheduling, additional supports in the iAPX432 system allow the operating system to implement and enforce a large variety of long-term process scheduling policies. Each process object, in fact, contains a service period field and a period count field in its data part. The first parameter is the maximum number of system time units or clock periods that the process can execute without being suspended and dispatched again; in other words, the service period represents the time-slice interval for the process. The period count parameter is used to control the number of time slices assigned to a task for its execution. When the process has been scheduled a number of times equal to the period count and its execution time becomes equal to (period count) × (service period) time units, it is sent to a suitable scheduling port where the system software can decide to stop the execution definitely or to dispatch the task after modifying its scheduling parameters, for example. Scheduling policies can then make use of the service period and period count mechanisms, together with additional queuing supports at the dispatching ports.

Two basic mechanisms have been introduced to queue objects (processes to be dispatched or messages in surrogate operations) at a dispatching or communication port. In general, simple ports support a first-in–first-out (FIFO) queuing discipline, where objects are obtained from the port in the same sequential order in which they are appended to it. However, a more complex class of ports based on a **priority/deadline strategy** has been introduced to allow sophisticated scheduling policies. For this purpose, each carrier object has an associated queuing value both for the first and second port, as shown in Figure 9.16. The queuing value consists of a deadline and priority 16-bit fields. Processes, or messages in surrogate operations, with different priorities are queued or dequeued to or from a non-FIFO port, according to the value of the priority field, zero being the lowest priority. The deadline parameter is an integer used to indicate the time interval that a process can wait for dispatching, relative to other tasks. When a carrier is queued to a priority or deadline port, the processor or system clock value is copied into the port time field (see Figure 9.15), to update the last port queuing operation time. Carriers having the same priorities are then ordered according to their absolute deadline periods, given by the sum of the port time (updated by the GDP) plus the relative deadline value contained in the carrier queuing value field. The iAPX432 system defines either priority/deadline ports or priority ports, where the deadline mechanism is disabled, by means of the port status field shown (see Figure 9.15). When a port is organized with the priority/deadline discipline, processes or messages are ordered according to their priorities and by absolute deadline within the same priority. When both the priority and deadline parameters are equal, processes are then ordered FIFO.

9.8.3 Mutual exclusion

Each multitasking system must provide the user with some mechanisms to grant mutual exclusion in accessing shared objects. The iAPX432 architecture based on port communications allows applications tasks to achieve synchronization and exclusive access to common resources by means of message exchange operations. However, other low-level mechanisms are also embedded in the system to be used by operating system programmers, or by designers of applications tasks, who need to bypass the operating system services and to obtain mutual exclusion on the hardware-recognized objects. These supports are also used by the general data processors and interface processors in the system, to avoid interference in their operations on shared object representations.

Several iAPX432 objects, such as processors, processes, ports and so on, have a 16-bit object-lock field in their data part. When the lock field is set, it means that the related object is currently being used by some entity in the system and it is not presently available to others. The lock field structure is shown in Figure 9.17. Objects can be locked by the hardware (that is, the general data process or the interface processor) or by the system software. Processors lock objects when operations requiring exclusive access must be performed on the object itself. On the other hand, there are two different kinds of software locking: short-term locking is performed by a processor, but long-term locking is obtained via two instructions – lock object and unlock object – used to mark the beginning and the end of the locking software section.

The status field in Figure 9.17 is used by the system to keep track of the locking conditions and of the current lock type. When the related object is hardware locked, the unique identifier associated with the locking processor is copied in the locker-identifier field.

Another support for implementing exclusive access to particular operands in the iAPX432 system is represented by the indivisible operators. These are special processor instructions that allow the system programmer to modify the value of a short ordinal, or of an ordinal variable, in a single, uninterruptable step. This is achieved in the

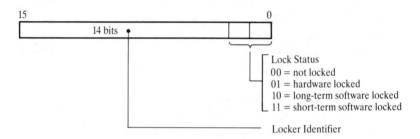

Figure 9.17 Object lock field.

hardware by a particular type of bus cycle called read–modify–write, which a general data processor can start and complete without releasing the system bus mastership.

Two different kinds of indivisible operator are provided: add and insert functions. The first class sums two ordinal operands indivisibly, whereas the second replaces a corresponding subfield in an ordinal variable with a certain bit pattern.

9.8.4   Inter-processor communications

The multiprocessing supports implemented in the iAPX432 system also include facilities for inter-processor communications (IPC) and processor management. The message exchange among different processors in the system is based on **inter-processor message objects**. In fact, each processor object contains two access descriptors in its access part for a couple of **processor communication objects** (**PCOs**), whose structure is shown in Figure 9.18. Two processors can communicate when they have an access descriptor for the same processor communication object. The first local processor communication object is used when a message must be sent to a single different processor, whereas the second or global processor communication object broadcasts the same message to all other processors in the system. The processor-identifier field in Figure 9.18 contains the hardware-defined identifier of the processor associated with the processor communication object, for the local processor communication objects, while a global processor communication object has this field set to zero. The processor count fields are set to one, in local processor communication objects, or are set by the system software to a value equal to the number of processors building up the system in global processor communication objects.

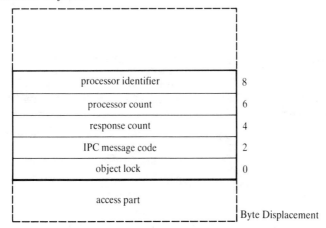

processor identifier	8
processor count	6
response count	4
IPC message code	2
object lock	0
access part	Byte Displacement

Figure 9.18   iAPX432 processor communication object.

When a processor sends a message to another CPU, the processor communication object processor count is copied into the response count field; then the system-defined message code is loaded in the inter-processor communications message code field, and a hardware signal is transmitted to the destination processors. In this way, the receivers can read the message accessed by the global or local processor communication object access descriptors. Each destination processor acknowledges receipt of the message by decrementing the processor communication object response count field by one. When the response count field is reset to zero, the issuing processor is then told that the message was correctly received by all the destination CPUs.

The iAPX432 system defines several kinds of inter-processor message, which can be grouped according to their functions. For example, some messages are used by operating system procedures to flush selectively the on-chip cache memories located on each general data processor when particular events occur, such as object relocation in main memory and/or object swapping to a backing store.

Other messages change the general data processor dispatching mode, when necessary. General data processors, in fact, can use four different dispatching ports according to their current working mode. For this purpose, three additional access descriptors are included in the process object, as alarm, diagnostic and reconfiguration ports, respectively. These ports are used by the processor to search for tasks ready to run, when its operation mode (normal, alarm, reconfiguration, diagnostic) is changed by an inter-processor communications message.

Other messages start and stop the processor operation, and activate an idle CPU when a new process can be bound to it. Finally, messages to initialize or reset a processor and to enable or disable the inter-processor global communication mechanism are also included in the system-defined message codes.

9.9   Objects for memory management

Machines as complex as the iAPX432 must have powerful support for memory management to allow the whole system to work and to provide satisfactory performance levels. Memory management is largely carried out by operating system procedures designed to grant transparent use of the storage devices to the user programs. Nevertheless, as discussed in Chapter 4, some basic mechanisms must be implemented in hardware both to make the implementation of sophisticated memory management strategies possible and to increase the system efficiency when this kind of operation is executed. The iAPX432 implements a number of tools on silicon that are particularly useful to operating system programmers in designing management software. For example, the iMAX432 operating system [9], developed by Intel for multiprocessor machines based on the iAPX432, relies strongly on on-chip support.

Memory management mechanisms are mainly based on another kind of system object, called a **storage resource object (SRO)**, whose structure is shown in Figure 9.19. A storage resource object is used, in fact, to collect all the information related to memory used and needed by the associated processes. The AD to **physical storage object (PSO)**, for example, is used to access physical storage block descriptors. On the other hand, the AD to object table header allows access to the object table, where object descriptors for objects created using the storage resource object itself are located.

When a new system or user object is created, a suitable storage resource object has to be specified. There are two basic requirements for creating an object. First, a suitable object descriptor must be allocated; that is, the object must be inserted in the iAPX432 logical address space. Furthermore, a block of physical storage must be assigned to the representation – the object must be loaded into memory. This happens for every object, except for refinements. When a refinement is defined, only the associated object descriptor is created, since its representation is a physical subset of the parent object.

9.9.1 Object life and memory resources

Some relevant points concerning object life must be explained at this point. Operands in a program can be grouped roughly into two classes. The first contains all the variables and constants used during the whole program execution, while the second includes local variables and data

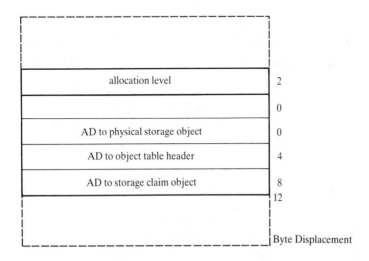

Figure 9.19 Storage resource object organization.

required only during some procedure executions. The latter are used, for example, to store intermediate results, which are no longer needed when the associated procedure returns. These variables are said to be local as their scope is restricted to the subprogram they belong to. Object scopes in the iAPX432 system can also be unlimited, or restricted to the lifetime of the context or procedure that created the objects themselves. For this purpose, the hardware supports two different kinds of storage resource object: **heap** and **stack**. Heap storage resource objects are used to create global objects that can exist in the system indefinitely, unless they are explicitly destroyed, or can no longer be accessed. Stack storage resource objects, in comparison, create local objects that can be accessed only from within their creating context, or from other subordinate contexts. In other words, objects created within a context using a stack storage resource object cannot be passed to any parent subprogram, but only to other procedures called by the current context in turn.

To handle the scope mechanism correctly, the iAPX432 uses a level number field in each object descriptor (see Figure 9.4). Objects created using heap storage resource objects have the level number field reset to zero to indicate that their scope is unlimited. When a stack storage resource object is used for object creation, however, the allocation level field (see Figure 9.19) is copied into the level number field, to mark the object with the nesting level of the associated context. When a context having access to a stack storage resource object calls another subprogram, which can use the same storage resource object, the allocation level field is automatically incremented by the hardware to keep track of the context nesting level.

Since objects allocated from stacks can only be accessed by the creating context, and possibly by the subordinate procedures, checks must be performed when access descriptors are copied. When copying an access descriptor, each iAPX432 processor verifies that the level number field in the object descriptor referred by the access descriptor is greater than or equal to the level of the destination context. This prevents access descriptors for objects created by a context being passed to procedures with lifetimes longer than the source procedure. In fact, because local objects are destroyed when the subprogram returns, some dangling reference to non-existent objects could be contained in the copied access descriptors, thus threatening system integrity.

A. STACK OBJECTS

Physical storage associated with stack storage resource objects consists of a single contiguous block of memory, which is used by the hardware in the same way as stacks are implemented in traditional microprocessor architectures. This means that the object representations in main memory, and corresponding object descriptors in the object table, are allocated or de-allocated with a last-in–first-out (LIFO) strategy. Moreover, the free memory space is maintained in stack storage resource objects as a single contiguous block.

One stack storage resource object is associated with each process in the system and processes cannot share stack storage resource objects. However, there is no support for stack storage resource objects in iAPX432 machines, apart from stacks corresponding to processes.

Stack storage resource objects are not accessed by means of access descriptors; instead, they are implemented as a part of the associated process object, even though they can be considered logically independent objects. In fact, the first three access descriptors in the process object access part (Figure 9.14) are used to build up the process stack storage resource object.

B. HEAP MEMORY OBJECTS

Heap storage resource objects are accessed by means of access descriptors. Heap storage resource objects can be shared by several different processes, and the physical memory associated with them is managed completely differently from the stack storage resource objects. In particular, storage is not allocated or de-allocated in a nested fashion, but is structured as a set of blocks used independently. Both free and used elements in object tables and physical storage objects are generally mixed; that is, they do not constitute two separate and contiguous spaces.

Objects created from heap storage resource objects are global, meaning that they are not automatically destroyed when a procedure returns. On the contrary, they can exist indefinitely and have a longer lifetime than the program that created it. Destruction of objects created from heap storage resource objects can be either automatic or explicitly requested by the user. In an iAPX432 machine, the system software usually deletes unused heap objects transparently to the user. Generally speaking, an object can be removed from memory when it becomes unreachable, because no access descriptor for that object exists in the system. In this case, the operating system must be able to recognize these garbage objects and to delete them to save memory space. For example, the iMAX432 operating system [9] supports a complex garbage-collector process, which runs in parallel with other user tasks. Garbage collection must be implemented in software and is usually a time-consuming process. However, the hardware must offer some mechanisms to the operating system so that it can distinguish between accessible and no-longer accessible objects. For this purpose, the iAPX432 architecture includes a copied bit in each object descriptor (Figure 9.4). This is set automatically by the general data processor when an access descriptor referring to the object is copied. This bit can periodically be reset by the operating system and is used to check whether access descriptors for the object are still present in the system.

C. LOCAL HEAPS

In addition to heap and stack storage resource objects, another kind of storage resource object exists in the iAPX432: a local heap. This combines characteristics of both heap and stack memory pools. Local heap storage resource objects, in fact, are bound to contexts in the same way as stacks. Objects created from a local heap, however, can be passed back to a caller when it is the context or subordinate context associated with the heap storage resource object. In other words, when a subprogram is called by another procedure, and an access descriptor for a local heap is passed from one to the other, the called routine is able to create objects from the heap, and to return valid access descriptors to the caller. The scope of a local heap is, however, limited to the associated context. When the context returns, the local heap (and hence all the objects created from it) can be destroyed by the operating system software, but no automatic memory reclamation is carried out by the hardware. However, during the lifetime of a heap, objects no longer needed can be deleted by the system software by means of the same garbage collection procedure used for global heap storage resource objects. The iMAX432 operating system carries out this process.

9.9.2   Physical storage objects

As already mentioned, another system object involved in memory management is the **physical storage object (PSO)**, whose structure is shown in Figure 9.20. Physical storage objects are used to store information about the blocks of physical memory associated with storage resource objects. It is easy to see that there is no system-defined access part in a physical storage resource object representation. The whole object consists of a storage specification area and two index fields. The storage specification area is an array of storage block descriptors, each containing status and addressing information related to a single contiguous block of memory. A block descriptor includes the 24-bit addresses of the first and last bytes in the block, as well as a bit indicating whether the descriptor is the last block specifier in the specification area, and a dirty bit. The latter is used to find out whether the associated block of memory must be initialized or zeroed when it is allocated.

The beginning block index in Figure 9.20 marks the first storage block descriptor in the storage specification area. The current block index is a pointer to the block descriptor where the search for a block of free memory starts when a new object is allocated. In fact, when an object must be created using a physical storage object, the iAPX432 hardware looks for a suitable block of storage. The strategy used in this search is a first-fit policy, where the selected block is the first that is found to be large enough to contain the created object. To avoid excessive memory

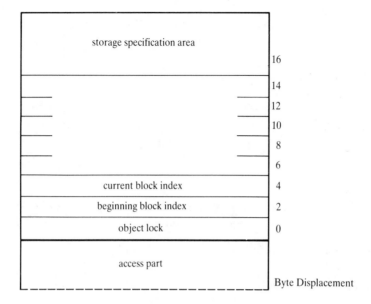

storage specification area	
	16
	14
	12
	10
	8
	6
current block index	4
beginning block index	2
object lock	0
access part	
	Byte Displacement

Figure 9.20 Physical storage object.

fragmentation by this technique, block descriptors in the specification array are analyzed in a circular fashion, starting with the first specifier not reached in the previous search operation and pointed out by the current block index field in Figure 9.20.

Physical storage objects referred to by both heap and stack storage resource objects have the same format. However, stack physical storage objects contain a single storage block descriptor in the storage specification area. Moreover, while different heap storage resource objects can share the same physical storage object, each stack physical storage object must be addressed by only one stack storage resource object via an access descriptor.

The third access descriptor in a storage resource object points to a **storage claim object (SCO)**. The structure of this hardware-recognized object is shown in Figure 9.21. A storage claim object is a mechanism offered to the system software to control the amount of memory allocated by the associated storage resource object. Storage claim objects have no predefined access parts and their data segments contain only a 32-bit storage claim field. This is a counter that indicates how many bytes of memory can still be allocated using the storage resource object. When a new object is created, this field is automatically decremented by the hardware by the amount of allocated memory, thus updating the storage resource object storage claim. The operating system must then suitably increment the storage claim field, when unnecessary objects, created using the storage resource object, are deleted by garbage collection.

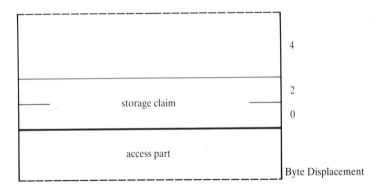

Figure 9.21   iAPX432 storage claim object.

9.9.3   Additional support for virtual memory

Complex systems such as the iAPX432 usually implement sophisticated techniques for virtual memory management, as pointed out in Chapter 4. Several operations concerning this task are necessarily carried out by the operating system, but some hardware mechanisms must nevertheless be provided to obtain satisfactory performance. The iAPX432 offers system programmers basic facilities for implementing virtual memory management schemes based on variable length segments. In other words, the iAPX432 memory space is not structured in a set of fixed-length pages. The operating system must be able to swap single objects, or groups of related objects between main memory and the backing storage.

Many policies can be used to search for objects that must be replaced or swapped out from physical memory at a given time, because other segments, not present in main memory, must be accessed by the running programs. However, most of the algorithms try to detect the less recently accessed segments for their replacements. The accessed bit in each object descriptor (see Figure 9.4) is automatically set by each processor when accessing the associated object. The operating system is able to detect long unused segments by periodically clearing this bit. On the other hand, the altered bit in the object descriptor (see Figure 9.4) increases the system performance. When a selected object has to be swapped out, it is necessary to copy its current representation back into mass storage. Nevertheless, if the representation has not been modified since the object was loaded in main memory, an updated object instance already exists in the backing storage; so the copy operation can be avoided, thus saving CPU time.

The altered bit is automatically set by the hardware when a processor writes to the corresponding object representation; the system software is therefore notified that the segment has been modified and must be copied when swapped out.

Finally, a third bit, called an allocated bit, is included in the object descriptor to support object relocation in memory. It is used by the operating system to signal to the hardware that the associated object is or is not currently allocated in physical memory. When an object must be relocated or swapped, the software clears the allocated bit. If a general data processor tries to access the not present segment, a fault is generated, to be managed by a suitable fault-handling process. This can, for example, load the required object into main memory and restart the suspended task transparently to the user.

9.10 The iAPX432 interconnect system

The most relevant characteristics of the iAPX432 fall into two main classes: first, the processor design has been oriented towards complex object management, rather than for conventional operand processing; secondly, a considerable effort has been made to obtain a truly reliable and fault-tolerant machine [10].

As error generation ranges from hardware failures to software bugs, the fault management system can be thought of as consisting of a hierarchy of error-handling levels. As the model in Figure 9.22 shows, these levels refer to components in the machine hardware modules con- sisting of several components, a hardware system composed of these modules, system software and, finally, applications software. When a fault is generated, a detection and recovery operation is required at each level. If the level cannot handle the error adequately, a message is passed to a higher layer, which will consider the error as generated inside the same higher level. In this way, fault recovery is carried out in a more complex environment by means of slower tasks; moreover, the real error source may be hidden, and the unnecessary interaction between different subsystems increased.

The iAPX432 error-handling mechanism has been designed to avoid hardware failures being reflected in the system and applications software. The architecture raises an ideal barrier between levels 3 and 4 in Figure 9.22, to minimize the traffic of error messages from system hardware to software, and, in practice, the hardware fault may be ignored in each fault-tolerant application.

At present, the iAPX432 is based on five VLSI chips. Besides the general data processor (consisting of two chips: 43201 and 43202) and the interface processor (43203), the **bus interface unit** (**BIU**, 43204) and the **memory control unit** (**MCU**, 43205) have been designed to enhance the modularity and reliability characteristics of each iAPX432 multiprocessor system [11].

Figure 9.23 shows the general topology of an iAPX432 machine: several general data and interface processors are connected to memory

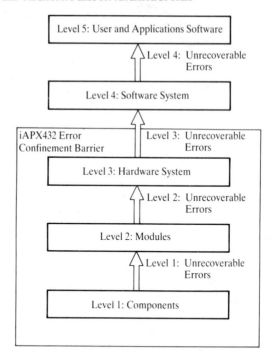

Figure 9.22   Error-reporting layered model.

arrays by a set of buses forming a cross-bar network. Each processor in the system is associated with a processor address, control and data bus (ACD). Memory arrays, in comparison, are connected to a memory address, control and data bus (MACD). Up to eight MACDs can be included in the system to achieve high bandwidth and fault tolerance. Each bus interface and memory control unit represents a node in the interconnect system and is linked to a unique node address. Since a six-bit name is used for identifying each processor or memory array, a maximum of 31 general data processors and interface processors, and 63 combined processors and memory modules are allowed in the system.

The bus interface unit acts as an intelligent switch, capable of accepting requests from a processor and performing the memory access by means of the right MACD. Moreover, it arbitrates the MACD use. As Figure 9.23 shows, there must be a bus interface chip for each MACD, and together the central processor and associated bus interface units constitute an iAPX432 processor module.

The memory control units allow dynamic RAM arrays to be interfaced to the MACD bus. Each memory control unit manages its associated memory, structured in 40-bit words: 32 bits are interpreted as data, seven bits as error correcting code (ECC) and one (optional) bit is spare. A memory module in the iAPX432 system consists of a memory array and its associated memory control unit.

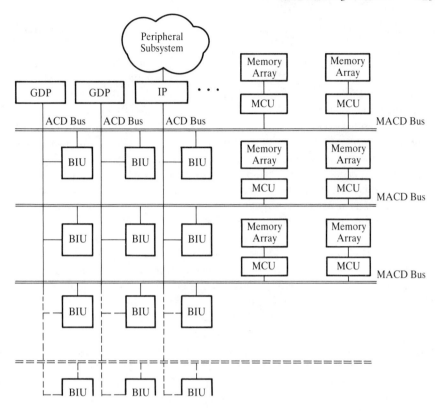

Figure 9.23 iAPX432 interconnect system architecture.

The MACD bus carries all the memory access requests and handles the inter-processor communications. The MACD bus protocol requires that each memory access consists of a request, issued by a processor, and a reply, from a memory array. By pipelining requests and answers on an MACD, bus throughput is greatly increased. Each MACD can queue a maximum of three memory requests and answers. Since each request can be separated in time by the corresponding reply, keeping track of all demands issued on an MACD is the job of the bus interface and memory control units connected to that MACD. In this way, fully distributed bus control is obtained. Requests are issued as packets of information from 1 to 16 bytes long.

The iAPX432 can also support direct inter-processor communication for signalling special conditions. This is achieved by a particular type of MACD message, which does not require reply packets.

To increase performance when several processors have access to the same memory area, memory bus interleaving is provided. In this way, different MACDs are used for distributing and alternating accesses to consecutive regions of the processor physical address space under software control. Interleaving is selected by the mid-order address bits at

64-, 128- or 256-byte boundaries and is controlled by the bus interface units.

The error confinement principle is fundamental for achieving most reliability goals. The iAPX432 recognizes four types of confinement areas: those built around a general data processor, an interface processor, a memory array and an MACD bus. As Figure 9.24 shows, the processor and the memory confinement areas consist of a processor module (a general data or interface processor and bus interface units) and a memory module (memory array and memory control unit). The MACD confinement area, on the other hand, consists of a memory bus and attached bus interface and memory control units. When a failure is detected inside a region in Figure 9.24, it is automatically confined, as no data can leave an area and pass to another without first being tested for accuracy.

All the iAPX432 chips – general data processor, interface processor, bus interface unit and memory control unit – provide basic mechanisms for supporting hardware self-checking module design. **Functional redundancy checking (FRC)** in the iAPX432 allows the replication of each VLSI chip and achieves high reliability. Figure 9.24 shows redundant processor and memory modules structured in master and checker units. In each master/checker pair, one component or master performs its normal functions, while the other, or checker, compares its outputs with the master's, testing for a possible disagreement. Functional redundancy checking does not consist of the replication of processing modules from a functional point of view. In fact, when either the master or the checker is permanently damaged, the other element in the

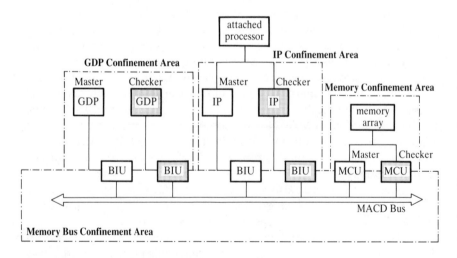

Figure 9.24 iAPX432 error confinement areas and functional redundancy checking module structures.

functional redundancy pair cannot continue to carry out its functions alone, nor can it be dynamically joined to a spare module to form a new functional redundancy couple. The main reason for this is that the master and checker must use the same signal lines for driving the bus buffers. In this way, the checker only acts as a watchdog processor, able to point out the incorrect behaviour of its companion. Errors detected in this way are quickly reported to other modules by a special error-reporting network whose topology is the same as the system cross-bar. However, the error-reporting network is totally independent of the buses devoted to normal operations.

The error transmission protocol consists of three basic phases. As Figure 9.25 shows, when a fault is detected at a node (i, j), an error message is first sent to all the devices connected to the same MACD bus. In a second step, the components that received the error message re-broadcast it along their module ACD bus. Finally, all the components send the message along their own MACD buses. In this way, all the nodes in the system receive the fault information, even if some ACD or MACD bus lines have failed.

The recovery action can be carried out by redundant resources available in the system. The iAPX432 builds fully fault-tolerant modules, such as QMR or quad modular redundant, by pairing two self-checking master or checker units, as in Figure 9.26. This is called **module shadowing**, since if a primary module fails the shadow module can be used in its place. The primary and shadow units work in a lock-step operation and, when a permanent error is detected in the main module, the other is switched in to replace the failed companion. Switching is made possible as the shadow provides a complete and current backup for the primary unit. During a memory write operation, in fact, the primary and shadow bus interface units in the quad modular redundant processor module perform the accesses to the MACD bus strictly alternately, while the memory read operations are carried out in parallel, by both units.

In the QMR memory module, in comparison, the primary and shadow memory control units accept data to be written into memory in parallel, simultaneously updating both the primary and the shadow storage array. Data are then retrieved from the physical memory alternately, by the main and backup memory control units. Unlike the master and checker units in a functional redundancy pair, primary and shadow modules that became spare during a fault in the associated unit can once again be coupled to form a new full quad modular redundant pair. The reconfiguration is totally controlled by software. Only the spare interface processor modules cannot be paired dynamically in a single quad modular redundant module: both the primary and the shadow interface processor, in fact, must be connected to the same attached processor bus to allow the correct operation of the module.

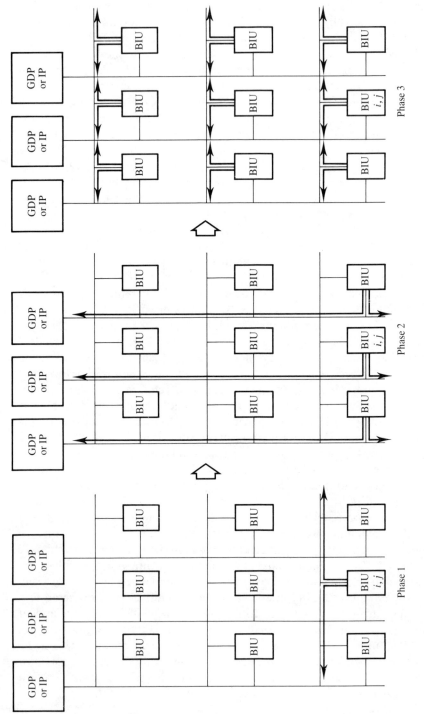

Figure 9.25   Error-reporting protocol.

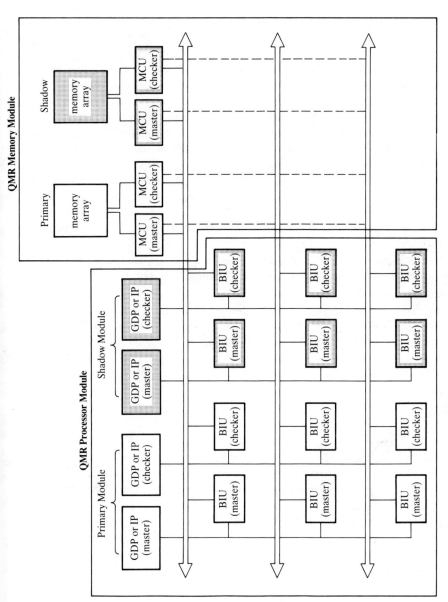

Figure 9.26 Quad modular redundant module architecture.

9.11   Fault handling in the iAPX432 system

9.11.1   Fault handling in the processor area

The processor confinement area handles errors in the general data and interface processors' operations and those in their associated bus interface units. There are no real differences between a general data and an interface processor module, as far as fault detection and recovery are concerned. The interface processor area is identical to that in the general data processor, but it also has an interface to the peripheral subsystem, which is controlled by the interface processor. The error-handling mechanisms are, however, the same for both processors.

Reliability is achieved by using a loop-back check for each memory bus interface, and by applying functional redundancy checking to the whole processor module. The loop-back check detects common mode errors in the TTL drivers that interface the MACD bus. In each interface buffer chip, a spare driver is reserved for the check: the bus interface (or memory control) unit connected to the buffer sends an oscillating signal through all the connected spare drivers, cascading one with another, as shown in Figure 9.27. The signal is then returned to the generating bus interface unit and is correct only if all the drivers in the interface are working well. This mechanism detects single failures in control signals, such as a stuck buffer enable line.

On the other hand, functional redundancy checking is based on two processor modules used in the master or checker configuration. The master selection is made at initialization by the software. The master module can then carry out its normal functions. The checker block, however, has its outputs disabled and tests the master outputs instead of presenting its own. Master and checker run in a clock cycle lock step.

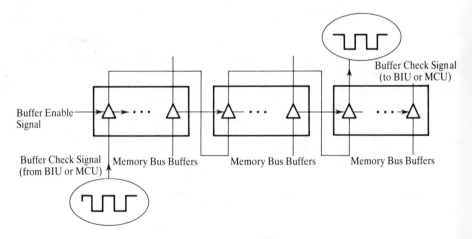

Figure 9.27   Buffer-checking mechanism.

Functional redundancy checking in a processor module is obtained with all the components working normally, except the MACD bus drivers in the checker bus interface units. Errors in the master or checker blocks (including general data processor, ACD bus and bus interface units) are then detected when corresponding bus interace units in both modules disagree.

Because the functional redundancy checking can detect errors generated in the master or the checker, but not in both simultaneously, the detection logic must be periodically tested for possible faults. The comparison and fault-reporting circuits of the checker, in particular, must be tested. This enhances reliability. Some software commands are provided for this purpose. A test error report function allows the system software to ask either the master or the checker explicitly for an error-check answer. A fault is assumed if there is no reply from the devices. Another special command allows the user to toggle between the master and checker functions of the module; eventual faults, such as erroneous mastership required and assumed by the checker, can then be detected, as after the toggle operation the module will probably consist of a checker/checker instead of a master/checker pair. Another software-controlled mechanism – test detection command – tests the error-detection circuits in the functional redundancy checking module. This forces error conditions in the functional redundancy checking comparators and in the buffer check logic, and a fault is assumed if any detection mechanism does not signal the error introduced into the system.

Finally, in the interface processor confinement area, the functional redundancy checking is also used to check the interface between the peripheral subsystem and the interface processor module. In contrast, no check is performed on the I/O operations of the peripheral subsystem.

9.11.2   Fault handling in the memory area

The memory error confinement area consists of the memory array and its associated memory control unit. As Figure 9.28 shows, each unit is directly connected to two MACD buses. In this way, when an MACD becomes unavailable, because a fault has been detected in the bus confinement area, for example, the memory array and its stored information can still be accessed by the second MACD.

The memory area protection mechanisms can be divided into two main classes, according to whether they concern the MACD interface or the array side of the storage module.

A.   MACD BUS INTERFACE

As with the processor area, functional redundancy checking is used to test the outputs of the master memory control unit to the MACD, in the same way as the master bus interface unit outputs are controlled by the checker

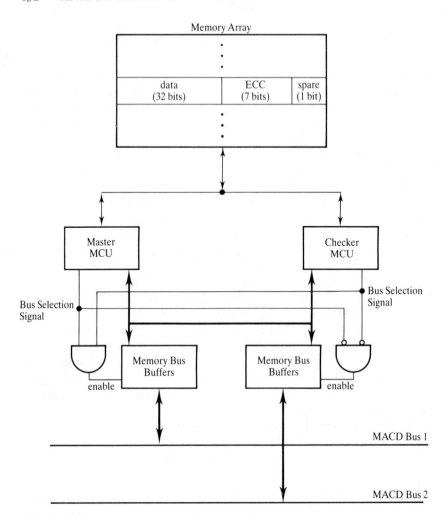

Figure 9.28 Master and checker memory control unit connections.

bus interface units. The loop-back check of the bus drivers is also performed by the memory control units. However, since each memory control unit is connected to two buses, two different sets of drivers must be checked. The loop-back check is applied in such a way as to verify that all the drivers on the active bus are working correctly, while the buffers on the backup bus should all be inactive. To avoid the corruption of data on each MACD when a fault is detected, the bus drivers can be enabled only if the master and the checker memory control units agree which bus must be activated. For this reason, a single fault in the bus interface cannot invalidate both the MACD buses.

B. MEMORY ARRAY INTERFACE

On the array side of the storage module, functional redundancy checking checks all the array signal lines to grant a correct management by the master memory control unit. A loop-back check for the memory or SLAD bus drivers is also carried out. If a fault is detected on the array side, an unsafe error message is broadcast through the system, as the stored information may or may not be corrupted. Data written into or read from the memory array are checked by means of a 7-bit ECC Hamming code appended to the 32 information bits, and computed from the data themselves and their memory addresses. The ECC is able to detect and correct all the single-bit errors in the data field. Each single- and double-bit error in the memory address can be discovered, together with the odd numbered bit errors in the data and address fields. The ECC is also used by the memory control unit when the refresh cycle of the memory locations is performed. This is called **scrubbing**. In fact, when a refresh operation is carried out, the ECC field is tested, and if a correctable error is detected the memory control unit writes the corrected value back into the array location. Since each memory cell is periodically accessed for scrubbing, the probability of an undetected double-bit error in the array is virtually nil. The reliability is further increased because the memory control unit performs each write operation as a read–modify–write cycle. By checking the ECC in this way, the memory controller is able to verify that the right address has been reached before changing the stored information.

Each memory location contains 39 bits of information and an ECC; since the physical interface to the memory control unit handles 40 bits in parallel, a spare bit is left over, and can be used for fault recovery. One of the 39 data bits can be replaced, if necessary, by the spare bit, and its selection is controlled by software. When the spare bit must be switched the memory control unit reports a burst of single-bit errors in the bit location replaced by the spare bit. During scrubbing, the spare bit at each location is updated to the value that a replaced bit should have. Of course, the ECC performs this operation.

C. DETECTION MECHANISM CHECKING

System software can check the memory area detection mechanisms by using one of six available commands. As in the processor confinement area, the master/checker functions are tested with a toggle operation. A test detection function verifies that functional redundancy checking comparators (both on the SLAD and MACD buses) and the buffer-check mechanisms are working well. Three software commands check the ECC circuits: they allow a diagnostic process to write bad data into the information and ECC fields of any memory location, and verify the ECC mechanism-correct operation during scrubbing or normal accesses to the location performed by the memory control unit.

9.11.3   Fault handling in the memory bus area

The MACD error-confinement area consists of the MACD bus, the buffers, and the arbitration sections of each bus interface and memory control unit connected to the bus. Two main mechanisms are provided for fault detection. As shown in Figure 9.29, the arbitration lines and circuits of the MACD are duplicated: one set is used by the masters and the other by the checkers.

Any single error in the arbitration signals is detected as a functional redundancy checking error on the arbitration line outputs by the master. On the other hand, parity is used to detect errors on the MACD bus lines. For this purpose, two parity bits are provided to test the 16 data and three control bits of the memory bus. The first or odd parity bit is applied to the even-numbered lines, while the second or even parity is referred to the odd-numbered signals. This parity control scheme detects all the single-bit and multiple, odd-numbered errors. Double-bit errors are also detected, if each parity bit covers only one of the errors. Stuck-at-zero faults are always discovered.

Associated with the 19 information signals is an error-reporting line used for broadcasting 16-bit error messages to the nodes connected to the memory bus. A parity bit, appended to each message, is capable of detecting each single-bit error, multiple and odd-numbered bit errors, and stuck-at-zero faults. A time-out function is also provided, and its period length is controlled by software. Time out, however, is not capable of detecting hardware failure. In fact, this mechanism is only used at

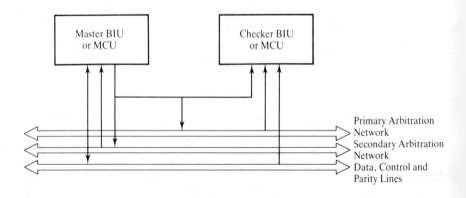

Figure 9.29   Duplication of the error-reporting network.

initialization for detecting configuration errors by the system software. Time out does not generate error messages, only a pseudo-reply in each node connected to the bus. Both the parity and the functional redundancy checking detection mechanisms can be checked by means of a software test-detection command. This can be carried out even if a detection mechanism is disabled. The master/checker functions of the bus interface units connected to the MACD are tested by the toggle and test report commands, as previously discussed.

9.11.4   Configurations

The mechanisms previously described are only capable of performing some reconfiguration within each subsystem, be it memory, processor or bus. In general, system reconfiguration is applications dependent when a spare for the faulty module is no longer available. Hence, the reconfiguration strategy is implemented in the iAPX432 system by the software, by means of a special set of processes, one per processor. Each process waits at a reconfiguration port corresponding to a specific processor [4]. When a message reporting information on a permanent fault is issued, it is transformed into a special inter-processor communications message, which suspends the process currently being executed by each processor. The processors re-dispatch themselves from their own reconfiguration-dispatching ports, and the processes waiting there are executed. In addition, the interface processors send an interrupt to the attached processors, so that the whole system is aware that some resource has a permanent fault.

The processes queued at the configuration-dispatching ports are the software fault handlers for the different processors. When these fault handlers are activated, they perform house-keeping actions, then send messages to the reconfiguration software and return the processors to their normal dispatching ports.

Of course, when the fault handlers recognize that recovering from the fault which caused the reconfiguration inter-process communications, requires software actions, in addition to the mechanisms provided by the hardware, they activate high-priority reconfiguration processes.

One of the simplest configurations, from the fault-tolerance point of view, is that shown in Figure 9.23, (where the general data and interface processor, and the bus interface and memory control modules do not have any hardware mechanism to check the accuracy of their operations). The redundant buses can be used during the checks as the memory arrays are protected by the ECC and spare-bit mechanisms.

When a fault occurs in a general data processor module, including the processor and connected bus interface units, it may not be immediately detected because no functional redundancy checking is used. However, the errors due to the fault are confined by the capability-addressing mechanism, which is also capable of detecting the fault when it causes unauthorized accesses. When this condition is discovered, the general data processor can detach its own bus interface units from the buses, or they can be detached by other processors. Thanks to the barriers between processes, built in by the capability-checking mechanism, only the database of the process running on the faulty module can be corrupted. However, the process can be re-initialized if cold start is allowed, by reading the initial state of the database from mass storage devices.

An additional reconfiguration action required when a general data processor module fails, is the de-activation of the processor object; that is, the software image of each processor in the system. This corresponds to the faulty general data processor module, so no process will be scheduled for that processor.

Once the software has been reconfigured according to the new hardware situation, the independence of the software in the system processors will do the rest. They redistribute the work load over the working processors. The final result is a decrease in system performance, without a decrease in functionality. In some applications, it might be desirable to keep the level of performance constant, as it may not be necessary to perform all tasks. In this case, the reconfiguration process will terminate one or more non-essential processes, so that the essential ones can be executed at the required speed, even with a reduced number of working processors.

The configuration of Figure 9.24 represents a further step towards enhancing systems' fault tolerance, as the introduction of functional redundancy checking allows a fault to be detected as soon as its effects become evident. Hence, faster reconfiguration procedures can be used. The failure of a general data processor module, for example, is detected immediately, and it is possible to disable the faulty processor module before it can perform an incorrect operation on the database of the process running on it. This feature restarts the process by simply continuing its operations on a different processor, taking advantage of the dynamic task-allocation mechanism provided by the system.

Finally, the configuration of Figure 9.25 ensures that the system still works, even when there is a single failure. This is achieved using the iAPX432 shadowing technique, because each primary shadow pair is seen as a single logical module, although both components execute the same operations in lock step. In this way, when the functional redundancy checking mechanism detects the failure of one element, and it issues the corresponding error-reporting message, the other partner recognizes that it is the only surviving component of the primary shadow pair, and will continue its operations, taking account of the new situation.

The failure of one element in a primary shadow pair does not require any software action to create a new working configuration;

however, the software should recognize that the system is now exposed to a crash if a second failure occurs in the same pair. Hence, if the system has been designed to obtain high reliability or availability, this exposure time should be kept as short as possible, either by invoking the field maintenance service, or by using some other spare module in the system to recast a new primary shadow pair.

In Figure 9.25, each system component has its own duplicate, in addition to its checker. Another interesting configuration is obtained when only the memory modules are organized in primary shadow pairs, while general data and interface processor modules only have functional redundancy checking. In this case, the integrity of the memory contents is also assured, even when a single module fails. Hence, the processes that were running on any faulty processors will always have a warm start. In this configuration, each general data processor module is a possible active spare for other modules. Software actions are, however, required to perform the reconfiguration described for the system illustrated in Figure 9.30.

9.12 Conclusion

The Intel iAPX432 is the only microprocessor commercially available that has a true capability-based and object-oriented architecture. The integration of hardware and software design has produced a uniform system that includes a large number of sophisticated supports for exploiting reliability and protection at the circuit, operating system and application levels.

The iAPX432 is capable of processing conventional operands and complex objects represented by means of special data structures. The system is oriented to high-level language programming in general and Ada in particular; thus, the iAPX432 hardware can recognize and process a number of objects intended to simplify the execution of Ada programs and to allow the implementation of separate addressing environments for procedures and tasks.

In addition, special mechanisms have been introduced to extend to the user-defined objects the same degree of protection as for system objects.

A number of system objects was foreseen to support transparent multiprocessing, inter-process communications, process scheduling and processors binding to processes. Some other iAPX432 objects are responsible for memory management and can be used to design complex virtual memory systems.

The iAPX432 architecture is suitable for implementing several variants of fault-tolerant systems with different degrees of reliability. In fact, special mechanisms included in the iAPX432 allow hardware faults

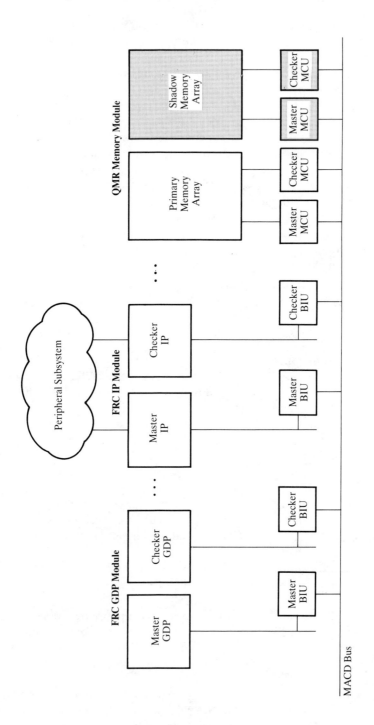

Figure 9.30   An additional fault-tolerant architecture.

to be confined within the area from which they originated. In this way, it is possible to insulate the faulty units from the system and to start some machine reconfigurations.

EXERCISES

9.1 What are the main advantages of having run-time support for operating systems operations and high-level languages directly in hardware?

9.2 Explain the iAPX432 technique for object addressing.

9.3 What are the main advantages and drawbacks of having a two-level addressing mechanism?

9.4 What is a refinement?

9.5 What is a domain?

9.6 How can an applications program use an object without being able to access its representation?

9.7 Try to write the design specifications of a simple system to simulate concurrent access by several users to a common database containing several pages of information. Each user can perform the following basic operations: find an entry in a page; read an existing entry; update an entry; or add a new entry to a page. How can the iAPX432 supports for user-defined data types, mutual exclusion and package implementation be conveniently used in this project?

9.8 What happens in the iAPX432 system when a send instruction is executed? (Try to outline the differences between the blocking and non-blocking cases.)

9.9 Why are carriers used in process communication rather than process objects themselves?

9.10 Design the structure of a data acquisition system consisting of the following processes: $S1$, $S2$, . . . , Sn are devoted to sample data from peripheral devices; $P1$ and $P2$ process the data obtained from each Si, (where $i = 1...n$) and pass the result to the client processes $C1$, $C2$, . . . , Cn. The system must be based on the iAPX432 communication mechanisms. When a datum is produced by a Si it can be processed only once by either *P*1 or *P*2. The system must prevent deadlocks and work efficiently, avoiding busy forms of waiting whenever possible.

9.11 Explain why global variables in high-level languages must be allocated from a heap storage resource object, while local variables are placed in the procedure stack storage resource object.

9.12 What are functional redundancy checking and quad modular redundancy?

References

[1] J. Rattner and W. W. Lattin, 'Ada Determines Architecture of 32-bit Microprocessor', *Electronics*, February 1981, pp. 119–126.

[2] V. Berstis, 'Security and Protection of Data in the IBM System/38', in *Proceedings of the 7th Symposium on Computer Architecture*, May 1980, pp. 245–252.

[3] Intel Corporation, *iAPX432 General Data Processor Architecture Reference Manual*, 1983.

[4] G. W. Cox, W. M. Corwin, K. K. Lai and F. J. Pollack, 'Inter-process Communication and Processor Dispatching on the Intel iAPX432', *ACM Transactions on Computer Systems* **1**(1), February 1983, pp. 45–66.

[5] Intel Corporation, *iAPX432 Interface Processor Architecture Reference Manual*, 1983.

[6] B. Liskov, A. Snyder, R. Atkinson and C. Shaffert, 'Abstraction Mechanisms in CLU', *Communications of the ACM* **20**(8), August 1977, pp. 564–576.

[7] R. S. Fabry, 'Capability-Based Addressing', *Communications of the ACM* **17**(7), July 1974, pp. 403–411.

[8] *Reference Manual for the Ada Programming Language*, 1983.

[9] Intel Corporation, *iMAX432 Reference Manual*, 1983.

[10] D. P. Siewiorek and R. S. Swarz, *The Theory and Practice of Reliable System Design*, Digital Press, 1982.

[11] Intel Corporation, *iAPX432 Interconnect Architecture Reference Manual*, 1983.

CHAPTER 10
REDUCED ARCHITECTURES

OBJECTIVES

The aims of this chapter are:

- to illustrate the reasons behind the development of the reduced instruction set computer (RISC) approach;
- to discuss the main features of three major examples of RISC microprocessors: Berkeley RISC, microprocessors without interlocked pipe stages (MIPS) and the Inmos Transputer.

10.1 Introduction
10.2 RISC approach
10.3 Berkeley RISC

10.4 MIPS
10.5 The Inmos Transputer
10.6 Conclusion

10.1   Introduction

The evolution of the microprocessor, briefly outlined at the beginning of this book, shows that designers have always used an increased chip area to introduce new and sophisticated instructions, addressing modes and other mechanisms. The new features support the execution of high-level languages as well as the complex functions of operating systems. In other words, the evolution of microprocessor architecture is closing the semantic gap (see Section 1.2).

This trend was constant until the 1980s, when a design philosophy based on a simplification of the architecture emerged. The basis of this approach is the fact that the computing power of a microprocessor does not necessarily depend on how wide or narrow the semantic gap is between the high-level languages and the machine; it depends on which aspects of this gap, critical to performance, are supported in hardware. For example, assume that there is a machine that can directly execute programs written in a high-level language; such a machine would be ideal because the semantic gap would not exist. Nevertheless, it highlights the following drawbacks:

- it is necessary to build one such machine for each high-level language used;
- syntactical errors are detected at run time, so only one error can be discovered at each run of the same program, because the detected error blocks the exectuion.

These drawbacks stem from the fact that some functions, such as language translation, are better implemented in software, rather than in hardware. The closure of the semantic gap is, therefore, not a goal in itself. It is more important to study which aspects of this gap have a strong influence on the computer's performance, in order to improve it.

The solutions discussed in this chapter are all based on a simple architecture, and have simple instructions, so they can be seen as different applications of the design philosophy called the **reduced instruction set computer** (**RISC**). However, the Inmos Transputer architecture highlights another issue, because it is intended to work in a system composed of several identical processors; in this way, the improvement in speed is achieved through the execution of several operations in parallel, rather than by implementing a very fast CPU.

10.2   The RISC approach

One consequence of narrowing the semantic gap is that nowadays microprocessors are complex instruction set computers (CISC), because they have repertoires of hundreds of instructions and several addressing modes. The RISC supporters argue that all these new instructions complicate the design of the control unit, slowing down the execution of basic operations. As the simpler operations tend to be used more frequently than the complex ones, this can have a serious effect on overall performance. A simple instruction set allows, in principle, a simple, fast implementation, so the larger number of instructions that it requires can be more than compensated for by the increased speed.

CISC machines implement their instructions in microcode, so the sequence of elementary operations (microinstructions) required to perform an operation is encoded and optimized during the design of the microprocessor. This removes the opportunity to achieve the best performance from the specific operations required by the program. In contrast, if the instruction set is so simple that there is no, or little, difference between assembly and microcode languages, the code generator of the compiler can optimize the operations, and so improve the speed of the resulting code.

Another advantage claimed by RISC supporters is that the simplification of the control unit helps to save chip area for the control implementation. This can be used to implement some special features in the operating unit, aimed at improving the execution speed. While all the RISC architectures have a small, fast instruction set, they can differ to a large extent in their use of the chip area that is made available by their simple control units. This means that a wide range of architectural choices is possible within the RISC family, each characterized by the ability to use the area that a simple instruction set frees.

10.3 Berkeley RISC

This section looks at the main features of the RISC project developed at the University of Berkeley [1]. In the rest of this section the acronym RISC will be used to indicate the project name rather than the design philosophy.

The main characteristics of the RISC microprocessor can be summarized as follows:

- each instruction is executed in a single cycle, so instructions are no more complex than microinstructions;
- all the instructions are the same size, which is equal to a 32-bit word;
- the access to memory is possible only through load/store instructions, while other accesses operate on internal registers;
- the internal organization, or the register file, is designed to support some operations required by high-level languages.

The last point here is particularly important, because it is the basis of the internal design of the Berkeley processor. A preliminary study on the characteristics of programs written in high-level languages showed that the call/return procedure is the syntactical construct with the highest value for the product (frequency of occurrence)×(execution time), where the frequency is obtained by counting the occurrences in the source program, given the difficulty of recognizing different syntactical constructs at run time.

The call/return procedure seems to be the most time-consuming operation, so the design team concentrated on implementing fast mechanisms aimed at supporting this type of operation efficiently.

10.3.1   Register organization

The silicon area saved in the design of the control unit by the simplicity and small number of instructions has been used in the RISC to implement a large number (128, in the first version) of registers. However, not all registers are visible to the programmer at the same time. A study [2] on the influence of the number of registers on the performance of programs written in high-level languages has shown that increasing the register number beyond five does not give remarkable advantages.

At a given time, only a window of 32 registers, each consisting of 32 bits, is available to the programmer. The window is moved over the whole register file whenever a call or return operation is performed. The mechanism for changing the window is illustrated in Figure 10.1, where it is assumed that procedure A calls procedure B, which in turn calls procedure C.

The first ten registers (R0–R9) are common to all the windows, so when the window is changed, these registers are not altered. For the other registers, when a procedure is called, the window of the called program overlaps with the window used by the calling procedure. This means that registers R26–R31 of the called procedure correspond to the registers R10–R15 of the calling procedure.

When a return from a procedure is performed, the calling procedure is executed with the register set that was used before the procedure call.

The rationale underlying this register organization is clear when the mechanisms for procedure call presented in Section 1.4 are considered. The window movements mimic the operations performed in main memory, which suggests a simple scheme for register usage, minimizing the number of memory accesses required to implement a procedure call/return operation, because almost all the information to be passed between the different procedures is kept in registers. The scheme is as follows:

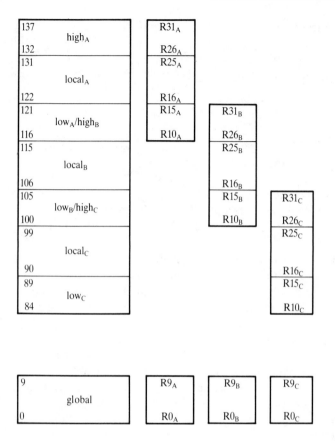

Figure 10.1 Example of window changes for three different procedures.

- R0–R9 are used to store global information, because their contents are visible to all the procedures (like global variables);

- R0–R15 are used to store parameters for the procedure called by the current one, as these registers will be part of the register window of any procedure called by the current one;

- R11–R25 are used for totally local information, because they are not part of any other register window;

- R26–R31 are used to store parameters of the current procedure, as they are also part of the register window used by the procedure that called the current one.

Of course, it is possible to have overflow or underflow in the register file: the first occurs when a procedure is called and no more registers are available; the second corresponds to a procedure return, when all the other registers hold no valid information. In both cases, a trap is activated, which is responsible for downloading part of the register file into memory in the case of overflow, or uploading from memory part of the register file that was previously downloaded in the case of underflow.

10.3.2   Instructions

The general format of a RISC instruction is shown in Figure 10.2. Because most of the instructions operate only on registers, both the DEST and SOURCE1 fields are only 5-bits long. But because they should specify one of the 32 internal registers, there is also a field SOURCE2, used to specify immediate or displacement values for the instructions using this feature.

The instruction set is shown in Table 10.1. The only addressing mode allowed is the base displacement mode, with the two particular cases of register indirect (if the displacement is zero) and address stored in the instruction (if the contents of the base register is zero); immediate operands are also allowed. The value of the displacement field is limited to 13 bits. The instructions for procedure call and return modify the register window as explained in Section 10.2.1.

The instruction execution is pipelined; that is, each instruction is executed while the next one in the instruction flow is decoded. These overlapping operations increase speed, but they may cause problems when conditional jumps are executed. In such a case, the instruction to be executed after a conditional jump is not known until the condition is evaluated. While this operation is being carried out, however, the instruction following the jump has already started the decoding phase, so the machine is forced to execute it after the completion of the jump instruction, regardless of the evaluation of the jump condition.

To prevent incorrect instructions from being executed, the code has to be restructured so that the instruction following each jump is executed before the actual jump effect is produced. For example, if a conditional jump is used to close a loop, it may be followed by one of the instructions in the body of the loop, but this does not stop the program exiting from the loop. For this reason, the instruction following the jump

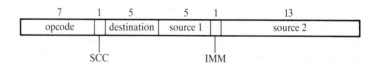

Figure 10.2   Instruction format of the Berkeley RISC.

Table 10.1 Instruction set of the Berkeley RISC I.

Instruction	Operands	Operation	Comments
Arithmetic and logic operations			
ADD	Rs, S2, Rd	Rd ← Rs + S2	Integer add
ADDC	Rs, S2, Rd	Rd ← Rs + S2 + carry	Add with carry
SUB	Rs, S2, Rd	Rd ← Rs − S2	Integer subtract
SUBC	Rs, S2, Rd	Rd ← Rs − S2 − carry	Subtract with carry
SUBR	Rs, S2, Rd	Rd ← S2 − Rs	Integer subtract
SUBCR	Rs, S2, Rd	Rd ← S2 − Rs − carry	Subtract with carry
AND	Rs, S2, Rd	Rd ← Rs & S2	Logical AND
OR	Rs, S2, Rd	Rd ← Rs	S2	Logical OR
XOR	Rs, S2, Rd	Rd ← Rs xor S2	Logical EXCLUSIVE/OR
SLL	Rs, S2, Rd	Rd ← Rs shifted by S2	Shift left
SRL	Rs, S2, Rd	Rd ← Rs shifted by S2	Shift right logical
SRA	Rs, S2, Rd	Rd ← Rs shifted by S2	Shift right arithmetic
Transport operations			
LDL	(Rx) S2, Rd	Rd ← M [Rx + S2]	Load long
LDSU	(Rx) S2, Rd	Rd ← M [Rx + S2]	Load short unsigned
LDSS	(Rx) S2, Rd	Rd ← M [Rx + S2]	Load short signed
LDBU	(Rx) S2, Rd	Rd ← M [Rx + S2]	Load byte unsigned
LDBS	(Rx) S2, Rd	Rd ← M [Rx + S2]	Load byte signed

Table 10.1   (cont.)

Instruction	Operands	Operation	Comments
Transport operations (cont.)			
STL	Rm, (Rx) S2	M [Rx + S2] − Rm	Store long
STS	Rm, (Rx) S2	M [Rx + S2] − Rm	Store short
STB	Rm, (Rx) S2	M [Rx + S2] − Rm	Store byte
Control transfer operations			
JMP	COND. S2 (Rx)	pc − Rx + S2	Conditional jump
JMPR	COND, Y	pc − pc + Y	Conditional relative
CALL	Rd, S2 (Rx)	Rd − pc, next	Call
		pc − Rx + S2, CWP − CWP − 1	and change window
CALLR	Rd, Y	Rd − pc, next	Call relative
		pc − pc + Y, CWP − CWP − 1	and change window
RET	Rm, S2	pc − Rm + S2, CWP − CWP + 1	Return and change window
CALLINT	Rd	Rd − last pc; next CWP − CWP − 1	Disable interrupts
RETINT	Rm, S2	pc − Rm + S2; next CWP − CWP + 1	Enable interrupts
Other operations			
LDHI	Rd, Y	Rd < 31:13 > − Y; Rd < 12:0 > − 0	Load immediate high
GTLPC	Rd	Rd − last pc	to restart delayed jump
GETPSW	Rd	Rd − PSW	Load status word
PUTPSW	Rm	PSW − Rm	Set status word

must always be executed, regardless of the jump result. If it is not possible to find such an instruction, the insertion of a no-operation instruction solves the problem. This technique is called **delayed jump**.

10.4   MIPS

The MIPS (microprocessor without interlocked pipe stages) [3] is another application of the RISC design philosophy. It shares some important features with the Berkeley RISC; namely, the simplicity of the instruction set, and the ability to execute each instruction in the same time and the same size (one 32-bit word) for all the instructions. However, several other characteristics, such as the register organization, make these two machines very different.

10.4.1   Instruction execution

The internal organization is based on a set of 16 general-purpose registers, each 32-bits long, which are uniformly used by the instruction set. The repertoire of instructions is listed in Table 10.2. Like the Berkeley RISC, MIPS is a load/store machine, because only such instructions can access the external memory, rather than operate with registers. Three operand instructions are included in the instruction set. The addressing modes include base displacement indirect with the displacement either in the instruction itself or in a register, base indexed indirect and direct addressing.

The distinctive feature of MIPS is its extensive use of pipelining to execute instructions fast. While the Berkeley RISC uses this technique to implement only two pipe stages, decoding and execution, the MIPS divides each instruction into five phases, as shown in Table 10.3. This finer subdivision allows the instruction stream to be executed with greater overlapping.

The ideal condition for this pipelined machine is as follows: while the instruction i is in phase OF, the instruction $i + 1$ would be in phase SX, the instruction $i + 2$ in phase OD, and so on. Unfortunately, this is not possible because different phases generally require the use of the same resources; for example, both OD and SX use the ALU. The solution to this problem reduces the degree of overlapping. Figure 10.3 shows how the instructions are executed in the MIPS: each pipe stage is composed of two phases, so the machine completes the execution of one instruction every two phases.

The overlapping execution of the instructions, as in the Berkeley RISC, gives rise to the problem of the correct execution of jumps. Once

Table 10.2   Instruction set of MIPS.

Instruction	Operands	Operation	Comments
Arithmetic and logical operations			
ADD	src1, src2, dst	dst:= src2 + src1	Integer addition
AND	src1, src2, dst	dst:= src2 & src1	Logical and
IC	src1, src2, dst	dst:= byte src1 of dst is replaced by src2	Insert byte
OR	src1, src2, dst	dst:= src2 | src1	Logical or
RLC	src1, src2, src3, dst	dst:= src2||src3 rotated by src1 positions	Rotate combined
ROL	src1, src2, dst	dst:= src2 rotated by src1 positions	Rotate
SLL	src1, src2, dst	dst:= src2 shifted left by src1 positions	shift left logical
SRA	src1, src2, dst	dst:= src2 shifted right by src1 positions	Shift right arithmetic
SRL	src1, src2, dst	dst:= src2 shifted right by src1 positions	Shift right logical
SUB	src1, src2, dst	dst:= src2 − src1	Integer subtraction
SUBR	src1, src2, dst	dst:= src1 − src2	Reverse integer subtraction
XC	src1, src2, dst	dst:= byte src1 of src2	Extract byte
XOR	src1, src2, dst	dst:= src2 ⊕ src1	Logical xor
Transport operations			
LD	A[src], dst	dst:= M[A + src]	Load based
LD	[src1 + src2], dst	dst:= M[src1 + src2]	Load based-indexed
LD	[src1 >> src2], dst	dst:= M[src1 shifted by src2]	Load based-shifted

Table 10.2 (cont.)

Instruction	Operands	Operation	Comments
Transport operations (cont.)			
LD	A, dst	dst:= M[A]	Load direct
LD	I, dst	dst:= I	Load immediate
MOV	src, dst	dst:= src	Move (byte or register)
ST	src1, A[src]	M[A + src]:= src1	Store based
ST	src1, [src2 + src3]	M[src2 + src3]:= src1	Store based-indexed
ST	src1, [src2 >> src3]	M[src2 shifted by src3]:= src1	Store based-shifted
ST	src, A	M[A]:= src	Store direct
Control transfer operations			
BRA	dst	PC:= dst + PC	Unconditional relative jump
BRA	Cond, src1, src2, dst	PC:= dst + PC if Cond(src1, src2)	Conditional jump
JMP	dst	PC:= dst	Unconditional jump direct
JMP	A[src]	PC:= A + src	Unconditional jump based
JMP	○ A [src]	PC:= M[A + src]	Unconditional jump indirect
TRAP	Cond, src1, src2	PC:= 0 if Cond(src1, src2)	Trap instruction
Other operations			
SAVEPC	A	M[A]:= PC$_{-3}$	Save multi-stage PC after trap or interrupt
SET	Cond, src, dst	dst:= −1 if Cond(src, dst)	Set conditional
		dst:= 0 if not Cond(src, dst)	

Table 10.3   Execution phases of an instruction.

Phase	Name	Operations
Instruction fetch	IF	Send out the PC, then increment it
Instruction decode	ID	Decode instruction
Operand decode	OD	Compute effective address and send it to memory if load or store, or compute the new PC, if jump, otherwise, use ALU for register to register operations
Operand/store/execute	SX	Write operand, if store, or use ALU for comparison, if compare and branch, otherwise, use ALU for register-to-register operations
Operand fetch	OF	Read operand, if load

again, the solution of the delayed branch, illustrated in Section 10.3, is adopted in MIPS.

Another characteristic of the MIPS organization is the absence of condition codes; comparisons are performed using a single compare and branch instruction. This choice simplifies the problem of overlapping instructions, because conditional branches do not rely on operations by other previously performed instructions.

10.4.2   Traps and interrupts

Exception and interrupt handling in a pipelined machine is complicated by the fact that, when an exception occurs, the different instructions will have altered the state of the machine. Therefore, either their operations must be undone or, after the exception, each instruction has to be resumed at exactly the stage reached when the exception occurred.

MIPS adopts the first strategy, but it is not necessary to undo any operation, thanks to the careful design of the phase overlapping. The possible combinations of exceptions for each phase are shown in Figure 10.4.

When an exception is detected, a jump is performed to the address 0, where a single exception-handling routine is stored. This unique routine plays the same role that the microcode portion does in CISCs, determining the type of exception and activating the corresponding handler. In MIPS, with the low level of its instruction set, this operation is put at the assembly language level.

Three addresses, at most, need to be saved on the stack when an

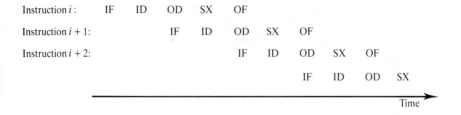

Figure 10.3 Overlapped execution of a stream of instructions in MIPS.

exception is being carried out. This is because up to three instructions can be executed at the same time. Hence, two instructions are always executed after a jump, because their decoding begins before the jump instruction is completed. This means that if the instruction following a jump causes an exception, then it is necessary to save the address of that instruction, the address of the following one and the address of the target of the jump. The three last program counters are, therefore, saved automatically by the hardware and put on to the stack whenever an exception occurs.

10.4.3 Support for the operating system

Support provided by MIPS for the implementation of an operating system consists of two privilege states and some mechanisms intended to support virtual memory.

The privilege states are implemented to ensure that some important instructions are used only by tested and certified software

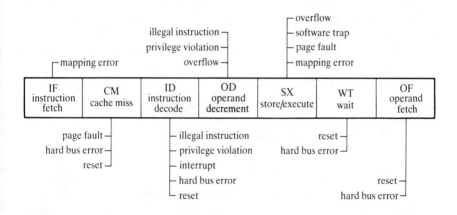

Figure 10.4 Possible exception occurrence in the different execution phases of an instruction.

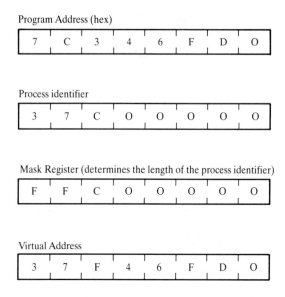

Program Address (hex)

| 7 | C | 3 | 4 | 6 | F | D | O |

Process identifier

| 3 | 7 | C | O | O | O | O | O |

Mask Register (determines the length of the process identifier)

| F | F | C | O | O | O | O | O |

Virtual Address

| 3 | 7 | F | 4 | 6 | F | D | O |

Figure 10.5   Address formation in MIPS.

(operating system). A trap detecting illegal use of such instructions is implemented in the CPU, along with a trap instruction, which can be used to invoke operating system functions, causing a switch to the more privileged state.

The virtual addressing scheme in MIPS includes a process identification number in the higher order bits of each address. In this way, the separation of the different virtual address spaces is implemented straightaway, and page or segment descriptors of different processes can be held in the same cache simultaneously to avoid cache flushing on each context switching.

The size of the process identification code is not fixed, because a mask register holds a 1 for each bit of the address occupied by such a code. Figure 10.5 illustrates the whole address assembly process.

10.5   The Inmos Transputer

10.5.1   System architecture

Another example of reduced architecture is the Transputer manufactured by Inmos Ltd. The general Transputer architecture includes a whole family of general- and special-purpose processors, rather than just a CPU.

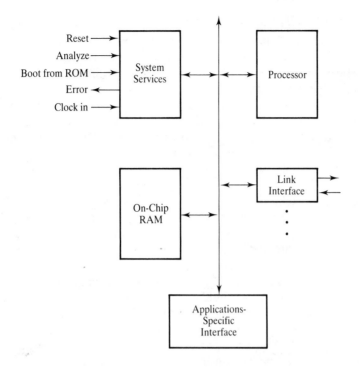

Figure 10.6 General block diagram of a Transputer.

The generic block diagram of a Transputer is shown in Figure 10.6; the same block diagram is used to describe the architecture of a Transputer, regardless of specific type. As it is possible to use Transputers for general data processing (CPU) as well as special purposes, such as I/O interfacing, CRT or disk controllers, the different applications are obtained by implementing different versions of the blocks, processor and applications specific interface, as shown in Figure 10.6. This tailors the general architecture to the applications considered.

Two features distinguish Transputers from the other reduced architectures (RISC and MIPS) presented in this chapter:

(1)   a block of RAM is implemented on the chip, enabling a Transputer to work without external memory, as long as the size of data and code fit into the on-chip memory (external memory is also allowed to obtain larger memory sizes);

(2)   a set of high-speed (10 Mbytes/s) serial links allows the processes running on a Transputer to communicate with processes running on a different Transputer.

The second feature outlined here allows the straightforward implementation of multiprocessor systems by interconnecting several Transputers through their serial links. The network can take any theoretical structure suitable for the class of algorithms to be executed by the multiprocessor system.

Multiprocessor systems obtained in this way have a static interconnection structure (see also [4]), as each link is used for communications between the same pair of processors during the system's lifetime. Static multiprocessors allow fast communications by avoiding any delay caused by signal switching or routing shown by dynamic interconnections. However, high performances can be obtained only when the data exchanges take place between directly linked processors. In fact, a static multiprocessor, with a given interconnection structure, may achieve good performances for a set of algorithms where the data exchanges match the structure well, and poor performances for a different set of algorithms requiring data exchanges between processors placed far apart in the interconnection structure. The first problem implied by the design of a multiprocessor system based on Transputers, therefore, is the choice of the interconnection structure for a given class of algorithms.

Adherence to a general architectural scheme (Figure 10.6) for general- and special-purpose processors allows the straightforward interconnection of Transputers, regardless of their specific internal structure. As general data processors are the most interesting members of the Transputer family, the remainder of this section is devoted to this type of processor.

10.5.2 Process execution on transputers

The basic unit for software running on a Transputer is the process, as defined in Chapter 3: each application may be seen as a set of interconnected (that is, communicating) processes.

Process communication takes place by means of channels, as defined in the Occam programming language [5]. A channel is like an unbuffered mailbox (normal ones are discussed in Section 3.7), since it is not possible for the process sending data to leave the message for the receiving process in the channel. If a process tries to send data on a channel and the receiver is not waiting for the transmission, the sender is put in a wait state until a receive operation is attempted on the same channel. Only when both sender and receiver are ready to communicate on the same channel is the data exchange performed.

Several communicating processes may be run on the same or on interconnected Transputers. Channels between processes executed by the same Transputer are implemented in shared memory; channels between processes running on different Transputers are implemented by using the hardware serial links. The decision as to which implementation to use for a channel is taken when the programs are prepared, by indicating the group of processes running on each Transputer, and mapping on to the serial links all the channels connecting local processes to processes running on an external Transputer.

In the group of processes represented by the graph in Figure 10.7(a), each node is a process and the edges connect two processes communicating through a channel. Figure 10.7(b) and Figure 10.7(c) show two different allocations for the group of processes; in the first, processes *A* and *B* are executed on a Transputer, represented by a square block, while *C* and *D* run on a different one; in the second figure, each process is executed by a different Transputer, with all the channels mapped on to serial links. It is possible to switch from one configuration to the other by changing declarations in the source programs, because the logical behaviour is not changed by the allocation scheme of the processes to the processors.

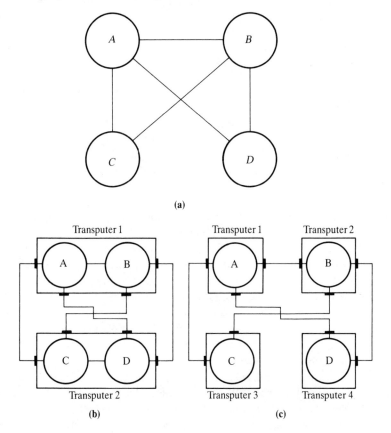

Figure 10.7 Example of process allocation: (a) graph of communicating processes; (b) allocation on two Transputers; (c) allocation on four Transputers.

10.5.3   Process multiplexing

Scheduling activities for multiplexing different processes on the same processor (see Section 3.8) are directly supported in hardware by the Transputer; mechanisms are almost transparent to the programmer.

Each process may belong to one of two priority classes: low-priority processes are executed only when no high-priority process is ready to run. When several high-priority processes are ready, one is selected and executed until either it is waiting for communication or it terminates.

When no high-priority process can be run, the low-priority ones that are ready to run are executed periodically, using time slices. If the running process does not switch its state within the assigned time slice, it is suspended and placed on the tail of the ready list, while the process at the head of the list starts to run.

With this scheduling policy, high-priority processes are expected to complete their activities in short periods to avoid blocking the CPU.

10.5.4   Register and memory organization

The internal block diagram of a Transputer intended for general data processing is shown in Figure 10.8. It is apparent that the applications specific circuits block of Figure 10.6 is, in this case, the interfacing circuitry required to access external memory.

Internally, the processor is a stack machine. Three registers, A, B and C (see Figure 10.9), are used to store the uppermost locations of the stack, so that A is always the top of stack. This implies that when the stack grows or shrinks, the stack contents are moved from one register to another, to maintain A at the top. Overflows or underflows of the register file should be handled by the compiler.

This register organization allows instructions to be implemented without involving any field for specifying the registers. The stack organization leads to a load/store machine, as all the operations except those for data movement operate on the stack – that is, on registers.

In addition to the registers for the stack, a local frame pointer (see Chapter 1 for the use of such a register), a program counter and an operand register are also implemented; the latter is used to provide an additional operand for some instructions.

A uniform addressing space, including internal and, if any, external memory, is implemented. The whole memory space is a linear vector of words, the size of which depends on the specific model (32-bits for T424). Addresses range from the minimum negative to the maximum positive value supported by the word size required for address manipulation, so avoiding the need for unsigned arithmetic and comparison instructions. In

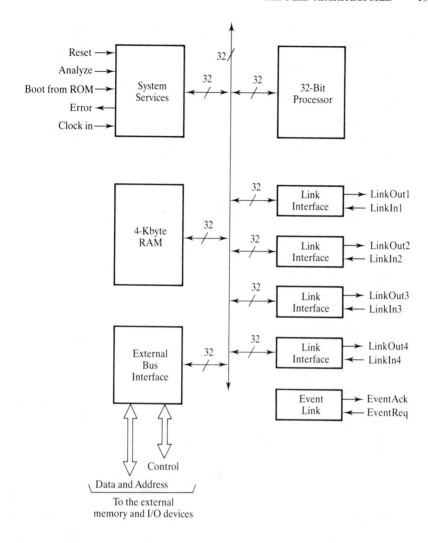

Figure 10.8 Internal block diagram of a Transputer for general data processing.

addition to the word address, a byte selector, composed of a number of bits depending on the word size, is used to obtain access to operands shorter than a word.

10.5.5 Instructions

The instruction format is simple, consisting of only one byte. The instruction is divided into two 4-bit nibbles: the most significant is the function field, the least is the data field.

Registers   Locals   Program

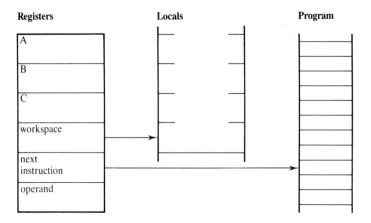

Figure 10.9 Register organization.

The whole instruction set is divided into three classes.

(1)   Direct functions: These have the opcode in the function field and the data field reserved for the operand.

(2)   Prefixing functions: These have the same encoding as direct ones. They are intended to be used in conjunction with other instructions requiring data in the instruction larger than those allowed by the single instruction format.

(3)   Indirect functions: These have a special pattern in the function field and a specific operation in the data field. Using this special feature, it is possible to construct an instruction code by means of the prefixing instructions, and then execute it.

Direct functions, shown in the list in Table 10.4, are the most common operations performed in a program. Local variables are accessed using a base displacement indirect mode (see Chapter 1), where the base register is represented by the frame (workspace) register and the displacement is obtained by adding the operand register and the instruction data field. Similarly, the immediate operands to be used as constants are obtained by adding the operand register content to the instruction data field. Non-local variables are accessed using the same addresing mode as the local ones; however, load and store instructions on non-local instructions use the register A as a base, while the displacement is obtained as for local variables. This implies that the whole addressing mechanism of non-local variables requires the correct frame pointer to be loaded on the stack before the load or store non-local instruction can be executed.

Table 10.4   Functions of a Transputer.

Functions	
Direct	
load constant	Load non-local
add constant	Store non-local
load local	Jump
store local	Conditional jump
load local pointer	Call
Prefixing	
prefix	Negative prefix
Indirect	
operate	

For small constants and displacements, the byte used to encode the instruction is sufficient to perform the operation. If larger data are required, it is necessary to use the prefixing instructions to build a large number in the operand register before applying the instruction. Prefixing functions add the constant stored in their data field to the operand register and perform a four-position left shift out of that register. In this way, any number can be built in the operand register, by a nibble-by-nibble insertion into the register, starting with the most significant one. The operand register is cleared at the end of each instruction, apart from prefixes.

To illustrate how prefixing functions can be used, the following instruction sequence shows how to load the hexadecimal constant 356F on top of the stack:

	operand register	*A register*
prefix 3	30	–
prefix 5	350	–
prefix 6	3560	–
load constant F	0	356F

One prefix function for negative and one for positive constants are allowed in the instruction set.

The indirect functions are obtained from a remaining function which corresponds to the operate opcode. This function causes the execution of the instruction, the code of which is obtained by adding the data field to the operand register contents. With this mechanism, 16 indirect functions (the most frequently used ones) can be encoded using a single byte, while the rest require a prefix instruction to obtain the most significant nibble in the operand register.

Indirect functions operate on registers, so they do not require any constant or displacement.

10.5.6 Serial links

Inter-Transputer communications are implemented by the four on-chip link interfaces shown in Figure 10.8. Each link implements a pair of channels, as it is composed of two unidirectional communication ports. The data transmission takes place in bit serial form, and each message comprises a sequence of data packets; the format is shown in Figure 10.10. Each data packet is composed of two start bits, one stop bit and an 8-bit datum. An acknowledge packet, the format of which is also shown in Figure 10.10, must be received after the transmission of each data packet to notify the transmitter that both the destination process was able to receive the byte and that another byte may be transmitted.

In addition to the four normal links, an EventReq input provides the interface to a running process with external logic different from that of other Transputers. These two signals can be used to implement interrupt request (EventReq) and acknowledge (EventAck).

When EventReq is activated by the external logic, a channel different from those implemented by normal links becomes ready for communication. As soon as a process is waiting to receive from the channel concerned with the EventReq, it becomes active and the EventAck signal is activated, informing the external logic that EventReq can be de-activated.

Any other communication between the process activated by this mechanism should be programmed explicitly. In other words, the process activated plays the role of the interrupt-handling routine, which explicitly reads all the additional information required to service the interrupt request.

10.6 Conclusion

The debate on CISC and RISC philosophies is increasingly significant for the design of new architectures. In the previous chapters the micro-processors mentioned were all in the CISC category; this chapter has looked at three instances of RISC architecture, two developed in universities and the other commercially available.

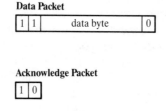

Figure 10.10 Packet formats used for inter-Transputer communication.

Besides their common characteristics of small, simple and fast instruction sets, the three machines have quite different features. The Berkeley RISC attempts to reach a high execution efficiency by using a suitable register organization, which supports the most time-expensive operations required by high-level languages. The MIPS bases its speed on extensive use of the pipeline technique and provides some mechanisms to support basic operating system functions. The Inmos Transputer is designed to be used as a basic block in multiprocessor systems built up by interconnecting several microprocessors.

As the RISC/CISC debate is still far from reaching a conclusion, the interested reader should refer to the papers listed at the end of this chapter.

References

[1] D. A. Patterson and C. H. Sequin, 'A VLSI RISC', *Computer* **15**(9), September 1982, pp. 8–21.

[2] W. A. Wulf *et al.*, *The Design of an Optimizing Compiler*, Elsevier, North-Holland, Amsterdam and New York, 1975.

[3] S. A. Przybylsky *et al.*, 'Organization and VLSI Implementation of MIPS', *Journal of VLSI and Computer Systems* **1**(2), 1984, pp. 170–209.

[4] T. Y. Feng, 'A Survey of Interconnection Networks', *Computer* **14**(12), December 1982, pp. 12–27.

[5] Inmos Ltd, *Occam Programming Manual*, Prentice Hall International, London, 1984.

Further reading

C. Barney, 'RISC Supermini has Stellas Performances', *Electronics*, August 1983.

I. Barron *et al.*, 'Transputer Does 5 or More MIPS Even When Not Used In Parallel', *Electronics*, November 1983, p. 109.

E. Basart, 'Ridge 32 – A RISC Variation', *Proceedings of the ICCD*, October 1983.

R. P. Colwell *et al.*, 'Peering Through the RISC/CISC Fog: An Outline of Research', *Computer Architecture News* **11**(1), March 1983, pp. 40–50.

R. P. Colwell *et al.*, 'Computers, Complexity and Controversy', *Computer* **18**(9), September 1985, pp. 8–20.

L. Foti *et al.*, 'Reduced-Instruction Set Multi-Microcomputer System', *Proceedings of the National Computer Conference*, June 1984, pp. 69–75.

J. R. Goodman *et al.*, 'PIPE: A VLSI De–coupled Architecture', *Proceedings of the 12th Annual Symposium on Computer Architecture*, June 1985.

M. G. H. Katevenis, *Reduced Instruction Set Computer Architecture for VLSI*, University of California Berkeley, Technology Report UCB/CSD 83/141, October 1981.

V. Milutinovic, D. Fura and W. Helbig, 'An Introduction to VLSI Computer Architecture for GaAs', *Computer* **19**(3), March 1986, pp. 30–42.

D. A. Patterson, 'RISC Watch', *Computer Architecture News* **12**(1), March 1984, pp. 11–19.

D. A. Patterson *et al.*, 'Architecture of a VLSI Instruction Cache for a RISC', *Proceedings of the 10th Symposium on Computer Architecture*, June 1983, pp. 108–116.

G. Radin, 'The 801 Minicomputer', *IBM Journal of Research and Development* **27**(3), May 1983, pp. 237–246.

A. Silbey, V. Milutinovic and V. Mendoza-Grado, 'A Survey of Advanced Microprocessors and HLL Computer Architectures', *Computer* **18**(8), August 1985, pp. 72–85.

C. Whitby-Stevens, 'The Transputer', *Proceedings of the 12th Symposium on Computer Architecture*, June 1985, pp. 292–300.

APPENDIX

FURTHER PROBLEMS

Problems proposed in this appendix are presented in general form. They can be solved for each microprocessor family by using the corresponding set of components.

In the following exercises, a target system is assumed to contain the following elements:

(a)   central processing unit;

(b)   floating-point co-processor;

(c)   system ROM/RAM (128 Kbytes);

(d)   application RAM (512 Kbytes);

(e)   interrupt controller;

(f)   real-time clock unit.

A1.1   Several microprocessor-based systems, such as personal computers and CAD/CAE workstations, rely heavily on support for floating-point computations. The aim of this exercise is to design a floating-point library for the target system mentioned above. Its main requirements are:

- The library must contain basic trigonometric and transcendental functions, such as $\sin(x)$, $\cos(x)$, $\tan(x)$, square-root(x), $\ln(x)$ and $\exp(x)$.

- Two library versions must be designed. The first should be used in systems including the floating-point co-processor, while the second must work when no floating-point unit is available.

- The applications software interface should be the same for the two versions. In other words, the user must not be aware of the floating-point unit's presence/absence except for different performance indices.

465

- When designing the non-floating-point unit version, assume that basic procedures for floating-point addition, subtraction, multiplication and division are available.

- The library must also be able to work in a multitasking environment. This requires, for example, particular attention in designing procedures to save/restore the floating-point unit internal status and to manage floating-point exceptions.

A1.2 Virtual memory systems include special support for managing exceptions caused by page faults. Design a page fault handler for the target system based on the following requirements:

- The exception handler must be able to save modified pages when they are swapped out, and to load missing logical pages when needed.

- Pages can be read from and written to the backup store by using a pair of suitable primitives – write (task, physical page, logical page) and read (task, physical page, logical page).

- A suitable algorithm must be implemented to select pages to be swapped out – a least recently used strategy variant.

- The handler must work in a multitasking environment.

The goal of Exercises A1.3–A1.5 is the design of simple mechanisms for an operating system kernel to be used in the target system. The main requirements are as follows:

(a)   Hierarchical design: The kernel structure is assumed to consist of nested levels. Each level i offers to the user (that is, level $i + 1$) services implemented by invoking functions supported by the $(i - 1)$th, $(i - 2)$th. . .1st levels.

(b)   Modularity, simplicity and efficiency.

(c)   Applications are interfaced to the outermost level.

(d)   No applications task must be able to invoke services by layers other than the user-interface layer (services by the inner layers are 'hidden' to the user).

(e)   The kernel must provide suitable mechanisms for implementing a multitasking environment (process management).

A1.3 Design the procedures belonging to the first level, to be used for obtaining mutual exclusion on shared variables:

- *LOCK(var A, time T)* allows the caller to lock the variable

A. When A is already locked by another entity, it enters a busy form, waiting for T time units before attempting to lock A again;

- UNLOCK(var A) allows the caller to unlock the variable A.

A1.4 Design the procedures belonging to the second level, to be used for obtaining queuing/dequeuing services and physical memory allocation/de-allocation:

- QUEUE(queue descriptor QD, element E) appends the element E to the queue described by QD.

- DEQUEUE(queue descriptor QD) removes and returns the first element in the queue described by QD to the caller.

- ALLOCATE(mem-area M, block B) allocates a block B of memory from the memory pool M. Several different strategies can be used for this purpose; for example, M can be a stack area and blocks can be allocated using different algorithms, such as first fit, best fit and so on.

- DEALLOCATE(mem-area M, block B) returns the block B to the memory pool M.

A1.5 Design the primitives belonging to the third level, to be used for creating/destroying process descriptors and semaphores, to assign the CPU to the running process and to manage the process ready list. Each process in the system can be in one of the following states: *inactive* – the process exists but does not compete for the CPU; *running* – the process has acquired the CPU; *ready* – the process competes for the CPU (it is ready to run) but it is not the running process; or *waiting* – the process is blocked in the system in some waiting queue and must be unblocked before becoming ready.

- CRPD(PD) allows the caller to create a process descriptor structure (PD) for a new task to be included in the system. The PD is a data structure containing all the information concerning the associated process. This includes information such as: process state (inactive, running, waiting, ready); hardware and software process context (that is, registers, instruction pointers and stack pointers); process priority; process stack width; and process name. Define the process descriptor information for the target system and the associated data structure.

- CRSEM(sem) allows the caller to create and initialize a semaphore structure.

- *ASSIGN(PD)* assigns the CPU to the process whose state is described by the process descriptor.
- *RESIGN* pre-empts the CPU with the process currently running and saves the process status in the associated PD.

INDEX

Access descriptor   392
Access list   171
Access rights   171, 174
Access time, in memory hierarchy
    153
Accumulator   73
Active state   134
AD   392
Addition   29
Addition instruction
    iAPX286 addition instructions   344
    MC68020 addition instructions   250
    NS32032 addition instructions   299
    Z80000 addition instructions   203
Address bus/data bus   190, 234, 284,
    331
Address field   57
Address of memory locations   16
Address register   75
Address space   146, 336
Address translation   160, 162, 167,
    212, 268, 316, 352
Address translation trap   210
Address unit   331
Addressing expression   29
Addressing mode
    autoincrement/decrement addressing
        33
    autoincrement/decrement indirect
        addressing   36, 244, 293, 343
    base displacement indexed indirect
        addressing   41, 202, 245, 293
    base displacement indexed indirect
        displacement indirect

addressing   40, 245
base displacement indirect
    addressing   37, 202, 293, 343
base displacement indirect
    displacement indirect addressing
    49, 294
base displacement indirect
    displacement indexed indirect
    addressing   50, 245, 294
base displacement indirect indirect
    addressing   40
base displacement indirect indexed
    indirect addressing   47
base indexed indirect addressing
    41, 343
base indirect displacement indirect
    displacement indirect addressing
    54, 294
base indirect displacement indirect
    displacement indexed indirect
    addressing   55, 294
direct addressing   36, 202, 244, 342
postincrement indexed indirect
    addressing   43
postincrement indirect indexed
    indirect addressing   46
predecrement indexed indirect
    addressing   44
register indirect addressing   30, 32,
    202, 244, 293, 342
register operand addressing   30, 32,
    244, 293, 342
iAPX286 addressing modes   341
MC68020 addressing modes   244

NS32032 addressing modes   292
Z80000 addressing modes   199
ALU   189, 284
Am9511   3, 73
American Standard Code for
    Information Interchange   22
AND instruction
    iAPX286 AND instructions   345
    MC68020 AND instructions   300
    NS32032 AND instructions   250
    Z80000 AND instructions   204
Arbitration   93, 118
Architecture
    classification   5
    direct execution   8
    language corresponding   7
    language directed   7
    reduced   6, 441
Argument passing for subroutines   10,
    41, 360
Arithmetic logic unit   189, 284
Array-oriented instructions   205, 251,
    301, 348
Arrays   19, 23
    element addressing in   43, 46, 49, 64
ASCII code   22
Associative cache   152
Attached processor   390
AU   331

Barrel shifter   17
Base register   30, 37, 74
Basic format   84
BCD   23, 195, 239, 288, 337
BCD instruction
    iAPX286 BCD instructions   345
    MC68020 BCD instructions   250
    NS32032 BCD instructions   299
    Z80000 BCD instructions   203
Berkeley RISC   443
Binary coded decimal   23, 195, 239,
    288, 337
Bit   195, 239, 288
Bit field
    addressing   16, 19, 21, 196, 239, 288
    instruction   205, 251, 301
Bit instruction
    MC68020 bit instructions   251
    NS32032 bit instructions   301

Z80000 bit instructions   205
BIU   423
Block architecture   189, 233, 285, 332,
    389, 425
Block size   151
Booleans   196, 288
Bound check   25, 64
Breakpoint   97
Breakpoint trap   211, 263, 275, 308,
    370
BU   33
Burst bus transfer   192
Bus error   209, 236, 260, 262, 287
Bus, external   15
Bus interface unit   423
Bus standard   118, 138
Bus unit   33
Byte   17
    address   21

Cache control registers   193, 242
Cache memory
    on board   150
    on chip   148, 193, 236
Call gate   360
CAM   168
Capability   171, 174, 357, 392
Capability list   394
Carrier object   410
Carry bit   199, 240, 290, 340
Channel   456
Character   22
CISC   442
Closed environment   170
Code
    ASCII   22
    BCD   23, 195, 239, 288, 337
    binary   21
    Hamming   178
    two's complement   21
Code segment   161, 338
Communication invariant   122
Compare instruction
    iAPX286 compare instructions   348
    MC68020 compare instructions
        250, 251
    NS32032 compare instructions   300
    Z80000 compare instructions   204
Comparison of microcomputer features

addressing modes, tables 58
array-oriented instructions 64
data types 28
memory organization 27
procedure call supports 62
register organization 78
Compiler 8, 23
Complex instruction set computers
 442
Conditional jump instruction
 iAPX286 conditional jump
  instructions 348
 MC68020 conditional jump
  instructions 252
 NS32032 conditional jump
  instructions 303
 Z80000 conditional jump
  instructions 206
Conforming segment 363
Content addressable memory 168
Context object 399
Context switching 76, 113, 365
Co-processor 217, 263, 312, 374
 instruction trap 266, 370
 instructions 218, 265, 377
 interface 218, 263, 312, 375
 registers 219, 264, 322, 376
CPL 343, 360, 362, 369
CPU control instructions 207, 257,
 303
CPU utilization 107
Critical region 115
Current privilege level 343, 360, 362,
 369

DAA instruction 204, 337
Daisy-chain for interrupt priority 94
Data address registers 196, 240, 289,
 338
Data segment 38, 161, 338
Data transfer instruction
 iAPX286 data transfer instructions
  343
 MC68020 data transfer instructions
  249
 NS32032 data transfer instructions
  298
 Z80000 data transfer
  instructions 203

Data types 14, 195, 238, 287, 336
Debug supports 97
Decimal adjust accumulator instruction
 204, 337
Delayed jump 449
Demand paging 165
Descriptor privilege level 359, 362,
 369
Destination register 59
Direct addressing 36, 202, 244, 342
Direct memory access 117
Displacement 30, 37
Display field 10, 39, 348
Division
 BCD 345
 binary 345
 floating point 381
 signed number 345
Division instruction
 iAPX286 division instructions 345
 MC68020 division instructions 250
 NS32032 division instructions 299
 Z80000 division instructions 203
DMA 117
Domain object 397
Domain of access 171
Double-precision format 84
DPL 359, 362, 369
Dynamic object typing 403

ECC 424, 433
Enable interrupt flipflop 90
Environment, execution 110
Error
 confinement 426
 correction 178
 detection 176
 Hamming codes 178
 overflow 88
 parity check 176
 transmission protocol 427
 underflow 88
Error correcting code 424, 433
EU 331
Exception frame 259
Exception vector 259
Exceptions 87, 208, 259, 305, 360,
 382
Execution efficiency 8

Execution unit   331
EXOR (exclusive-or) instruction
  iAPX286 EXOR instructions   345
  MC68020 EXOR instructions   250
  NS32032 EXOR instructions   300
  Z80000 EXOR instructions   204
Exponent   82
Extended format   84
External operand addressing   295

Flag bits   199, 240, 290
Floating point
  exceptions   87, 377, 382
  format   82, 84
  instructions   226, 277, 324
  operations   87, 377
  registers   219, 276, 322
  representation   82
Floating-point unit   *see* co-processor
FPU   *see* co-processor
Frame, procedure   11
FRC   426
Functional redundancy checking   426

GDP   388
GDT   352, 357, 369
General data processor   388
Global descriptor table   352, 357, 369

Hamming code   178
Handlers   88, 96, 368
Heap memory   8, 419
High-level language   4, 37
  memory allocation in   8
  variable addressing in   13
History of microprocessor   2

ICU   309
IDT   369
IEEE 754 Standard   84, 218, 277, 322,
  376
Immediate   30, 34
Inactive state   134
Index register   74
Indexed addressing   41, 202, 245, 293,
  294, 343
Indexed cache   152
Indirect addressing   202, 244, 245,
  293, 294, 343

Indirection   29
Indivisible instructions   116
Infinity   86
Inmos Transputer   73, 454
Instruction encoding   57
Instruction format   245, 296
Instruction overlapping   223, 234, 444
Instruction queue   148, 331
Instruction set   202, 249, 298, 343,
  446, 449, 459
Instruction unit   331
Integer   21, 195, 238, 287, 336
Intel 80287 floating-point co-processor
  73, 374
Intel iAPX286 microprocessor   27, 64,
  329
  addressing modes   341
  CPU registers   338
  handshake lines   331
  instruction set   343
  interrupt handling   368
  memory management   351
  task management   363
Intel iAPX432 microprocessor   387
Interface processor   388
Interleaving, program   106, 110, 458
Interrupt   88
  acknowledgement   90, 262
  control unit   309
  controller   93, 137, 309
  descriptor table   369
  dispatch table   306
  gate   369
  interprocessor   137
  mask   90
  non-maskable   90, 209, 308, 368
  non-vectored   91, 209, 308
  priority   92
  request   90, 209, 262, 308
  restartable   91, 369
  service routine (handler)   306, 88,
    452
  vectored   90, 209, 308, 369
IOPL   340, 343, 350
I/O control   88
I/O instructions   206, 343
I/O privilege level   340, 343, 350
I/O space   192, 206
IP   388

IU   331

Jump instruction
  iAPX286 jump instructions   348,
    360
  MC68020 jump instructions   252
  NS32032 jump instructions   303
  Z80000 jump instructions   206
Jump-to-subroutine instruction
  iAPX286 jump-to-subroutine
    instructions   348, 360
  MC68020 jump-to-subroutine
    instructions   252
  NS32032 jump-to-subroutine
    instructions   304
  Z80000 jump-to-subroutine
    instructions   206

Latency time   91
LDT   352, 357
Local descriptor table   352, 357
Local frame pointer   39, 458
Longword   18
Loop instructions   348
Loop-back check   430

Machine cycle   162
Magnetic memory   153
Mailbox   126
Mantissa   82
Maskable interrupt   90, 369
Mass storage   153
MCU   423
Memory
  deallocation   13, 349
  efficiency   153
  fragmentation   161
  hierarchy   146, 155
  organization   16, 336
  protection   169, 216, 273, 319, 351
  reconfiguration   180
Memory allocation   11, 18, 348
Memory area   431
Memory banks   156
Memory bus area   434
Memory control unit   423
Memory management unit   147, 160,
  212, 266, 313
Message   410, 415

Microcomputer   2
Microprocessor
  iAPX286 microprocessor   329
  iAPX432 microprocessor   387
  MC68020 microprocessor   231
  NS32032 microprocessor   283
  Z80000 microprocessor   187
Microprocessor without interlocked
  pipe stages   449
MIPS   449
MMU   147, 160, 212, 266, 313
Module   253, 294
Module descriptor   254, 295
Module shadowing   427
Motorola MC68020
  microprocessor   21, 27, 231
  addressing modes   244
  block architecture   232
  CPU registers   240
  data types   238
  exception handling   259
  instruction set   249
  signals   234
Motorola MC68851 memory
  management unit   266
Motorola MC68881 floating-point
  co-processor   275
Multimicroprocessor   111, 117, 155,
  389, 456
Multiple domains   172
Multiplication
  BCD   344
  binary   344
  signed number   344
Multiplication instruction
  iAPX286 multiplication instructions
    344
  MC68020 multiplication instructions
    250
  NS32032 multiplication instructions
    299
  Z80000 multiplication instructions
    203
Multiprocessing   407
Multiprocessor   111, 117, 137, 155,
  407
Multiprogramming   106
Multitasking   106, 407
Mutual exclusion   114, 414

NaN (not a number) 84, 86
National Semiconductor NS32032
   microprocessor 15, 19, 21, 54,
      283
   addressing modes 292
   block architecture 284
   CPU registers 289
   data types 287
   exception handling 305
   instruction set 298
   signals 284
National Semiconductor NS32081
   floating-point co-processor 322
National Semiconductor NS32082
   memory management unit 313
Nested procedure support 402
Non-maskable interrupt 90, 369
Normalized numbers 83
Number representation 21, 23, 84

Object descriptor 392
Object lock 414
Object programming 391
Object table 393
Object table directory 394
Objects 391
   addressing in the iAPX432
      system 392
   representation in the iAPX432
      system 392
Occam 456
OD 392
Opcode 57
Operand 578
Operating system kernel 109
OR (inclusive-or) instruction
   iAPX286 OR instructions 345
   MC68020 OR instructions 250
   NS32032 OR instructions 300
   Z80000 OR instructions 204
Orthogonality 61
OSK 109
Overflow 88
Overlay 158

Package (Ada) 396
Page descriptor 166
Page selection 213, 271, 316

Page size 214, 272, 316
Page table 212, 271, 316
Page table organization 167, 213, 271,
      316
Paging 164
   with segmentation 168, 174
Parity bit 176
Parity error 176
Pascal language 9, 24
PCO 415
Phase 145
Physical address 146
Physical storage object 417
Pipelining 190, 444, 449
Pointer table 271
Pointer to memory 11
Pointer use 41
Pointer validation 172, 267, 320, 360
Polish notation 71
Port object 408
Prefetch queue 148, 331
Privilege state 153, 198, 242, 290, 359
Priority/deadline strategy 413
Procedure addressing
   environment 398
Procedure call 10, 41, 62, 343
Procedure descriptor 173
Process 110
   communication 126, 408, 415, 456
   descriptor 113, 363
   isolation 170
   object 407
   queue 409
   scheduling 412
   starvation 120
   state 132
   synchronization 121, 408
Processor communication object 415
Processor object 412
Program counter 33, 199, 241, 290,
      340
Program debugging 274, 320
Program flow control
   instructions 206, 252, 303, 348,
      360, 449
Program locality 145
Protected address mode 351
Protection checks 357
PSO 417

Quadword   18
QMR (quad modular redundant)   427

Radix   82
Read–modify–write cycle   117
Ready queue   135
Ready state   135
Real address mode   336
Record   19, 26, 50
Reduced architecture   442
Refinement object   398
Registers   30, 113, 147
  organization   70
  iAPX286 registers   337
  MC68020 registers   240
  MIPS   449
  NS32032 registers   289
  RISC   444
  Transputer   458
  Z80000 registers   196
Reset   209, 236, 262
Return-from-subroutine instruction
  iAPX286 return-from-subroutine
      instructions   362
  MC68020 return-from-subroutine
      instructions   252
  NS32032 return-from-subroutine
      instructions   305
  Z80000 return-from-subroutine
      instructions   207
RISC   443
RISC, Berkeley   443
Rotate instruction
  iAPX286 rotate instructions   345
  MC68020 rotate instructions   251
  NS32032 rotate instructions   301
  Z80000 rotate instructions   204
Rounding   86
RPL (relative privilege level)   351,
    359, 362
Running state   132, 136

Scalar   38
Scheduling   132, 367
SCO   421
Scrubbing   433
Segment
  descriptor   162, 352
  register   338, 356

selector   336
Segmentation   161, 336
  paging   168, 174
Semantic gap   4, 442
Semaphore   121
Serial link   455, 462
Set associative cache   152
Set size   151
Shift instruction
  iAPX286 shift instructions   345
  MC68020 shift instructions   251
  NS32032 shift instructions   301
  Z80000 shift instructions   204
Shift operations   29
Sign bit   82, 199, 240, 290, 340
Signals   190, 234, 284, 331
Significand   82
Single-precision format   84
Single step   97, 368
Source register   57
Spare bit   180
SRO   417
Stack   8
Stack instruction   344
Stack machine   71, 458
Stack pointer   33, 74, 197, 240, 290,
    338
Step-by-step execution   97, 371
Storage claim object   421
Storage descriptor   393
Storage resource object   417
String   22, 196
String instructions   205, 301, 346
Subroutine
  instructions for   *see*
      jump-to-subroutine instruction
  Pascal   10, 41
  memory allocation   11, 18
Subscripts   23, 64
Subtraction instruction
  iAPX286 subtraction instructions
      344
  MC68020 subtraction instructions
      250
  NS32032 subtraction instructions
      299
  Z80000 subtraction instructions   203
Supervisor state   199, 236, 290
Syndrome   178

System call   208, 210, 258, 262, 305, 311
Swapping   160

Tag memory   148
Task alias   272
Task gate   365
Task segment selector   364, 368
Task state descriptor   363
TCO   404
TDO   404
Test-and-set instruction   116, 344
Trace trap   97, 211, 263, 311, 371
Translation cache   215, 269, 318
Translation lookaside buffer   215
Trap   87, 95, 210, 262, 311, 368, 452
Trap gate   369
Tree, overlay   158
Truncation   86
TSS   364, 368
Two's complement   21
Type control object   404
Type definition object   404

Underflow   88
User-defined data types   403

Variables
  global   11, 50
  local   11, 39
VAX   21, 61
Virtual address   146, 351
Virtual memory   146, 163, 217, 274, 320

Wait state   135
Word   18
Word length   15
  data   15
  instruction   57

Zero in floating point   84
Zilog Z80000 microprocessor   187, 64
  addressing modes   199
  block architecture   188
  CPU registers   196
  data types   195
  exception handling   208
  instruction set   202
  signals   192
Zilog Z8070 floating-point co-processor 218

Notes